Nutrient Requirements of Sheep

Sixth Revised Edition, 1985

Subcommittee on Sheep Nutrition
Committee on Animal Nutrition
Board on Agriculture
National Research Council

NATIONAL ACADEMY PRESS
Washington, D.C.   1985

National Academy Press, 2101 Constitution Avenue, NW, Washington, DC 20418

NOTICE: The project that is the subject of this report was approved by the Governing Board of the National Research Council, whose members are drawn from the councils of the National Academy of Sciences, the National Academy of Engineering, and the Institute of Medicine. The members of the committee responsible for the report were chosen for their special competences and with regard for appropriate balance.

This report has been reviewed by a group other than the authors according to procedures approved by a Report Review Committee consisting of members of the National Academy of Sciences, the National Academy of Engineering, and the Institute of Medicine.

The National Research Council was established by the National Academy of Sciences in 1916 to associate the broad community of science and technology with the Academy's purposes of furthering knowledge and of advising the federal government. The Council operates in accordance with general policies determined by the Academy under the authority of its congressional charter of 1863, which establishes the Academy as a private, nonprofit, self-governing membership corporation. The Council has become the principal operating agency of both the National Academy of Sciences and the National Academy of Engineering in the conduct of their services to the government, the public, and the scientific and engineering communities. It is administered jointly by both Academies and the Institute of Medicine. The National Academy of Engineering and the Institute of Medicine were established in 1964 and 1970, respectively, under the charter of the National Academy of Sciences.

This study was supported by the Center for Veterinary Medicine, Food and Drug Administration of the U.S. Department of Health and Human Services, by the Agricultural Research Service of the U.S. Department of Agriculture, by Agriculture Canada, and by the American Feed Industry Association.

Library of Congress Cataloging-in-Publication Data

Main entry under title:

Nutrient requirements of sheep.

   (Nutrient requirements of domestic animals)
   Bibliography: p.
   Includes index.
   1. Sheep—Feeding and feeds.   2. Sheep—Feed utilization efficiency. I. National Research Council (U.S.). Subcommittee on Sheep Nutrition. II. Series.
SF376.N85 1985   636.3'0852   85-21562
ISBN 0-309-03596-1

Printed in the United States of America

Preface

This report is one in a series of reports entitled *Nutrient Requirements of Domestic Animals,* issued under the guidance of the Committee on Animal Nutrition, Board on Agriculture, National Research Council. It was prepared by the Subcommittee on Sheep Nutrition and updates the 1975 edition of *Nutrient Requirements of Sheep.*

The revisions made include the following:

• The values presented reflect new information available on sheep nutrition and are interpreted by the committee into useful form.

• The concentrations of nutrients in the diet for a specific stage of production are similar for all weights of sheep and include the ratio of concentrate to forage that would conventionally be fed.

• Specific diets and nutrient requirements are presented for ewe lambs during various stages of production.

• The energy requirements and energy concentration of the diet of ewes in the last 4 to 6 weeks of gestation with an expected lambing rate of 130 to 150 percent are reduced somewhat from the values reported in the 1975 edition of this report.

• The nutrient requirements and nutrient concentrations of the diet during the last 4 to 6 weeks of gestation for ewes with an expected lambing rate of 180 to 225 percent are a new addition and are distinctly different from requirements for ewes with lower lambing rates.

• The expected growth rate of light-weight finishing lambs was substantially increased, and dietary energy concentrations were increased for all weight lambs to accommodate these higher weight gains within the constraints of limited capacity to consume dry matter.

• Feed composition data are expressed on a dry matter basis.

• Feeds are named in accordance with nomenclature adopted by the Committee on Animal Nutrition (United States) and the National Committee on Animal Nutrition (Canada).

• Values for nutrient requirements are given in both the metric and English systems to broaden the application of the information.

• More husbandry information is included than in previous editions to better serve sheep producers who rely on this information source in managing their flocks.

• Formulas and tables have been developed to estimate energy requirements for maintenance and growth by animals of varying mature weight genotypes (see Table 3). Tables 1 and 2 were not developed from these formulas; thus, there may be some discordance between these estimates of average energy requirements.

The subcommittee wishes to express appreciation to the Committee on Animal Nutrition and most especially to Richard D. Goodrich, George E. Mitchell, Jr., and Duane E. Ullrey, whose support, encouragement, and scientific expertise contributed significantly to the completion of this report. Appreciation is also extended to Douglas E. Hogue, who served on the subcommittee during the early stages of preparing this report, and Arthur L. Pope and John E. Butcher, who reviewed an early draft and prepared comments for the subcommittee's consideration.

The subcommittee is also indebted to John A. Pino, who served as board reviewer; Margaret Benson, who provided data for consideration; and Selma P. Baron and Philip Ross, of the Board on Agriculture, for their assistance in the production of the report.

Subcommittee on Sheep Nutrition

iv

Contents

Figures and Tables

Nutrient Requirements of Sheep

Sixth Revised Edition, 1985

1 Introduction

The major nutrient requirements of sheep and the composition of typical diets that will supply those nutrients at specific stages of production are presented in Tables 1 and 2.

The values given are considered necessary for the levels of performance indicated in the tables for various stages of production and for the prevention of nutritional deficiencies.

When using these tables to determine feed rations, one should be aware of the following:

- Variation among sheep affects the utilization of and need for nutrients.
- Competition among sheep of different sizes, ages, and breeds may significantly affect the daily intake of an individual sheep, resulting in an excess intake by more-aggressive sheep and an inadequate intake by less-aggressive sheep.
- Dry matter (DM) intake is an important consideration in formulating sheep rations. Severely restricted DM intake often results in a 5- to 10-fold increase in salt and mineral intake when minerals are offered free choice. Restricted DM intake may result in wool picking or defleecing of self or penmates.

Conversely, feeds excessively high in fiber or water may restrict nutrient intake. This is particularly a problem during late gestation in twin- and triplet-bearing ewes, early weaned lambs, and finishing lambs fed for maximum gain.

- Performance level expected may differ from the levels indicated in the tables.
- Interrelationships among nutrients may affect need.
- Previous nutritional status of the sheep may influence requirements. Sheep previously fed carotene-deficient forage or sheep that are excessively thin or fat should be fed a diet different from sheep in average condition.
- Level of intake may affect utilization of nutrients (e.g., high intake, in general, depresses digestibility).
- Disease, parasites, environmental stress, and other less-obvious conditions may influence nutritional requirements.

Most of the values given in Tables 1 and 2 are based on research results. Some were determined by extrapolation from research data.

The nutrient values presented are for feedstuffs of average composition, digestibility, and quality. In special cases, adjustments in intake should be made. Amounts of feed refer to the amount actually consumed, not offered. Failure to account for wasted food may result in gross underfeeding.

Except for maintenance and early gestation diets, the amounts of dry matter indicated are near maximum without resulting in refusal. If higher levels or rates of production are sought via increased nutrient intake, an increase in the concentration of nutrients in the ration rather than an increase in the amount fed is necessary.

2 Nutrient Requirements and Signs of Deficiency

ENERGY

The term energy, when used to describe diet attributes, actually describes the end product rather than the inherent characteristics of compounds found in feedstuffs. Energy results from the utilization of the absorbed nutrients from metabolic processes such as oxidation and synthesis. It is generally measured as heat of combustion. The specific term used to describe the unit of energy depends on many factors; the most common include calorie and joule.

In the United States the calorie is the most common unit for measuring energy in feedstuffs and is used throughout this report. A calorie is the amount of heat necessary to raise one gram of water from 16.5° to 17.5°C. Since the calorie is a very small unit of measurement, energy values for feedstuffs are more commonly expressed as kilocalories (1 kcal = 1,000 calories) and megacalories (1 Mcal = 1,000,000 calories = 1,000 kcal). Internationally, the joule is frequently used (1 calorie = 4.184 joules).

The caloric values of individual constituents of feedstuffs are characteristic of their chemical compositions. The energy value of a constituent is measured as the heat released when the substance is completely oxidized to carbon dioxide and water. The amount of energy released is measured in calories and is referred to as the gross energy (E) contained in that constituent. For example,

Compound	Heat of Combustion, kcal/g
Ethanol	7.11
Glucose	3.74
Starch	4.18
Acetic acid	3.49
Propionic acid	4.96

Compound	Heat of Combustion, kcal/g
Butyric acid	5.95
Palmitic acid	9.35
Stearic acid	9.53
Glycine	3.12
Tyrosine	5.91

Generally, the proximate constituents of feedstuffs are considered to contain the following E:

Feedstuff Component	kcal/g
Carbohydrate	4.2
Fat	9.4
Protein	5.6

Although E is determined by burning a constituent in an atmosphere of oxygen, the yield of energy, whether via oxidation in biological systems or a furnace, is the same if taken to the same state of oxidation or end products.

Terminology for Discussing Energy Values of Feedstuffs

Gross energy is not particularly descriptive of the energy an animal can derive from a feedstuff. When a feedstuff or combination of feedstuffs (diet) is fed, the digestive process is generally not able to make all the E consumed available to the animal for absorption; thus, there is a loss of energy in the feces. Subtracting the energy excreted in feces from the E consumed yields digestible energy (DE). Digestible energy can be expressed in absolute terms per unit of weight (kcal/g) or as a percentage of gross energy. The term total digestible nutrients (TDN) also is used, but feed energy values are expressed in units of weight instead of calories. TDN is determined by

2

summing digestible crude protein, digestible carbohydrates (nitrogen-free extract and crude fiber), and 2.25 × digestible crude fat.

Although DE and TDN are frequently used to evaluate feedstuffs and to express nutrient requirements, the use of metabolizable energy (ME) instead of DE or TDN has important advantages for ruminants. Measuring only fecal energy losses does not accurately reflect the energy available to ruminants for use in productive processes. As feedstuffs are exposed to microorganisms in the rumen, a significant part of the E in the feedstuff is metabolized to methane (an end product of fermentation that is very high in energy but of essentially no caloric value to the host animal) that escapes from the rumen in eructated gases. Loss of gross energy as methane varies with the type of diet (high concentrate versus low concentrate) and the level of feeding and ranges from 3 to 10 percent. The energy lost in urine also is not accounted for if only fecal energy is measured. The energy content of urine is rather constant and represents 3 to 5 percent of the E value of a diet. The major factors influencing the fraction of dietary DE in the urine are diet protein level, diet roughage levels, and essential oil content. The last is high in some range plants such as sagebrush (Cook et al., 1952). To determine ME, subtract gaseous and urine energy losses from DE. The conversion of DE to ME generally is estimated as DE × 0.82. This estimation is accurate except for high-grain diets, where higher ratios are observed (Johnson, 1972).

Net energy (NE) is the most refined expression of the value of energy in a feedstuff. Although not as commonly used in evaluating feedstuffs and expressing requirements as ME, NE represents the amount of energy available to the animal for maintenance and productive processes. Determination of NE requires one measurement in addition to those required for calculating ME. This is the heat increment (HI), which is the increase in heat produced as a result of digestion and metabolic processes in response to increased ME intake. Thus, HI is the inefficiency of ME use for any given function. Subtracting HI from ME yields NE. This assumes that HI includes both the heat from fermentations in the digestive tract and the heat liberated during nutrient metabolism. Under most conditions, HI is of no value to the animal and frequently is a burden, since it requires that additional energy be dissipated. However, when ruminants are exposed to low environmental temperatures and must increase heat production to maintain normal body temperatures, then HI may be useful in maintaining body temperature. Heat increment varies with diet and physiological function of the animal and can range from 10 to 90 percent of the ME.

Net energy is subdivided into that used for maintenance (NE_m) and that recovered as some useful product (NE_p) (recovered energy [RE], body tissue, milk, or wool). NE_m and NE_p may be further subdivided.

Net energy for maintenance includes the NE for basal metabolism that relates to muscular activity, tissue repair and replacement, and involuntary metabolic processes such as maintenance of ionic gradients. Also included as NE_m is the minimal voluntary activity necessary to sustain life. The amount of energy needed to satisfy voluntary activity needs (sometimes called the activity increment) varies widely depending on the availability of feed, water, and shade and the topography of the environment. Extreme examples of management systems—confinement versus arid range—may cause the activity increment to be a major factor in determining NE_m. During hot or cold weather, the animal uses ME to cool or heat its body; the energy required for this is also part of NE_m and is widely variable depending on several environmental factors.

Net energy available to the animal in excess of that required for maintenance is used in a variety of productive processes. These include the net energy for growth (NE_g), lactation (NE_l), reproductive processes (NE_y), and production of wool and hair (NE_v). Where applicable, the net energy for physical work, in addition to that required by the activity increment, may also be included.

The efficiency with which metabolizable energy above maintenance is used as net energy for various functions varies with quality of diet and physiological function. For example, the process of milk production is more efficient than growth as empty body gain.

Signs of Deficiency and Toxicity

Meeting energy requirements without over- or underfeeding animals is one of the producer's most difficult tasks. Energy deficiency or insufficiency is likely the most widely occurring nutritional deficiency within the sheep industry. Likewise, oversupplying energy to sheep is one of the most wasteful practices.

An energy deficiency will manifest itself in a variety of ways depending on its severity. In growing animals an early sign is reduced rate of gain, which progresses to cessation of growth, weight loss, and ultimately death. In reproducing females early signs of energy deficiency are reduced conception rate, reduced reproductive rate (i.e., reduced number of multiple births), and reduced milk production, with progressively worse deficiencies causing reproductive failure, cessation of or lack of initiation of lactation, and death. Similar problems develop in the male, with an initial reduction and eventual cessation in reproductive activity and performance and finally death. With restrictions in energy, wool growth slows; fiber diameter is reduced; total production of wool decreases; and in severe cases wool growth ceases, creating a "break" (weak spot) in the staple of wool. Energy deficiency will cause a reduction in the function of the immune system, resulting in a lowered resistance to disease. Undernourished sheep also will have an increased susceptibility to parasite infestation.

On the other hand, an animal consuming more NE than required must find a way to handle the excess. Excesses are stored as adipose tissue and are a valuable reserve until obesity ensues. Signs of NE toxicity are gross excesses in adipose deposits and ultimately a reduction in reproductive performance in both males and females. In pregnant, obese females, NE toxicity manifests itself shortly prior to parturition as ketosis.

Maintenance

An animal's energy requirement for maintenance is that amount of dietary energy it must consume daily to neither gain nor lose body energy. Experimentally it is the amount of metabolizable energy resulting in zero change in body energy and zero product. Energy maintenance occurs when daily ME intake equals daily heat production. This ME requirement is not independent of kind or quality of diet fed, however. Fasting heat production is most commonly used as a baseline for describing the maintenance requirement of the animal independent of diet. This daily quantity of energy is defined as the net energy required for maintenance (NE_m). Measured fasting heat production is used to set maintenance requirements in some systems (ARC, 1980). However, because of the limited data base available and questions about the validity of fasting measurements, particularly on young animals, an extrapolated fasting heat production is used as the reference base for maintenance requirement in the present system (Rattray et al., 1973b). The experimentally derived kilocalorie value of 63 $kg^{0.75} \times d^{-1}$ has been adjusted from an empty body weight (EBW) basis to a live weight (W) basis assuming a 6.1-kg fill for a 40-kg sheep (ARC, 1980). The resulting daily NE_m kilocalorie requirement is approximated as 56 $W^{0.75}$.

Growth

Energy requirements for tissue deposition reflect the proportions of lipid, protein, and water deposited. Each kilogram of empty body gain requires between 1.2 Mcal (mainly protein and water) and 8.0 Mcal (mainly fat and water). Changes in the live weight of sheep also reflect changes in the weight of ingesta in the gastrointestinal tract, which can vary from 60 to 540 g/kg of empty body weight.

Chemical analyses of the empty bodies of 20- to 50-kg growing sheep representative of genotypes produced in the United States show that caloric densities of empty body weight gains (EBG) vary from 3 to 4 Mcal/kg gain in light-weight lambs to 5.5 to 7.5 Mcal/kg in heavier lambs. If these caloric densities of gain are scaled to the empty body weight of the animal raised to the 0.75 power ($EBW^{0.75}$), the variation within genotype drops perceptibly. Variation in caloric density from one genotype to another remains considerable, ranging from approximately 300 to 440 when expressed as kcal $\times$ EBG $\times$ $EBW^{0.75}$.

The requirement for growth across this 20- to 50-kg weight span appears to be closely related to the yearling ram weight of the genotype, which, in turn, is closely related to genotype mature weight (Parker and Pope, 1983). Relating the caloric densities of gains of nine genotypes (Reid et al., 1968; Burton and Reid, 1969; Drew and Reid, 1975b) to a measure of the yearling ram weights (Figure 1) of those genotypes (Parker and Pope, 1983) yields the following equation:

$$NE_g = 644 - 2.61W; r = -0.883$$

where NE_g equals Mcal of retained tissue energy per day in empty body gains per kg EBG per $EBW^{0.75}$, and W equals the yearling ram weight of the genotype. This relationship extrapolated to an average mature ram weight genotype of 115 kg corresponds to an average requirement of 344 kcal $\times$ EBG $\times$ $EBW^{0.75}$.

Calculation of energy requirements for gain also requires extrapolation from an empty body basis to a live weight basis. Two adjustments are necessary, since requirements are described per kilogram gain per unit body weight. Live weight gains are predicted as 9 percent higher than empty body gains, and empty body weight is multiplied by 1.195 to predict live weight and to adjust for fill at a 30 kg EBW similar to ARC values (1980). Tissue energy retained, which is the net energy for growth (NE_g), can now be calculated from live lamb gains and weights. NE_g (kcal $\times$ d^{-1}) equals 276 LWG $\times$ $W^{0.75}$ for medium mature ram weight (115-kg) genotypes. For every 10 kg mature weight less than 115 kg, the energy requirement increases by 21 kcal $\times$ LWG $\times$ $W^{0.75}$, or 7.6 percent. For each 10 kg over 115 kg, a like amount would be subtracted from this requirement for live weight gain (Table 3).

Rams deposit less energy than ewes of the same genotype at equal live weights (Bull et al., 1970; Ferrell et al., 1979). These limited data suggest that caloric densities of energy gains in rams can be estimated at 0.82 times those for ewes. Castrated males may also have somewhat lower requirements than females (Kelloway, 1973; ARC, 1980); however, the quantitative differences are not well established (Rattray et al., 1973a) and no adjustment is recommended at this time.

Level of diet intake, rate of gain, and concentration of

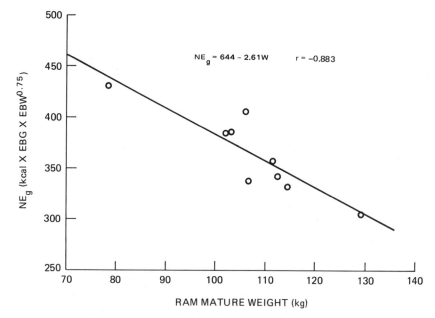

FIGURE 1   Relationship between the energy density of empty body weight gain (NE_g) and genotypic mature weight (W) as estimated by yearling ram weight.

dietary DE have generally had a small long-term effect, if any, on the composition of weight gain in growing lambs after weaning (Reid et al., 1968; Theriez et al., 1982a,b). Very low rates of growth may sometimes result in increased caloric density in body gains (Rattray et al., 1973a; Graham and Searle, 1982), presumably because of the demand for protein resources for wool growth. Very high rates of gain in milk-fed lambs have been associated with greater fat deposition (Black, 1974). On the other hand, high-protein diets in early weaned fast-growing lambs have been associated with depressed fat deposition (Andrews and Ørskov, 1970). The energy requirements for gain in castrated or ewe lambs from medium-sized genotypes are very similar under the present system to the ARC (1980) values for wethers (Figure 2). Increased requirements for small-genotype lambs are similar to increases that ARC (1980) relates to ewe lambs. Gain requirements per kg LWG increase linearly as animals get heavier in the ARC (1980) system and increase slightly curvilinearly in the present system.

Pregnancy

Sheep utilize metabolizable energy for conceptus development with an efficiency of 12 to 14 percent and for pregnancy (gravid uterus plus mammary gland development) with an efficiency of 16 to 18 percent for diets containing 2.4 to 2.6 Mcal ME/kg DM (Rattray et al., 1973b, 1974). (The efficiency of ME utilization may vary with diets that differ markedly from those used to establish the above values.) The NE_y requirements (above NE_m and NE_g) of ewes bearing single, twin, and triplet fetuses that have a total fetal weight of 5.0, 9.0, and 11.5

kg, respectively, are given in Table 4 for different stages of late pregnancy (Rattray et al., 1974). Actual NE requirements may differ from those listed if the fetuses or placental tissues differ markedly in size or composition from those studied by these workers.

Rattray et al. also obtained data indicating that the maintenance requirement of ewes and the efficiency of utilization of ME for maternal maintenance and gain were not changed by pregnancy. The extra heat production that occurs in pregnancy appears to be primarily fetal in origin.

Total feed requirements of pregnant sheep can be obtained by summing the various diet amounts needed to meet each NE requirement (e.g., feed for NE_m + feed for NE_g + feed for NE_y for a pregnant ewe lamb or feed required for NE_m + feed for NE_y for a pregnant adult ewe). Fetal growth and pregnancy requirements are substantial in the last 6 weeks of pregnancy and average approximately 0.5 × maintenance for single-bearing ewes and 1.0 × maintenance for twin-bearing ewes. Total feed requirements would thus increase to 1.5 to 2.0 × maintenance for this physiological phase.

Lactation

Few estimates of the utilization of ME for lactation in sheep are available. Sheep have a relatively short lactation period, and the actual quantity and composition of milk produced by animals suckling young are difficult to determine. Gardner and Hogue (1964) have estimated that 65 to 83 percent of ME is converted to milk energy during 12 weeks of lactation. Higher values were obtained for ewes suckling twins than for ewes with single

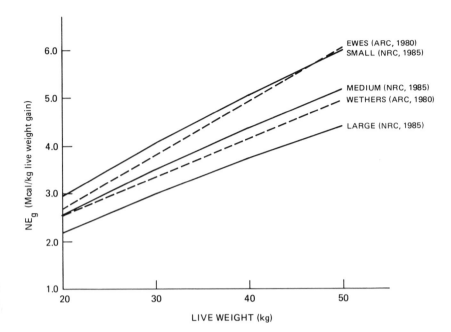

FIGURE 2 Energy density of live weight gains of large, medium, and small genotypes compared with ARC data (1980).

lambs. The average of these values is slightly above that calculated for dairy cattle.

NE Value of Feedstuffs

The NE value of feedstuffs in meeting the NE_m and NE_g requirements of animals has been established from the following. The widest data base and the one most applicable to production situations was developed from the relationships established by Garrett (1980) relating NE_m and NE_g to the ME concentration of the diet:

$$NE_m = 1.37ME - 0.138ME^2 + 0.0105ME^3 - 1.12$$
$$NE_g = 1.42ME - 0.174ME^2 + 0.0122ME^3 - 1.65$$

The data reported by Rattray et al. (1973b) are applicable to pelleted diets. Pelleting changes the relationship between NE and ME, particularly when predicting NE_g (Blaxter and Boyne, 1978). Ovine and bovine partial efficiencies of ME use for maintenance and gain can be interchanged (Blaxter and Wainman, 1964; Garrett et al., 1959; Rattray et al., 1973c; ARC, 1980). The NE_y value of the diet can be estimated as 0.17 ME.

Gut Fill Variation

The large and variable ingesta fraction of sheep weight and gain complicates requirement definitions. Gut fill varies from 6 percent of live weight in milk-fed lambs to 30 or 35 percent in forage-fed lambs soon after weaning. Gut fill assumptions used in this publication are typical for mixed-grain/forage-fed animals, unshrunk but before the morning meal. Gut fill will be higher on forage diets

and lower on very high concentrate diets. Animal handling procedures, feed processing, and quality will cause considerable variation.

Environment

Ambient temperature, thermal radiation, humidity, air movement, contact surfaces, and precipitation may all have a positive or negative effect on a sheep's energy requirement, depending on where they put the animal in relation to its thermoneutral zone. For instance, environmental temperatures above or below the thermoneutral zone will increase energy needs. More specific information is available in *Effect of Environment on Nutrient Requirements of Domestic Animals* (NRC, 1981).

Wool is a very effective insulation against cold and heat; however, reports on the insulating effect of wool against heat are rare (Curtis, 1981). Several scientists (Blaxter, 1966; Ames, 1969; and Brink and Ames, 1975) have reported the influence of fleece on lower critical temperature (LCT) in sheep. Length of fleece and level of feeding (fasting, maintenance, or full feed) interact in influencing LCT. At a given level of feeding, the shorter the fleece the higher the LCT. Thus, shearing increases energy needs when the environmental temperature is below the LCT. NRC (1981) reports LCTs of 25° to 31°C for shorn sheep and −3°C for sheep with full fleece. Diet digestibility by shorn sheep generally declines approximately 0.001 units per degree centigrade fall in ambient temperature; however, unshorn sheep show no digestibility change between −10° and +20°C (Christopherson and Kennedy, 1983).

A distinct seasonal shift in the maintenance energy requirement of sheep, probably modulated by photoperiod, has been noted in thermoneutral environments (Blaxter and Boyne, 1982). The sine wave fluctuation increases to a peak (14 percent above average) in July and decreases a similar magnitude in winter. Parallel fluctuations in voluntary dietary intake also occur.

Level of energy intake or rate of gain to which a sheep has been accustomed has been shown to shift maintenance requirements (Koong et al., 1982). Fast growing, ad libitum-fed sheep have a fasting heat production 30 to 40 percent higher than those of matched weight and age but accustomed to zero gain and low intakes. High basal metabolism appears related to high vital organ mass (i.e., 30 to 40 percent higher liver and small intestine organ weights). These adaptations to low energy intakes are likely to be important to animal survival during periods of scarce feed supplies. Also, low metabolism and renewed increases in vital organ mass likely are important contributors to compensatory gains when animals are refed after a period of scarce feed supply.

Management Considerations

Ewes that begin pregnancy in a very thin condition and weigh, for example, 60 kg (132 lb) are about as large physiologically (i.e., capacity of digestive tract, body fluids, and body surface) as they are when fat and weigh 70 to 75 kg (154 to 164 lb). When thin, they must be fed more energy and protein during gestation than the tables suggest for their particular weight. Feeding at levels suggested for a ewe 10 kg heavier would enable the thin ewe to regain some of the weight lost due to the stress of lactation and/or inadequate feed.

Conversely, an overly fat ewe whose weight suggests she is physiologically larger than she actually is can be fed less during the first 3.5 months of gestation without affecting lamb and wool production. Consideration of an ewe's initial body condition and its effect on subsequent nutrient needs is as vital as consideration of size and age. Figure 3 shows the daily and cumulative weight changes of a 60-kg ewe during various stages of production.

Depending on the desired response of the animals, their existing body condition, their appetite, and environmental conditions, the amount of feed given to sheep may be varied from the levels recommended in Tables 1 and 2. If diets are more concentrated than those indicated in Table 2, the level of dry matter fed may be reduced accordingly. Regardless of the concentration of energy in the diet, however, amounts of feed given should provide the suggested daily requirements of energy, protein, minerals, and vitamins. Figure 4 gives the approximate daily DE requirements of 65- to 70-kg ewes at various stages of production.

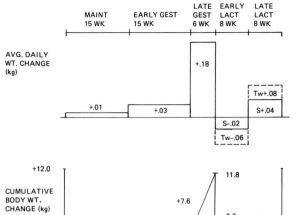

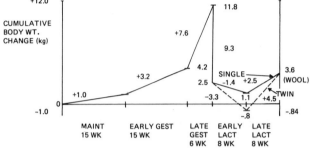

FIGURE 3   Daily and cumulative weight changes of a 60-kg ewe during maintenance, gestation, and lactation.

EWES—FIRST 15 TO 17 WEEKS OF GESTATION

The requirements given in Tables 1 and 2 are intended to provide for maintenance, wool growth, and a small daily gain. If ewes are fat, a submaintenance diet is permissible during the first 3.5 months of gestation (noncritical period) to avoid overly fat ewes at lambing time. No allowance has been made for flushing the ewe to increase lamb production (see the subsection on Flushing, p. 30). The nutrients required for wool production depend on the genetic potential of the sheep to produce wool. The energy required for wool production represents a small fraction of the total energy consumed.

EWES—LAST 4 WEEKS OF GESTATION

In early pregnancy, fetal growth is very small, and the total feed requirement of the ewe is not significantly different from the feed requirement during periods of maintenance. During the last 4 to 6 weeks of gestation, ewes need more energy to meet increased nutrient demands for fetal growth and the development of the potential for high milk production. The nutrient levels recommended in Tables 1 and 2 are adequate for normal fetal and mammary development in single- and twin-bearing ewes.

Excessive energy intake may lead to fattening with resultant birth difficulties in single-bearing ewes. Excessively low energy intakes can result in impaired milk

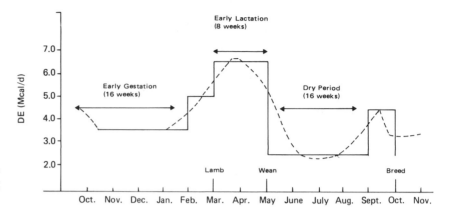

FIGURE 4 Approximate daily digestible energy (DE) requirements of 65- to 70-kg breeding ewes at various production stages.

production capability, reduced mothering instinct, and lower birth weights, leading to reduced viability in the lambs. Either low energy intakes or excessive fattening may result in pregnancy toxemia in the ewe (see the section on Pregnancy Disease, p. 28).

EWES—LACTATION

In Tables 1 and 2, energy requirements are estimated for four groups of lactating ewes: those in the first 6 to 8 weeks of lactation, suckling singles; those in the last 4 to 6 weeks of lactation, suckling singles; those in the first 6 to 8 weeks of lactation, suckling twins; and those in the last 4 to 6 weeks of lactation, suckling twins.

A ewe nursing twin lambs produces 20 to 40 percent more milk than a ewe nursing one lamb. Within the genetic capability of the ewe, milk production responds to nutrient intake of the ewe and demand for milk by the lamb or lambs.

Requirements for the last 6 to 8 weeks of lactation are based on the assumption that milk production during that period is approximately 30 to 40 percent of the production during the first 8 weeks. Thus, nutrient intake during the last 6 to 8 weeks of lactation may be reduced. For example, the weaning weight of lambs nursing ewes fed 20 percent less total digestible nutrients for 6 weeks postpartum than suggested (NRC, 1975) was no different from that of lambs nursing ewes fed 115 to 120 percent of NRC-suggested requirements (Jordan and Hanke, 1977).

In preparing these tables, it has been anticipated that ewes will lose a small amount of weight during early lactation. The amount of weight loss varies greatly, depending on management factors (e.g., the quality and amount of feed available), the number of lambs suckled, the environment, and the ewe's genetic background. Under some range conditions, ewes lose weight in winter (during pregnancy) and gain weight during lactation when grazing high-quality summer ranges.

REPLACEMENT LAMBS

Separate requirements are presented in Tables 1 and 2 for replacement ewes and rams. Ram lambs have the potential to grow at a faster rate than ewe lambs, especially after they reach 40- to 50-kg body weight.

Mature size for the breed will influence energy requirements. Smaller breeds tend to grow more slowly, whereas larger breeds grow more rapidly and have higher nutrient requirements.

Nutrients needed for gain by ewe and ram lambs have been compared. The performance of the ewe lambs fits the equations for maintenance and gain used in developing Tables 1 and 2. Ram lambs gain more rapidly than the equations suggest, have a higher feed intake, and use feed more efficiently for body weight gain. Gains in the body weight of intact males are higher in water and protein and lower in fat than in females.

Producers breeding ewe lambs to yearlings should feed at levels that will result in Finn cross ewe lambs weighing a minimum of 43 kg (95 lb) and other breeds weighing 50 kg (110 lb) at breeding. During the gestation period, sufficient additional feed should be provided to meet pregnancy requirements and weight gains of 0.12 to 0.16 kg daily. During lactation these ewes still require additional feed to ensure adequate milk production and continued growth. Usually this means providing up to 1 kg of grain per ewe daily in addition to a full feed of forage. Weaning at around 6 weeks coupled with sufficient feed postweaning will permit recovery of lactation weight loss and resumption of normal growth rates in preparation for subsequent breeding.

PROTEIN

The lamb is born with a nonfunctional rumen that requires dietary protein be provided through milk or a milk replacer until the rumen becomes functional. The rumen develops some degree of functionality by 2 weeks of age, primarily as a result of the consumption of dry feed (Poe et al., 1971, 1972). During early rumen development, creep feed should be provided to supplement milk or milk replacer. By 6 to 8 weeks of age, the functioning rumen has developed into a culture system for anaerobic bacteria, protozoa, and fungi. These microbes digest feedstuffs and synthesize protein to extents that allow efficient production without milk. Ruminal microorganisms can utilize either protein or nonprotein nitrogen to synthesize microbial protein. The microbial protein, along with undigested feed protein, passes from the rumen-reticulum through the omasum to the abomasum and small intestine where it is subjected to digestive processes similar to those of the nonruminant. Microbial protein reaching the small intestine usually accounts for 40 to 80 percent of the total protein reaching this area of the digestive tract (Owens and Bergen, 1983).

The requirements given in Tables 1, 2, and 5 apply to functioning ruminants and were determined factorially with the basic formula: Crude protein required in g/d = $\dfrac{PD + MFP + EUP + DL + Wool}{NPV}$ (where PD = protein deposited, MFP = metabolic fecal protein, EUP = endogenous urinary protein, DL = dermal loss, and NPV = net protein value). Protein deposited in gain was estimated by applying the following equation (NRC, 1984): PD in g/d = daily gain in kg × (268 − 29.4 × ECOG) when energy content of gain (ECOG) = $\dfrac{NE_g \text{ in kcal/d}}{\text{gain in g/d}}$ with NE_g values taken from Table 3. Protein deposited was set at 2.95 g/d for early gestation and 16.75 g/d for the last 4 weeks of gestation (ARC, 1980) for ewes with single lambs and increased proportionately for higher lambing rates. A milk production of 1.74 kg/d for ewes nursing a single lamb and 2.60 kg/d for those nursing twins and a crude protein content of 47.875 g/liter of milk (ARC, 1980) were used to determine PD need for lactation. Ewe lambs were assumed to produce 75 percent as much milk as mature ewes. Metabolic fecal protein in g/d was assigned a value of 33.44 g/kg DM intake (NRC, 1984). Endogenous urinary protein in g/d was calculated as 0.14675 × body weight in kg + 3.375 (ARC, 1980). Dermal loss in g/d was estimated to be 0.1125 × kgW$^{0.75}$ (ARC, 1980). Crude protein in wool in g/d of ewes and rams was assigned a value of 6.8 g, assuming an annual grease fleece weight of 4 kg. For lambs, crude protein in wool in g/d was calculated as 3 + (0.1 × protein retained in the fleece free body) (ARC, 1980). A net protein value of 0.561 was used based on a true digestibility of 0.85 (Storm and Ørskov, 1982) and a biological value of 0.66 (NRC, 1984). Expression of requirements as crude protein is consistent with the dairy (NRC,

1978) and beef (NRC, 1984) reports, but contrary to ARC (1980). The potential advantages of digestible protein are negated by the use of standard factors for conversions between crude protein and digestible protein by both NRC (1975) and ARC (1980). Development of a more-comprehensive system of expressing protein requirements of ruminants is being intensively studied, but a consensus has not developed. Some of the key issues are summarized later in this section. Numerous reviews are available that treat these issues more extensively (NRC, 1976, 1984, 1985; ARC, 1980; Huber and Kung, 1981; Ørskov, 1982; Owens, 1982; Owens and Bergen, 1983; Chalupa, 1984).

Microbial Nitrogen Requirements

Although a variety of anaerobic microorganisms inhabit the rumen, bacteria are most active in protein digestion and synthesis of microbial protein. Bacteria degrade dietary protein in the rumen to simpler nitrogen compounds such as ammonia, amino acids, and peptides and incorporate these materials into cellular protein. Ammonia also is derived from dietary nonprotein nitrogen sources such as urea. Ammonia is the nitrogen source preferred by the bacteria in the rumen for cellular protein synthesis (Bryant and Robinson, 1963; Hungate, 1966). Lack of ammonia in the rumen may limit microbial growth when the intake of protein or the ruminal degradation of the dietary protein is low. Although the concentration of ruminal ammonia-nitrogen required for optimal microbial growth is unclear, concentrations above 5 to 10 mg per 100/ml of ruminal fluid have not consistently increased bacterial protein production (Satter and Slyter, 1974; Pisulewski et al., 1981; Leng and Nolan, 1984).

Nonprotein Nitrogen

Substitution of dietary nonprotein nitrogen (NPN) for plant and animal protein sources often will lower the cost of the complete diet fed to sheep. Urea is the most common source of NPN fed. It is useful only when it is needed to provide a source of ammonia to ruminal bacteria. Since urea is rapidly hydrolyzed to ammonia by bacteria in the rumen, strict management techniques are essential when high levels of urea or other NPN sources are fed to prevent decreased feed intake and ammonia toxicity. Urea is utilized most efficiently when thoroughly mixed in high-concentrate, low-protein diets that are fed continuously. Urea concentrations should not exceed 1 percent of the dietary dry matter or one-third of the total dietary protein. High-concentrate diets provide more energy than high-roughage diets for bacterial protein synthesis from ammonia (Owens and Bergen, 1983). The resulting decrease in ammonia absorption reduces the likelihood of ammonia toxicity (Bartley et al., 1976). If NPN is substituted for dietary protein, special emphasis should be given to the supplementation of potassium, phosphorus, and sulfur, which are absent in urea. Particular attention should be given to sulfur supplementation, because wool contains a high percentage of sulfur-containing amino acids.

In attempts to reduce the threat of ammonia toxicity and/or improve the utilization of ruminal ammonia, other forms of NPN (biuret, triuret, and complexes of urea with formaldehyde or molasses) have been developed (Nikolic et al., 1980). These compounds have slower ammonia release, which should more nearly parallel energy availability and increase bacterial protein synthesis (Johnson, 1976). However, these slow release forms of NPN have not consistently improved nitrogen utilization (Owens and Bergen, 1983).

Ruminal Degradation and/or Bypass of Dietary Protein

Dietary protein is either digested in the rumen or escapes undigested to the omasum and abomasum. If it is not digested in the rumen, it is described as "bypass" or "escape" protein (Owens and Bergen, 1983). Bypass protein is either digested postruminally or excreted in the feces. Dietary protein degraded in the rumen yields ammonia (Chalupa, 1975), which can then be incorporated into microbial protein. Chalupa (1975), Satter and Roffler (1975), and ARC (1980) have classified protein sources on the basis of the extent to which they bypass ruminal degradation (percentage of dietary protein that reaches the small intestine undigested). Low-bypass sources (< 40 percent) include casein, soybean meal, sunflower meal, and peanut meal; medium-bypass sources (40 to 60 percent) include cottonseed meal, dehydrated alfalfa meal, corn grain, and brewers dried grains; and high-bypass sources (> 60 percent) include meat meal, corn gluten meal, blood meal, feather meal, fish meal, and formaldehyde-treated proteins. Feed processing conditions, animal variations, dietary alterations, and changes in microbial population affect extent of dietary protein bypass, but these effects have not been well quantitated. When high-bypass protein sources are fed, supplementation with NPN will be needed to maintain adequate ruminal ammonia levels for microbial protein synthesis.

Increased bypass of dietary protein does not always increase production, because bypassed protein may be poorly digested postruminally, the balance of amino acids available for absorption from the small intestine may be poor, or other nutrients may limit production (Young et al., 1981; Owens and Bergen, 1983). Conversely, if microbial protein is the only protein reaching the small intestine, animal production may not be maximal (Satter et al., 1977). Presentation to the small intestine of a mixture of microbial protein and complementary dietary protein is desired. Striving to optimize this mixture will undoubtedly be the subject of much research activity in the future, as it has been in the past.

Amino Acids

Amino acids available for absorption from the small intestine are supplied by microbial and/or bypassed dietary protein. The tissues of sheep require the same amino acids as those of the nonruminant (Black et al., 1957; Downes, 1961). In sheep, however, the relationship of dietary amino acid supply with tissue requirements has been difficult to define because of the intervention of the protein digestive and synthetic functions in the rumen. Also, amino acid requirements are difficult to quantitate because of variability in requirements for various productive functions. For example, wool growth responds to sulfur amino acid supplementation (Reis and Schinckel, 1963), whereas other functions do not. Hogan (1975) concluded that the amino acid composition of protein deposited in the tissues and that secreted in milk, plus the maintenance requirement, should equal the total needed by the animal. Owens and Bergen (1983) further concluded that the quantity, as well as the ratios, of amino acids required by the animal varies with both the productive function and the level of production.

Dietary amino acids are normally rapidly degraded in the rumen. To increase bypass, Neudoerffer et al. (1971) and Digenis et al. (1974) coated dietary amino acids so they would be ruminally stable but available for absorption postruminally, suggesting that the combination of amino acid and NPN supplementation may be feasible in the future.

Protein Deficiency and Toxicity

Ammonia deficiency in the rumen reduces the extent and efficiency of rumen function. Deficiencies or imbalances of amino acids at the tissue level result in decreased protein synthesis, as well as reduced feed intake and lower efficiency of feed utilization. Growth rate and milk and wool production all react to inadequate protein intake. Extreme deficiency results in severe digestive disturbances, loss of weight, anemia, edema, and reduced resistance to disease. Increased feed intake after protein supplementation is a good practical indication that protein was deficient (NRC, 1984).

Excess protein becomes an expensive and inefficient source of energy, but rather large excesses can be fed without producing acute toxicity (Fenderson and Bergen, 1976). Excesses of NPN or highly soluble protein may produce ammonia toxicity (Bartley et al., 1981). Affected animals may display nervousness, incoordination, labored breathing, bloating, severe tetany, respiratory collapse, and ultimately death.

MINERALS

Although the body contains many mineral elements, only 15 have been demonstrated to be essential for sheep. Seven are major mineral constituents: sodium, chlorine, calcium, phosphorus, magnesium, potassium, and sulfur. The other eight are trace elements: iodine, iron, molybdenum, copper, cobalt, manganese, zinc, and selenium. Additional elements under investigation with other species may eventually prove to be essential for sheep. Fluorine is discussed (p. 22) because of its toxicity to sheep.

The multiplicity of interactions among minerals makes it difficult to determine the requirements of sheep for specific minerals, because a lack or abundance of one mineral may render others deficient or toxic. Tables 6 and 7 present the mineral requirements of sheep and the toxic levels when known. In both tables, values are estimates based on available experimental data.

Sodium and Chlorine (Salt)

Sodium (Na) and chlorine (Cl) serve many functions in the body. They maintain osmotic pressure, regulate the acid-base balance, and control water metabolism in tissues. Sodium occurs primarily in extracellular fluids and bones. Chlorine is found within cells, in the body fluids, in gastric secretions such as hydrogen chloride, and in the form of salt (Underwood, 1981).

Animals that are deprived of adequate salt may try to satisfy their craving by chewing wood, licking dirt, or eating toxic amounts of poisonous plants. Inadequate salt may result in inappetence, growth retardation, inefficiency of feed use, and increased water consumption (Hagsten et al., 1975; Underwood, 1981). In addition, the concentration of sodium falls and that of potassium rises in the parotid saliva of sheep on low-sodium diets (Morris and Peterson, 1975). Signs of sodium deficiency occur without a significant decline in either plasma or milk sodium concentrations until a condition of extreme deficiency is reached (Morris and Peterson, 1975; Underwood, 1981).

Several feeding and metabolism studies have been conducted to determine the sodium and/or salt requirement of sheep. McClymont et al. (1957) reported that the addition of 1.2 to 2.6 g of sodium per day (as sodium chloride) to the diet of very thin wethers fed a low-sodium grain diet increased growth rate. They concluded that the sodium requirement was greater than 0.9 g/d (0.06 percent of the diet). From balance data, Devlin and Roberts (1963) estimated the sodium requirements for maintenance of wether lambs to be 1.01 g/d (0.18 percent of the diet). Hagsten et al. (1975) concluded that the dietary salt requirement for growing lambs ranged between 0.33 and 0.43 percent of the air-dry ration (90 percent dry matter). They further stated that since most sheep rations contain approximately 0.2 percent salt, a supplemental level of 0.2 percent is adequate. Based on the maintenance of a normal $Na^+:K^+$ ratio in the parotid saliva, Morris and Peterson (1975) concluded that a dietary sodium level of 0.09 percent met the requirements of lactating ewes. Apparently no feeding trials have been conducted in which the requirement for chlorine can be assessed independently of sodium; thus, the chlorine requirement is unknown.

When adding salt to mixed feeds, it is customary to add 0.5 percent to the complete diet or 1.0 percent to the concentrate portion. Range operators commonly provide 220 to 340 g of salt per ewe per month as a salt lick. Drylot tests show lambs consume approximately 5 to 10 g of salt daily (Denton, 1969). Mature ewes in confinement consume 15 to 30 g of salt daily when it is offered free choice (Jordan and Hanke, 1982). Salt may safely be used to limit free-choice supplement intake if adequate water is available. Such mixtures are usually 10 to 50 percent salt depending on the desired amount of ration to be consumed. Trace-mineralized salt should not be used for this purpose because of the possibility of excessive intake of various trace minerals, particularly toxic levels of copper. In many areas (commonly arid), feed and water may contain enough salt to meet the animal's requirements, and supplemental salt need not be offered.

On the basis of research conducted by Meyer and Weir (1954) and Meyer et al. (1955), the maximum tolerable level of dietary salt for sheep was set at 9.0 percent (NRC, 1980). Jackson et al. (1971), however, reported a linear decrease in weight and energy gains of growing-finishing lambs as salt content increased from 1.8 to 7.6 percent of the diet.

Calcium and Phosphorus

Calcium (Ca) and phosphorus (P) are closely interrelated, particularly in the development and maintenance of the skeletal system. Approximately 99 percent of the body's calcium and 80 percent of its phosphorus are found in bones and teeth. Diets lacking in calcium or phosphorus may result in abnormal bone development, a condition known as rickets in young animals and osteomalacia in adults. The 1 percent of calcium and 20 percent of phosphorus not present in skeletal tissues are widely distributed in body fluids and soft tissues, where they serve a wide range of essential functions (Underwood, 1981).

Signs of calcium deficiency due to a low intake of calcium develop slowly because the body draws on calcium in bone. Blood levels of calcium are normally not good indicators of calcium intake or status, as these levels are hormonally controlled (Care et al., 1980). Blood calcium levels below 9 mg/dl of plasma (hypocalcemia), however, suggest chronic low calcium intake or utilization at a rate that exceeds calcium mobilization from bone (as during lactation). In extreme cases, which may develop in lambs on high-grain diets, low intakes of calcium may result in tetany or precipitate an outbreak of urinary calculi in intact or castrated male sheep.

Sheep efficiently utilize phosphorus, partly by recycling considerable amounts in parotid and other salivary secretions. The phosphorus concentration of parotid saliva, rumen fluid, and serum is related to phosphorus intake (Tomas et al., 1967). In some cases, sheep recycle more phosphorus per day through parotid saliva than is required in the diet to maintain normal concentrations in body pools. This salivary phosphorus can moderate variations in rumen phosphorus due to diet, particularly at low phosphorus intakes (Cohen, 1980). A phosphorus deficiency may be manifested by slow growth, deprived appetite, unthrifty appearance, listlessness, low level of phosphorus in the blood (less than 4 mg/dl of plasma), and development of rickets (Beeson et al., 1944; Preston, 1977).

Calcium and phosphorus utilization are influenced by vitamin D. Dietary calcium is absorbed according to the nutritional requirements of the animal, and on a low-calcium diet the efficiency of absorption is increased. The efficiency of absorption also is increased in adult animals during pregnancy and lactation (Care et al., 1980; Scott and McLean, 1981; Braithwaite, 1983a). Differences have been observed in absorption of phosphorus within and between breeds of sheep. These differences appear to be partly heritable and vary as much as twofold (Field et al., 1983; Field, 1984). Adaptation to a low-phosphorus diet is due to an increase in the efficiency of intestinal absorption and a reduction in the salivary secretion of phosphorus (Care et al., 1980).

Calcium and phosphorus requirements were calculated using a factorial approach. First, a net requirement was calculated from estimates of the storage and excretion of these elements during growth, pregnancy, and lactation and of endogenous losses. The dietary requirement then was calculated by dividing the net requirement by the coefficient of absorption. Daily dietary requirements were converted to dietary concentrations (percent of diet) by dividing by daily DM intakes.

Endogenous fecal losses of calcium were assumed to vary in a linear relationship with DM intake, as described by Braithwaite (1982, 1983a). These values varied from 11.6 mg Ca/kg body weight per day for maintenance of mature ewes consuming 15.6 g DM/kg body weight per day to 43.2 mg Ca/kg body weight per day for a 10-kg, rapidly growing, early-weaned lamb consuming 60 g DM/kg body weight per day.

Total endogenous losses of phosphorus were assumed to be 20 mg/kg body weight per day for maintenance, early gestation, and growth. However, a higher value (30 mg/kg body weight per day) was used to calculate phosphorus requirements during the last 4 weeks of gestation and during lactation. ARC (1980) used a constant value of 14 mg P/kg body weight per day to calculate phosphorus requirements for all stages of production. The higher values used in this publication reflect the fact that there may be inevitable losses of phosphorus associated with the higher phosphorus intakes required to meet the demands of late gestation and lactation as suggested by Braithwaite (1984a), as well as evidence that the phosphorus levels recommended by ARC (1980) may be inadequate for pregnancy and lactation (Braithwaite, 1983b, 1984b) and growth (Field et al., 1982).

The calcium and phosphorus contents of gain were 11 and 6 g/kg empty body gain, respectively (ARC, 1980; Grace, 1983). Although it is recognized that numerous factors influence the birth weight of lambs, including breed, size, and age of ewe; breed of sire; season and type of birth; sex of lamb; and nutrition of the ewe (Neville et al., 1958; Jamison et al., 1961; Shelton, 1968; Rastogi et al., 1982; Stritzke and Whiteman, 1982), only the size of the ewe at mating and the type of birth (single or twins) were considered in estimating calcium and phosphorus requirements for gestation. It was assumed that single lambs were 22.6 percent and twins were 36.1 percent of the ewe's metabolic weight at the time of mating (Donald and Russell, 1970). Net calcium and phosphorus values for the gravid uterus were calculated as described in ARC (1980).

The calcium and phosphorus contents of ewes' milk, used to calculate nutritional requirements, were 0.18 and 0.14 percent, respectively. The milk production values used in estimating net calcium and phosphorus requirements for lactation in mature ewes were 1.74 kg/d, first 6 to 8 weeks of lactation suckling singles; 1.11 kg/d, last 4 to 6 weeks of lactation suckling singles; 2.60 kg/d, first 6 to 8 weeks of lactation suckling twins; and 1.67 kg/d, last 4 to 6 weeks of lactation suckling twins. The milk production of ewe lambs was 1.30 kg/d, first 6 to 8 weeks of lactation suckling singles, and 1.95 kg/d, first 6 to 8 weeks of lactation suckling twins (Langlands, 1973; Pert et al., 1975; Doney et al., 1979).

The values used for absorption of dietary calcium were 0.4 for maintenance, 0.5 for gestation, and 0.6 for lactation and rapidly growing lambs. These values were based on data summarized by ARC (1980) and on subsequent research by Braithwaite (1983a). The values used for absorption of phosphorus were 0.6 for maintenance and for the first 15 weeks of gestation and 0.7 for the last 4 weeks of gestation, for lactation, and for growing lambs. These values were based on research reported by Grace (1981), Field et al. (1982), Braithwaite (1983b, 1984a,b), and Field (1983a, 1984).

The supply of calcium found in most pasture and range forages usually is adequate. However, areas have been reported in Florida, Louisiana, Nebraska, Virginia, and West Virginia in which calcium supplementation is required for sheep consuming pasture or range forage. Legumes are excellent sources of calcium. Corn silage and most grasses, including small grain forages, are fair to poor sources. In some areas of the West, soils are formed largely from calcium carbonate and dolomite, and forage in these areas may have a calcium content up to nine times greater than the level considered adequate. Excessive intakes of calcium, however, are normally not detrimental when adequate phosphorus is supplied. Finishing-lamb diets that contain nonlegume roughage or that are high in grain usually require calcium supplementation (see Urinary Calculi, p. 28).

Pasture and range forages in North America are commonly low in phosphorus (Preston, 1977). Consequently, ewes (especially lactating ewes) fed primarily forages receive an inadequate supply of phosphorus and need a diet supplemented with phosphorus when a legume forage is fed and with calcium and phosphorus when nonlegume hay is fed. Furthermore, species and stage of maturity of forage significantly affect concentration, apparent absorption, and retention of major minerals by sheep (Powell et al., 1978).

Several factors may influence the calcium and phosphorus nutrition of sheep, necessitating a reevaluation of present recommendations. For example, chronic internal parasitic infections can have a serious negative impact on calcium and phosphorus status (Sykes et al., 1979). Magnesium deficiency interferes with calcium absorption; low levels of dietary phosphorus also decrease the rate of calcium absorption. Both aluminum and iron at elevated levels will increase the need for phosphorus (Rosa et al., 1982).

Although the oral intake of calcium compounds generally does not produce toxicity problems, addition of extra calcium to an otherwise adequate diet may precipitate a deficiency of other elements, including phosphorus, magnesium, iron, iodine, zinc, and manganese (NRC, 1980). Assuming adequate levels of dietary phosphorus, however, ruminants can tolerate a wide calcium-to-phosphorus ratio (as wide as 7:1) and as much as 2 percent calcium in the diet. But the long-term intake of phosphorus at levels 2 to 3 times the requirement for main-

tenance can cause increased bone resorption in adult animals, and a narrow calcium-to-phosphorus ratio (< 2:1) may contribute to an increased incidence of urinary calculi in intact and castrated male sheep (NRC, 1980).

Magnesium

Magnesium (Mg) fulfills many physiological functions. It is a constituent of bone (approximately 60 to 70 percent of the total body magnesium is present in the skeleton) and also is necessary for many enzyme systems and for the proper functioning of the nervous system (Martens and Rayssiquier, 1980; Underwood, 1981; Larvor, 1983). Skeletal magnesium serves as a reserve that can supply magnesium to soft tissues during dietary deficiency. Although approximately 30 percent of skeletal magnesium can be mobilized from bone in young animals, the value for adults is only around 2 percent (Rook and Storry, 1962; Martens and Rayssiquier, 1980).

Tetany is the classic sign of magnesium deficiency in sheep. A lamb with hypomagnesemic tetany may fall on its side with its legs alternately rigidly extended and relaxed. Frothing at the mouth and profuse salivation are evident, and death may occur. The signs of magnesium deficiency in adults are similar to those in younger animals, but death may occur more rapidly after convulsions (Ammerman and Henry, 1983). Other signs of magnesium deficiency in young lambs include loss of appetite, hyperemia, and calcification of soft tissues (Underwood, 1981; Ammerman and Henry, 1983). Outbreaks of tetany occur most frequently in nursing ewes shortly after they are turned out to pasture in the spring (grass tetany). Incidence is highest during the first 4 or 5 weeks after lambing, when magnesium requirements for lactation are maximal. Cases are most common where the grass is high in nitrogen and potassium and low in magnesium (Egan, 1969; Martens and Rayssiquier, 1980).

Information on dietary magnesium requirements is limited. In magnesium-deficient sheep around 18 months old, the minimum amount of magnesium (as magnesium oxide) required to restore feed intake is 0.33 percent (Ammerman et al., 1971). When a semipurified diet containing 0.02 percent magnesium was fed to 4- to 8-week-old lambs, serum magnesium levels decreased to 0.5 to 0.7 mg/dl and most lambs exhibited convulsions within 45 days. Addition of magnesium carbonate to the diet to provide 0.08 percent total magnesium maintained serum magnesium levels of approximately 2.0 mg/dl (McAleese and Forbes, 1959). Sheep with serum magnesium levels < 1.0 mg/dl are severely hypomagnesemic; serum levels > 1.0 but < 1.5 mg/dl are considered mildly hypomagnesemic (Amos et al., 1975). Hypomagnesemic tetany was reported in a flock of ewes grazing spring grass that was analyzed as 0.15, 4.1, and 2.6 percent magnesium, potassium, and nitrogen, respectively. In this case, dosing with magnesium alloy bullets (30 g) effectively controlled grass tetany (Egan, 1969). Lambs (6 to 12 months old), yearlings (1 to 2 years old), and adult sheep (2 to 3 years old) fed a semipurified diet containing 0.1 percent added magnesium exhibited a slight decrease in voluntary feed intake and plasma magnesium levels (Chicco et al., 1973a).

Although the results of the above studies vary, collectively they indicate that the levels recommended in the previous revision (NRC, 1975) for the magnesium requirements of sheep (0.04 to 0.08 percent) are too low. Therefore, the suggested minimum magnesium requirements are 0.12, 0.15, and 0.18 percent of dry matter for growing lambs, for ewes in late pregnancy, and for ewes in early lactation, respectively. Magnesium requirements may be increased when feeds contain high levels of potassium (Thomas and Potter, 1976; Greene et al., 1983a,b), calcium (Chicco et al., 1973b), and nitrogen in the form of nonprotein nitrogen or rumen-degradable protein (Fenner, 1979), since these dietary constituents decrease the efficiency of magnesium absorption and/or utilization. In situations where ewes in early lactation are grazing forage with high nitrogen and potassium contents, the minimum level of magnesium in the diet should be 0.2 percent.

Commonly used feedstuffs vary widely in magnesium content. Most cereal grains are fair sources of magnesium, varying from 0.13 to 0.22 percent Mg on a DM basis. Plant protein supplements are excellent sources (0.28 to 0.62 percent Mg), whereas protein supplements of animal origin are more variable (0.11 to 1.22 percent Mg). By-product feedstuffs derived from plants tend to be good sources of magnesium. The magnesium contents of forage plants vary but are normally higher in legumes than in grasses (NRC, 1982); magnesium fertilization has been used to increase the magnesium content of forages (Thompson and Reid, 1981; Fontenot, 1980). Based on absorption and retention data, magnesium in the forms of magnesium carbonate, magnesium oxide, and magnesium sulfate is well used by sheep. Magnesium in magnesite was essentially unavailable (Ammerman et al., 1972; Fontenot, 1980).

Magnesium toxicosis is unlikely except by accidental feeding of high levels. Oral administration of 0.5 percent magnesium to wethers did not produce toxicity, but administration of 0.8 percent or higher resulted in signs of toxicosis. Signs of magnesium toxicosis are lethargy, disturbance in locomotion, diarrhea, lower feed intake, lower levels of performance, and death (NRC, 1980).

Potassium

Potassium (K) is the third most abundant mineral in the body, accounting for approximately 0.3 percent of the body's dry matter. Potassium is primarily present in intracellular fluids (skin and muscle), where it affects osmotic pressure and acid-base balance within the cell. It also aids in activating several enzyme systems involved in energy transfer and utilization, protein synthesis, and carbohydrate metabolism (Clanton, 1980; Underwood, 1981).

Suboptimal levels of potassium result in decreased feed intake and decreased live weight gain. Listlessness, stiffness, impaired response to sudden disturbances, convulsions, and death have also been reported. Deficient lambs had low potassium levels in whole blood, plasma, and red blood cells, and red cell sodium was increased (Telle et al., 1964).

Brink (1961) found that KCl added to a semipurified diet containing 0.17 percent potassium improved performance of lambs, with a 0.5-percent potassium level yielding maximum performance. Telle et al. (1964) reported that a potassium level of 0.34 percent of the dietary DM was borderline for growing-finishing lambs, and that lower amounts of potassium resulted in growth depression almost immediately. Values for average daily gain and feed efficiency were not significantly different for lambs fed either 0.46 or 0.68 percent potassium. Campbell and Roberts (1965) determined that the level of potassium necessary to promote optimum performance of lambs fed a semipurified diet was 0.52 percent (DM basis). All the above estimates of the potassium requirements of growing-finishing lambs involved the use of $KHCO_3$ and K_2CO_3 as sources of potassium in semipurified diets (Brink, 1961; Telle et al., 1964; Campbell and Roberts, 1965). Thus, part of the responses observed may have been attributable to the buffering effect of HCO_3^-. This possibility is supported by research with growing-finishing lambs fed a high-concentrate diet (10 percent roughage). In this instance, there was a positive response when 1 or 2 percent $KHCO_3$ was added to the basal diet (0.46 percent potassium, air dry basis) but not when KCl was the source of supplemental potassium (Calhoun and Shelton, 1983).

The potassium requirement for growth in lambs appears to be no more than 0.5 percent of the diet (DM basis). Since potassium is a major mineral element present in milk, slightly higher levels (0.7 to 0.8 percent) may be required for lactation and during periods of stress (Beede et al., 1983). Hutcheson et al. (1979) has shown that receiving diets for shipped, stressed calves should contain between 1.2 and 2.2 percent potassium. Potassium content of the diet appears to have a curvilinear effect on urolith formation. In wethers fed calculogenic diets, maximum urolithiasis occurred with 0.64 percent potassium in the diet and decreased at levels above and below that (Lamprecht et al., 1969).

The potassium content of most grains is 0.4 percent or greater and in most harvested forages exceeds 1.0

percent of the dry matter. Therefore, the possibility of potassium deficiency is slight under most feeding conditions. Nevertheless, attention should be given to potassium supply when lambs are fed high-grain diets and when sheep are grazing mature range forage during winter or drought periods. Potassium levels in mature range forage have been reported to decrease to less than 0.2 percent. Under such grazing conditions beef cattle have responded favorably to the addition of potassium to the range supplement (Clanton, 1980).

The maximum tolerable level of potassium for sheep is approximately 3 percent of the diet DM (NRC, 1980). Magnesium absorption was depressed 24.4 and 61.2 percent when diets containing 2.4 and 4.8 percent potassium, respectively, were fed to wethers. Increasing the level of potassium in the diet also depressed serum magnesium levels (Greene et al., 1983a). The negative effect of high levels of potassium on magnesium utilization can help precipitate magnesium tetany in sheep on diets marginal in magnesium (Field, 1983b). Increasing the level of dietary potassium from 0.7 to 3.0 percent linearly decreased energy and weight gains in lambs (Jackson et al., 1971).

Sulfur

The signs of sulfur (S) deficiency are similar to the signs of protein deficiency (loss of appetite, reduced weight gain or weight loss, and reduced wool growth). In addition, they include excessive salivation, lacrimation, and shedding of wool. In extreme cases, emaciation and death may occur (Goodrich et al., 1978). Because sulfur functions in the synthesis of the sulfur-containing amino acids (methionine and cysteine) and B-vitamins (biotin and thiamin) during microbial digestion in the rumen, rumen microorganisms that are deficient in sulfur do not function normally. Addition of sulfur in such cases increases feed intake, digestibility, and nitrogen retention (Bray and Hemsley, 1969; Bird, 1974; Guardiola et al., 1983). Sulfur levels of 0.15 to 0.20 percent (DM basis) appear adequate for normal rumen function (Goodrich et al., 1978).

Sulfur has functions in the body in addition to those concerned with protein structure. Sulfate sulfur is an important constituent of the chondroitin sulfates and of the mucins of the gastrointestinal tract (including saliva), the reproductive tracts, and other duct systems (Moir, 1979; Goodrich and Thompson, 1981). Because wool is high in sulfur, this element is closely related to wool production.

Much information has been obtained in recent years about sulfur metabolism in the rumen, sulfur losses, sulfur requirements of microorganisms, and the recycling of sulfur and nitrogen (Goodrich et al., 1978; Bull, 1979; Moir, 1979). This information generally supports the recommendation that a dietary nitrogen-sulfur ratio of 10:1

be maintained. The percentages of sulfur required in diet dry matter are 0.14 to 0.18 for mature ewes and 0.18 to 0.26 for young lambs.

Practically all common feedstuffs contain more than 0.1 percent sulfur. Mature grass and grass hays (especially those grown on granitic soils), however, are sometimes low in sulfur and may not furnish enough for optimal performance. Where forages are low in sulfur, or where diets contain relatively large quantities of urea, weight gains and growth of wool can be increased by feeding a sulfur supplement, such as sulfate sulfur, elemental sulfur, or sulfur-containing proteins or amino acids. Most grains contain 0.10 to 0.15 percent sulfur, so it is conceivable that lambs on high-concentrate diets could lack adequate sulfur.

Although inorganic compounds are generally more convenient and economical for supplemental feeding, sulfur availability is greatest from methionine followed by sulfate sulfur and then elemental sulfur. Sulfur from sodium sulfate is around 80 percent as available as sulfur from methionine, and sulfur from elemental sulfur is about half as available as that from sodium sulfate (Johnson et al., 1970).

Available data do not allow the establishment of a safe upper limit for the different sulfur sources for sheep, but it appears that 0.4 percent is the maximum tolerable level for dietary sulfur as sodium sulfate (NRC, 1980). At levels slightly above 0.4 percent, there is a decrease in DM intake and rumen motility. At higher levels, complete anorexia, ruminal stasis, impaction, and a foul odor of hydrogen sulfide on the breath of sheep are observed. Since the availability of elemental sulfur is only 50 percent that of sodium sulfate, a correspondingly higher level of elemental sulfur would be required to induce signs of sulfur toxicosis (Johnson et al., 1970). Sulfur forms insoluble complexes with copper and molybdenum and decreases their utilization (Suttle and McLauchlan, 1976; Grace and Suttle, 1979; Suttle, 1983a). It also decreases selenium retention (Pope et al., 1968).

Iodine

Iodine (I) is necessary for the synthesis of the thyroid hormones, thyroxine and triiodothyronine (Underwood, 1977). In newborn lambs, the most common sign of iodine deficiency is enlargement of the thyroid gland. If the condition is not advanced, lambs may survive. Other signs are lambs born weak, dead, or without wool (Underwood, 1981). Signs of iodine deficiency in mature sheep seldom take the form of a change in the animal's appearance. Through the impairment of physiological functions, however, deficiency may result in reduced yield of wool and reduced rate of conception (Potter et al., 1980; Underwood, 1981).

Iodine requirements of sheep have been estimated

from heat production (Underwood, 1977), thyroxine secretion rate (Henneman et al., 1955; Singh et al., 1956; Falconer and Robertson, 1961; Robertson and Falconer, 1961; Falconer, 1963), and serum triiodothyronine levels (Barry et al., 1983). Based on heat production the minimum iodine requirement is between 0.05 and 0.10 mg/kg diet DM. Values based on the rate of thyroxine secretion vary from 0.05 to 1.25 mg/kg diet DM. Levels of 0.18 to 0.27 mg I/kg diet DM are necessary to maintain serum triiodothyronine levels in growing lambs.

The previous NRC (1975) publication for sheep reported the iodine requirement as 0.10 to 0.80 mg/kg diet DM in diets not containing goitrogens, the higher level being indicated for pregnancy and lactation. These levels are also being recommended in this revision. When goitrogens such as the glucosinolates found in kale (*Brassica oleracea*) or other thioglycosides found in cruciferous plants are present, the dietary iodine should be increased (Underwood, 1977; Barry et al., 1983).

Areas in the United States deficient in iodine are the northeastern section of the country and the Great Lakes and Rocky Mountain regions (Underwood, 1981). Serious losses of lambs can be prevented in these areas by feeding iodized salt to ewes during gestation. Iodized salt generally is formulated by adding 0.0078 percent of stabilized iodine to salt (Perry, 1982). Stabilization is necessary to prevent losses from exposure to sunlight or moisture. Iodized salt should not be used in a mixture with a concentrate supplement to limit feed intake, since the animals may consume an excessive amount of iodine.

Signs of iodine toxicosis are depression, anorexia, hypothermia, and poor body weight gain (McCauley et al., 1973). According to NRC (1980) the maximum tolerable level of iodine for sheep is 50 mg/kg diet DM. McCauley et al. (1973), however, reported that levels of 267 mg iodine (as ethylenediamine dihydroiodide) and 133 mg iodine (as potassium iodide) per kilogram had no effect on live weight gain and feed intake of lambs during a 22-day treatment period.

Iron

Iron (Fe) deficiency in animals is characterized by poor growth, lethargy, anemia, increased respiration rate, decreased resistance to infection, and in severe cases high mortality (Underwood, 1981). A primary iron deficiency in grazing sheep is very unlikely because of the iron content of pasture plants and the contamination of plants by soil (McDonald, 1968). Loss of blood resulting from parasite infestation, however, can produce a secondary iron-deficiency anemia (Silverman et al., 1970). Experimentally, iron-deficiency anemia has also been produced in milk-fed lambs (Thomas and Wheeler, 1932) and in lambs raised on slotted wooden floors and fed a semipurified diet (Lawlor et al., 1965). Anemia in suckling lambs can be prevented by administering intramuscular injections of iron-dextran or by offering a commercial oral iron compound free choice in the creep area. Two injections, 150 mg of iron each, given 2 to 3 weeks apart are preferable to a single injection (Holz et al., 1961; Mansfield et al., 1967).

The addition of 13 mg Fe/kg diet DM was reported to increase blood hemoglobin levels and total red cell volume in artificially reared lambs given a liquid diet of skimmed milk plus fat (Brisson and Bouchard, 1970). In another study, acute iron-deficiency signs were observed in lambs fed a semisynthetic diet containing 10 mg Fe/kg diet. A 25-mg Fe/kg diet did not support maximum growth, but 40 mg Fe/kg seemed adequate to meet the dietary requirement (Lawlor et al., 1965). Hoskins and Hansard (1964) estimated the gross requirements of ewes to be at least 34 mg iron per day during the final stages of pregnancy. This value is equivalent to about 20 mg iron Fe/kg diet DM. Based on the limited information available, 30 mg/kg would appear adequate to meet the dietary iron requirements for all classes of sheep.

Signs of chronic iron toxicity are reductions in feed intake, growth rate, and efficiency of feed conversion. In acute toxicosis animals exhibit anorexia, oliguria, diarrhea, hypothermia, shock, metabolic acidosis, and death (NRC, 1980). Feeding 1,600 mg Fe/kg of diet as either ferrous sulfate or ferric citrate reduced feed intake below maintenance in lambs (Standish and Ammerman, 1971). The ferrous sulfate diet was less palatable than the ferric citrate diet. In another study (Lawlor et al., 1965) an unexplained diarrhea occurred among lambs receiving diets containing 210 and 280 mg Fe/kg. A maximum tolerable level of 500 mg Fe/kg of diet has been suggested for sheep (NRC, 1980).

Molybdenum

Although molybdenum (Mo) occurs in low concentrations in all tissues and fluids of the body and is a component of three metalloenzymes, unequivocal evidence of molybdenum deficiency in sheep, unrelated to copper, has not been reported (Underwood, 1977; 1981). A significant growth response to added molybdenum and an improvement in cellulose digestibility were reported in one study with lambs fed a semipurified diet containing 0.36 mg Mo/kg (Ellis et al., 1958). This observation, however, was not substantiated in three subsequent experiments with semipurified and practical-type pelleted diets (Ellis and Pfander, 1960).

The minimum dietary requirements for molybdenum are not known but appear to be extremely low. Although the 1975 edition of this report stated the requirement as

> 0.5 mg Mo/kg diet DM, sheep regularly graze pastures containing less molybdenum with no adverse effects other than increased copper retention in the tissues (Underwood, 1981). The major concern about the level of molybdenum in the diet involves its interaction with copper and sulfur. Molybdenum forms insoluble complexes with copper and sulfur and decreases the utilization of dietary copper (Suttle, 1975, 1983a; Suttle and McLauchlan, 1976). Copper absorption is inhibited most by 4 to 6 mg Mo/kg diet DM. Higher levels of molybdenum inhibit sulfide production and may give rise to a recovery in copper absorption (Suttle, 1983a). The rates of absorption, retention, and excretion of molybdenum are inversely related to the level of dietary sulfur (Grace and Suttle, 1979; NRC, 1980).

Sheep appear more resistant to molybdenosis than cattle and tolerate plasma molybdenum levels of 0.1 to 0.2 mg/dl (approximately 20 to 40 times the normal plasma level), providing dietary sulfate is at least 0.1 percent (NRC, 1980). High levels of molybdenum induce a copper deficiency, and the signs of molybdenosis in sheep are the same as those described for copper deficiency ("stringy" wool, lack of pigmentation in black sheep, anemia, bone disorders, and infertility). Several of the western states have extensive areas where forage plants have 10 to 20 mg/kg or more of molybdenum (Kubota, 1975).

Sheep start to scour a few days after being turned on pasture with a high molybdenum content (5 to 20 mg/kg on a DM basis). The feces become soft, the fleece becomes stained, and the animals lose weight rapidly. When the dietary copper level falls below normal (5 to 8 mg/kg) or the dietary sulfate level is high (0.40 percent), molybdenum intake as low as 1 to 2 mg/kg may prove toxic. Molybdenum toxicity is controlled by increasing the copper level in the diet by 5 mg/kg.

Copper

A condition known as neonatal ataxia or "swayback" is characteristic of copper (Cu) deficiency in young lambs. Most often ataxia is apparent immediately after birth, but it may be delayed several weeks. Signs of ataxia, generally seen in suckling lambs, include muscular incoordination, partial paralysis of the hindquarters, and degeneration of the myelin sheath of the nerve fibers. Lambs may be born weak and may die because of their inability to nurse, a condition that occurs when the central nervous system develops during a time of maternal copper deficiency (Howell, 1970; Underwood, 1977; Miller, 1979a).

Sheep suffering from copper deficiency have "steely" or "stringy" wool, lacking in crimp, tensile strength, affinity for dyes, and elasticity. Lack of pigmentation of the wool of black sheep also occurs and appears to be a

sensitive index of copper deficiency (Underwood, 1977). The condition is similar to that noted in black sheep on high levels of molybdenum. Anemia, bone disorders (osteoporosis in lambs and spontaneous bone fractures in adult sheep), and infertility have also been associated with copper deficiency in sheep (Underwood, 1977).

Copper requirements of sheep are so dependent on dietary and genetic factors that it is difficult to state requirements without specifying the conditions for which they apply. Concentrations of sulfur and molybdenum are the major dietary factors influencing copper requirements. These minerals form insoluble complexes with copper, thereby reducing its absorption and increasing dietary levels needed to meet requirements. Sulfur appears to exert an independent effect on the availability of copper, but the effect of molybdenum is sulfur dependent (Suttle, 1975; Underwood, 1981; Suttle and Field, 1983). The relationship for the effects of sulfur and molybdenum on the true availability (A) of dietary copper for sheep fed semipurified diets is described by equation (1):

$$\log (A) = -1.153 - 0.76S - 0.013 (S \times Mo) \quad (1)$$

This relationship is based on the data from 10 repletion experiments with sheep fed semipurified diets varying from 0.8 to 4.0 g S/kg and from 0.5 to 1.5 mg Mo/kg (Suttle and McLauchlan, 1976). The relationship for summer pasture is given by equation (2):

$$\text{Copper Absorption (percent)} = \quad (2)$$
$$5.71 - 1.279 \, S - 2.785 \, \log_e Mo + 0.227 \, (S \times Mo)$$

where S and Mo are herbage concentrations of sulfur and molybdenum in g/kg and mg/kg, respectively (Suttle, 1983a). This equation differs substantially from that describing the effects of sulfur and molybdenum in semipurified diets and should be used to estimate the absorption of copper from pasture. Sulfur and molybdenum concentrations did not exceed 4g/kg and 6 mg/kg diet DM, respectively, in the data from which equation 2 was derived, and the equation should not be used to extrapolate to higher concentrations. High concentrations of zinc (Campbell and Mills, 1979), iron, and calcium (Miller, 1979a) have also been shown to decrease copper absorption.

Differences in copper metabolism within and among breeds also cause variation in the minimum copper requirements of sheep (Wiener, 1979; Woolliams et al., 1982; Wiener and Woolliams, 1983; Field, 1984). These differences, which are partly heritable, appear to be due to differences in absorption and are reflected in differences in blood and liver copper concentrations and in the incidence of copper deficiency (swayback) and toxicity exhibited by different breeds of sheep (Wiener and Woolliams, 1983). In fact, it has been shown that dietary amounts of copper that are adequate for some breeds are deficient for others and possibly toxic to some (Wiener and Woolliams, 1983). Finnish Landrace ewes have lower copper concentrations in their blood than Merino ewes, and the values for Merino ewes are lower than for some British breeds (Hayter and Wiener, 1973).

Although it is impossible to give exact requirements for copper, several estimates have been made of the amounts of copper that should be provided in the diet of sheep. In the 1975 revision of this report, 5 mg/kg diet DM was suggested for sheep fed diets with normal levels of sulfur and molybdenum. Merino sheep are less efficient in absorbing copper from feedstuffs than British breeds and therefore need an additional 1 to 2 mg/kg in their diet. Using a factorial approach, the ARC (1980) estimated the requirements of sheep for copper as follows: for growing lambs ranging from 5 to 40 kg live weight, 1.0 to 5.1 mg Cu/kg diet DM; for maintenance of adult sheep, 4.6 to 7.4 mg Cu/kg diet DM; for gestation, 6.2 to 7.5 mg Cu/kg diet DM; and for lactation, 4.6 to 8.6 mg Cu/kg diet DM. These recommendations do not take into account individual or genetic differences but do suggest adjustment factors for diets not containing normal levels of sulfur (2.5 g/kg DM) and molybdenum (2 to 3 mg/kg DM). More recently Suttle (1983c) recalculated the ARC (1980) estimates using a new value for the net copper requirement for growth and lower estimates of copper absorption that varied depending on the molybdenum content of diet as follows:

Recommended Copper Allowance

Mo Content of Diet (mg/kg)	Recommended Cu Allowance (mg/kg diet DM)		
	Growth	Pregnancy	Lactation
< 1.0	8-10	9-11	7- 8
> 3.0	17-21	19-23	14-17

Available data (Grace, 1975; Stevenson and Unsworth, 1978) suggest a variable availability of copper from natural sources. Availability from all forage diets ranged from 10 to 35 percent (Grace, 1975), whereas lower values were reported when high-concentrate diets and straw-based low-concentrate diets were fed (Stevenson and Unsworth, 1978).

Copper is found in adequate amounts over most of the United States, but deficient areas have been reported in Florida and in the coastal plains region of the Southeast. Also, in several of the western states there are areas where an excess of molybdenum induces copper deficiency (Kubota, 1975). (For additional discussion of molybdenum and copper interrelationships, see the section on Molybdenum on p. 16.) Copper can be provided conveniently in deficient areas by adding copper sulfate to salt at a rate of approximately 0.5 percent. Stores of copper in the body serve as a reserve for as long as 4 to 6 months when animals are grazing copper-deficient forage.

The differential between copper requirement and copper toxicity is very narrow. Errors in feed mixing frequently result in mortality due to copper toxicity. Complete manufactured feeds for sheep in the United States may contain 25 to 35 ppm copper. When vitamin-mineral preparations are added to feeds, the copper content of the diet may be excessive (Buck and Sharma, 1969). These levels of copper can be extremely harmful if the molybdenum level of the diet is low. In fact, if the molybdenum level is extremely low (< 1 ppm), forage with a normal copper content of 8 to 11 ppm can produce toxicity.

The normal concentration of copper in whole blood is 0.7 to 1.3 ppm and in liver (fresh basis) 12 ppm (Pope, 1971). The concentration of copper in liver gives a reliable indication of the copper status of sheep. The concentration in the kidney cortex provides an even better criterion for diagnosing copper poisoning. In most cases of copper poisoning, concentrations of copper, on a DM basis, exceed 500 ppm in the liver and 80 to 100 ppm in the kidney cortex (Pope, 1971). Hemolysis, jaundice (easily detected in the eyes), and hemoglobinuria are characteristic signs of toxicity and result in very-dark-colored liver and kidneys (Todd, 1969).

In treating copper toxicity, both molybdenum and sulfate should be administered. Dietary inorganic sulfate alone has less effect on uptake or reduction of copper in the liver and on utilization of copper for synthesis of ceruloplasmin (Ross, 1966). High dietary concentrations of zinc protect against copper intoxication. A diet of 100 ppm of zinc on a DM basis reduces liver copper storage (Pope, 1971).

An effective treatment for copper toxicity in lambs is to drench each lamb daily with 100 mg of ammonium molybdate and 1 g of sodium sulfate in 20 ml of water. Adding equivalent amounts of molybdenum and sulfur to the daily feed is equally effective. Either treatment usually requires a minimum of 5 to 6 weeks (Ross, 1966, 1970). The Food and Drug Adminstration does not recognize molybdenum as safe, and the law prohibits adding it to feed for sheep unless prescribed by a veterinarian. Copper toxicity can be prevented by reducing or eliminating extraneous sources of copper in the diet.

Cobalt

The only known function of cobalt (Co) in sheep nutrition is to promote synthesis of vitamin B_{12} in the rumen. Thus, signs of cobalt deficiency are actually signs of vitamin B_{12} deficiency. These are lack of appetite, lack of thrift, severe emaciation, weakness, anemia, decreased estrous activity, and decreased milk and wool production (Ammerman, 1981; Underwood, 1981).

For mature sheep grazing grossly cobalt-deficient pastures, the amount of cobalt necessary to ensure optimum growth is 0.08 mg/d when supplementary cobalt is administered orally 3 times per week. For young, rapidly growing lambs the requirement is greater and during the first few months is probably as much as 0.2 mg/d (Lee and Marston, 1969). With sheep confined to pens and fed a cobalt-deficient diet, 0.07 mg cobalt per day is required for maintenance of normal growth rate; however, for maintenance of maximum vitamin B_{12} status, based on serum and liver vitamin B_{12} concentrations, a supplement of between 0.5 and 1.0 mg Co/d is necessary (Marston, 1970).

Although levels of vitamin B_{12} in the contents of the rumen and in the blood and liver are indicators of the cobalt status of sheep, the vitamin B_{12} content of the feces is an indicator that can be used advantageously. Jones and Anthony (1970) developed an equation for estimating oral intake of cobalt on the basis of concentration of vitamin B_{12} in the feces:

$$Y = 0.0779X - 0.0757$$

where Y represents the oral intake of cobalt expressed as mg/kg in the dry feedstuff and X represents the concentration of vitamin B_{12} in the feces expressed as μg of vitamin B_{12} per gram of dry feces. In the study no signs of cobalt deficiency were observed in lambs fed a diet containing 0.09 mg Co/kg diet DM for a 7-month period. The corresponding level of vitamin B_{12} for this level of cobalt in the diet was 2.13 μg/g of dry feces.

In the 1975 edition of this report, the recommended amount of cobalt was 0.1 mg/kg diet DM. The same value is proposed here for all classes of sheep; however, young, rapidly growing lambs may have a slightly higher requirement, as suggested by Lee and Marston (1969).

Areas deficient in cobalt have been reported in the United States and Canada. The most severely deficient areas in the United States include portions of New England and the lower Atlantic Coastal Plain. Moderately deficient areas include New England, northern New York, northern Michigan, and parts of the Central Plains (Ammerman, 1981).

Research has demonstrated that cobalt should be ingested frequently (MacPherson, 1983). This can be accomplished by adding cobalt to salt at a rate of 2.5 g Co/ 100 kg salt using either cobalt chloride or cobalt sulfate. Other effective methods are the addition of cobalt to the soil (Griffiths et al., 1970; Burridge et al., 1983) or the administration of cobalt pellets (MacPherson, 1983) or a soluble glass containing cobalt that dissolves slowly in the reticulum (Telfer et al., 1984).

Sheep have been fed 350 mg Co/100 kg of live weight for short periods of time without ill effects. Levels of approximately 450 mg/100 kg of live weight have been suggested as toxic (Becker and Smith, 1951). The National Research Council (1980) suggests 10 mg Co/kg diet DM as a maximum tolerable level for ruminants.

Manganese

Manganese (Mn) deficiency in animals results in impaired growth, skeletal abnormalities and ataxia of the newborn, and depressed or disturbed reproductive function (Hidiroglou, 1979a; Underwood, 1981). The minimum dietary manganese requirements for sheep are not exactly known; however, it appears that the requirement for growth is less than for optimal reproductive performance. Requirements may also be increased by high intakes of calcium and iron (Underwood, 1981). Bone changes similar to those seen in other manganese-deficient animals were observed when early-weaned lambs received a purified diet containing less than 1 ppm of manganese over a 5-month period (Lassiter and Morton, 1968). When a diet containing 8 ppm of manganese was fed to 2-year-old ewes for a 5-month period prior to breeding and throughout gestation, more services per conception (2.5 versus 1.5) were required than for ewes fed a diet containing 60 ppm manganese (Hidiroglou et al., 1978). Levels of manganese in wool appear to be sensitive to changes in the manganese status of lambs (Lassiter and Morton, 1968).

The growth of female goats fed 20 ppm of manganese for the first year of life and 6 ppm during the following year was not affected, but the onset of estrus was delayed and more inseminations were required per conception (Anke and Groppel, 1970). No goats aborted in the control group (100 ppm), but 23 percent of those on the low-manganese diet aborted. The low-manganese diet also resulted in a 20-percent reduction in birth weights, the birth of more male than female kids, and the death of more female than male kids. Bone structure was not affected. In mature goats the manganese content of the hair was a better indicator of manganese status than the manganese content of any other part of the body.

Although the exact requirements of sheep for manganese are not known, 20 mg/kg, on a DM basis, should be adequate for most production stages. With a well-balanced diet, it appears that 1,000 mg/kg of dietary manganese is the maximum tolerable level for sheep (NRC, 1980).

Zinc

Zinc (Zn) deficiency in sheep is characterized by a decrease in appetite and a reduction in the rate of growth.

Other signs are brief periods of excessive salivation, parakeratosis, wool loss, reduced testicular development (or testicular atrophy), defective spermatogenesis, and delayed wound healing. In addition, all phases of the reproductive process in females from estrus to parturition and lactation may be adversely affected (Smith et al., 1962; Hidiroglou, 1979b; Miller, 1979b; Underwood, 1981).

Ott et al. (1965) found that a diet containing 18 mg Zn/kg diet DM did not support maximal live weight gains of lambs fed a purified diet. Mills et al. (1967) estimated that a dietary zinc level of 7.7 mg/kg diet DM satisfied the growth requirements of lambs but did not maintain the plasma zinc levels within the normal range. Data presented by Underwood and Somers (1969) indicate that a diet containing 2.4 mg Zn/kg DM is grossly inadequate for growth and metabolic requirements of ram lambs. A similar diet supplying 17.4 mg Zn/kg DM was adequate for body growth and for the maintenance of normal appetite, although this level was not adequate to permit normal testicular development and spermatogenesis. Histological and other evidence suggest that dietary zinc at a level of 32.4 mg/kg DM is adequate for maximal testicular development and function (Underwood and Somers, 1969). Pond (1983) concluded that a zinc level of 19 to 26 mg/kg DM was adequate for growth of lambs. Based on these reports it appears that the zinc requirements of ram lambs for testicular growth and development and for spermatogenesis are greater than the requirements for body growth.

Zinc requirements for pregnancy and lactation have not been established. The few studies that have been conducted indicate that the lactating ewe is clearly susceptible to zinc deficiency, but whether zinc is necessary for normal parturition in sheep (as it is in rats) requires further study (Apgar and Travis, 1979; Masters and Moir, 1983). Under Australian field conditions, Egan (1972) obtained an increased conception rate when grazing ewes were given supplemental zinc. The zinc content of the forage varied between 17 and 28 mg/kg DM.

The suggested minimum requirements are 20 mg Zn/kg DM for growth and 33 mg Zn/kg DM for maintenance of normal reproductive function in males and for pregnancy and lactation in females. Diets high in calcium (1.2 to 1.8 percent calcium) have been reported to adversely affect zinc utilization (Mills and Dalgarno, 1967).

Although there appears to be a wide margin of safety between requirements for zinc and amounts that are toxic, zinc toxicity has been described for growing lambs (Ott et al., 1966; Davies et al., 1977) and for pregnant sheep (Campbell and Mills, 1979). One gram of zinc per kilogram of diet caused reduced consumption of feed and reduced gain in lambs (Ott et al., 1966), and 0.75g Zn/kg diet induced severe copper deficiency in pregnant

ewes and caused a high incidence of abortions and stillbirths (Campbell and Mills, 1979).

Selenium

In the northwestern, northeastern, and southeastern parts of the United States, there are extensive areas where the selenium (Se) content of crops is below 0.1 ppm (Figure 5), which is the level considered adequate for preventing deficiency in sheep. Thus, selenium-responsive diseases are most likely to occur in these regions. In an area extending roughly from the Mississippi River to the Rocky Mountains, the selenium content of crops is predominantly in the nutritionally adequate but nontoxic range of selenium concentration. Parts of South Dakota, Wyoming, and Utah produce forage that causes selenium toxicity in farm animals (Kubota et al., 1967; Muth, 1970; NRC, 1983).

The most commonly noticed lesion in sheep resulting from an inadequate supply of selenium is degeneration of the cardiac and skeletal musculature (white muscle disease), but unthriftiness, early embryonic death, and periodontal disease are also signs of a possible selenium deficiency (McDonald, 1968; Muth, 1970; Underwood, 1981). Lamb production is seriously affected; the major manifestations of deficiency in lambs are reduced growth and white muscle disease, which affects lambs 0 to 8 weeks of age (Pope, 1971). Selenium-responsive infertility has been described in Australia (Godwin et al., 1970; Piper et al., 1980) and New Zealand (Hartley, 1963) but not elsewhere (Pope, 1971; Phillippo, 1983).

Supplementation with 0.1 mg Se/kg DM (as sodium selenite) of the diet of ewes during gestation through weaning consistently provided essentially complete protection against white muscle disease in their lambs (Schubert et al., 1961). Feeding ewes a natural diet containing 0.07 mg Se/kg DM or the addition of 0.1 mg Se/kg DM to a low-selenium diet (< 0.02 mg Se/kg DM) prevented white muscle disease in their lambs (Oldfield et al., 1963). Oh et al. (1976) concluded that the selenium requirement of reproducing ewes and their lambs fed a practical diet was 0.12 mg/kg DM. This conclusion was based on the dietary selenium level required to reach a plateau in tissue glutathione peroxidase levels. In contrast, Moksnes and Norheim (1983) found that tissue glutathione peroxidase activity plateaued above a level of 0.23 mg Se/kg diet. Glutathione peroxidase was the first selenoenzyme to be identified in animal tissues. The level of this enzyme in tissue and red blood cells can be considered a more sensitive indicator of dietary adequacy for lambs than tissue selenium content (Oh et al., 1976; Paynter et al., 1979).

An extensive review of New Zealand data indicated selenium-responsive unthriftiness in grazing lambs oc-

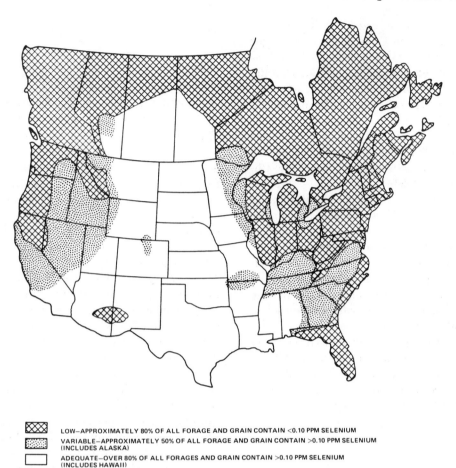

LOW—APPROXIMATELY 80% OF ALL FORAGE AND GRAIN CONTAIN <0.10 PPM SELENIUM
VARIABLE—APPROXIMATELY 50% OF ALL FORAGE AND GRAIN CONTAIN >0.10 PPM SELENIUM
(INCLUDES ALASKA)
ADEQUATE—OVER 80% OF ALL FORAGES AND GRAIN CONTAIN >0.10 PPM SELENIUM
(INCLUDES HAWAII)

FIGURE 5 The regional distribution of forages and grain, containing low, variable, or adequate levels of selenium, in the USA and Canada.

curred where the selenium content of spring pastures was < 0.02 mg/kg DM. Pastures containing > 0.03 mg/kg DM were apparently adequate, whereas intermediate levels were probably marginally deficient. An occasional positive response was obtained, however, with pastures having selenium levels in the range of 0.09 to 0.10 mg/kg DM (Grant and Sheppard, 1983). Whanger et al. (1978) have proposed that the selenium requirements for sheep be raised to at least 0.2 mg/kg diet DM when legume forages are fed.

Schubert et al. (1961) and Pope et al. (1979) found an antagonistic effect of dietary sulfur on selenium absorption and retention. Thomson and Lawson (1970) reported an interaction between selenium and copper in sheep. Adding selenium to the diet improved the copper status of sheep on deficient or marginally adequate copper diets.

A number of methods can be used to prevent white muscle disease in lambs caused by a selenium deficiency. The Food and Drug Administration has approved the following uses of selenium for ewes and ewes with lambs up to 8 weeks of age: (1) selenium can be added to a complete feed at a level not to exceed 0.1 mg/kg diet; (2) selenium can be added to a feed supplement at a level that, when consumed with the base feed, will not exceed an intake of 0.23 mg Se per sheep per day; and (3) up to 30 mg Se/kg diet can be added to a salt-mineral mixture for free-choice feeding at a rate not to exceed an intake of 0.23 mg Se per sheep per day (Federal Register, Vol. 43. pp. 11700-11701, 1978). These uses of selenium have been shown to be safe and effective (Paulson et al., 1968; Rotruck et al., 1969, Ullrey et al., 1977, 1978). One may also inject a commercial pharmacological product containing selenium and vitamin E (see the subsection on Vitamin E on pp. 24 for levels).

Other experimental methods of supplying selenium to sheep include an oral drench (Whanger et al., 1978; Paynter et al., 1979; Piper et al., 1980; MacPherson, 1983), subcutaneous or intramuscular injection (Kuttler et al., 1961; Whanger et al., 1978), application of selenium to the soil (Allaway et al., 1966; Watkinson. 1983), introduction of a heavy selenium pellet (composed of finely divided metallic iron and elemental selenium in a proportion of 20 to 1) into the reticulum (Kuchel and Buckley, 1969; Handreck and Godwin, 1970; Whanger et al., 1978; Paynter, 1979; MacPherson, 1983), and introduction of a soluble glass containing selenium to the reticulum (Telfer et al., 1984).

Chronic selenium toxicity occurs when sheep consume over a prolonged period of time seleniferous plants containing more than 3 ppm of selenium. Signs include loss of wool, soreness and sloughing of hooves, and marked reduction in reproductive performance (NRC, 1980; Underwood, 1981; Howell, 1983).

Toxicity of forage depends somewhat on its protein and sulfur content. The extent to which plants take up selenium varies greatly. Some species of plants grown on seleniferous soils contain as much as 1,000 ppm of selenium, whereas other species grown on the same soils contain only 10 to 25 ppm. The most practical way to prevent livestock losses from selenium poisoning is to manage grazing so that animals alternate between selenium-bearing and other areas.

Selenium is a cumulative poison, but mild chronic signs can be overcome readily. The mineral is eliminated rapidly from the body of an affected animal when it is fed selenium-low forage. Small amounts of arsanilic acids are effective in reducing the toxicity of selenium.

Fluorine

Fluorine (F) exerts a cumulative toxic effect. Signs may not be observed until the second or third year of intake of high levels of fluoride. Affected animals usually exhibit anorexia; the normal ivory color of their bones gradually changes to chalky white; bones thicken because of periosteal hyperostosis; and the teeth, especially the incisors, may become pitted and eroded to such an extent that the nerves are exposed (Underwood, 1977; NRC, 1980).

Fluorine rarely occurs free in nature but combines chemically to form fluorides. In some parts of the world fluoride occurs in the water supply in amounts that may be high enough to have deleterious effects. Another danger lies in the use of rock phosphate that contains fluorine in amounts sufficient to be toxic (O'Hara et al., 1982). Proper defluorination procedures are necessary to make rock phosphate safe for animal supplementation. Forage growing near manufacturing units processing minerals containing fluorides may be highly contaminated with fluoride.

Finishing lambs can tolerate up to 150 ppm of fluorine in the diet on a DM basis (Harris et al., 1963). Acute toxicity can occur at 200 ppm. Data are not available on lifetime tolerance levels for sheep; however, breeding sheep should not be fed diets containing more than 60 ppm fluorine on a DM basis (NRC, 1980).

VITAMINS

Vitamin A

In the previous revision of *Nutrient Requirements of Sheep* (NRC, 1975), 17 IU/kg of body weight for vitamin A alcohol (retinol) or 25 µg/kg of body weight for β-carotene were the values used to calculate the vitamin A and β-carotene requirements. An IU is defined as 0.300 µg of retinol or 0.550 µg of vitamin A (retinyl) palmitate. Requirements for late pregnancy, lactation, and early-weaned lambs were calculated by multiplying these values by 5; those for replacement lambs and yearlings were obtained by multiplying by 2.5; and those for finishing lambs and for ewes during maintenance and the first 15 weeks of gestation were calculated by multiplying by 1.5. These values were based on the amounts of retinol or carotene required to prevent night blindness in sheep and the amounts required for storage and reproduction (Guilbert et al., 1937, 1940).

Recent studies with growing calves have effectively demonstrated that elevated pressure in the cerebrospinal fluid (CSF) is a more sensitive indicator of vitamin A status than is night blindness. For example, Eaton (1969) reported that the minimum β-carotene or retinol requirement of calves (µg/kg live weight per day) based on prevention of night blindness was 24 to 35 µg for carotene and 5.1 to 6.4 µg for retinol (17 to 21 IU), whereas for prevention of elevated CSF pressures, the values are 66 to 73 µg for β-carotene and 14.1 µg for retinol (47 IU). Increased CSF pressure has also been observed in sheep deficient in vitamin A (Eveleth et al., 1949; May, 1982). Based on increased CSF pressure the minimum requirement for growing-finishing lambs appears to be between 8 and 16 µg of retinol/kg live weight per day (May, 1982). This is supported by the work of Faruque and Walker (1970), who reported that 14 µg retinyl palmitate or 69 µg β-carotene/kg live weight per day permitted the establishment of a small liver reserve of retinol in young lambs.

In the absence of more definitive information, the minimum carotene and vitamin A requirements of sheep are assumed to be 69 µg of β-carotene/kg live weight per day or 47 IU of vitamin A/kg live weight per day. These values were used as the basis for establishing requirements for vitamin A for all categories (Tables 1 and 2) except ewes in late gestation and during lactation, in which cases the requirements are 125 µg/kg live weight per day for β-carotene and 85 IU/kg live weight per day for vitamin A. During the first 6 to 8 weeks of lactation, the requirements for ewes suckling twins were further increased to 147 µg/kg live weight per day for β-carotene and 100 IU/kg live weight per day for vitamin A. Ewe milk contains about 1,500 IU vitamin A per liter and conceivably these additional amounts should be added per day to compensate for what is produced in milk.

Plant products do not contain preformed vitamin A, and sheep meet their vitamin A needs mainly from carotenoid precursors in the diet (Moore, 1957). Vitamin A compounds and carotenoids exist in many forms, each with different biological activity. The all-*trans* forms exhibit the highest biological activity.

The international standards for vitamin A activity as related to vitamin A and β-carotene are as follows: 1 IU of vitamin A = 1 USP unit = vitamin A activity of 0.300 μg of crystalline all-*trans* retinol, which is equal to 0.344 μg of all-*trans* retinyl acetate or 0.550 μg of all-*trans* retinyl palmitate (Anonymous, 1963). All-*trans* β-carotene is the reference standard for provitamin A. It is the major carotenoid pigment in most plant feeds. Although the vitamin A equivalence used for β-carotene in this publication is 681 IU of vitamin A/mg of β-carotene, this value probably only applies to all-*trans* β-carotene fed at a level to meet the minimum requirement. The biological potency of β-carotene, relative to preformed vitamin A, is not a single standard value but is dependent on a number of factors, such as the level of supplementation, the previous nutritional history of the animal, and the response criteria used to determine the relative potencies (Myers et al., 1959; Faruque and Walker, 1970). Other factors that have been reported to influence the biological availability of carotene in natural feedstuffs are the mixture of carotenoid isomers present, the digestibility of the diet, the presence of antioxidants, and the protein and fat contents of the diet (Ullrey, 1972). Both vitamin A and β-carotene are subject to loss by oxidation. Stabilized vitamin A, which is resistant to oxidation, may be added to diets of low-carotene content.

The vitamin A value of carotene from artificially dehydrated alfalfa meal ranged from 254 to 520 IU/mg in a study with growing lambs (Myers et al., 1959). The vitamin A activity of carotenes in corn silage fed to lambs was 436 IU/mg (Martin et al., 1968). Sun-cured hay is usually lower in carotene than dehydrated hay. With the exception of yellow corn, grains are poor sources of vitamin A activity.

Vitamin A is fat soluble and is stored in the body. Approximately 200 days are required to deplete entirely the vitamin A stores in the livers of ewe lambs previously pastured on green feed. Because of this storage, animals that graze on green forage during the normal growing season perform normally on low carotene diets for periods of 4 to 6 months. In situations where sheep are grazing forage low in carotene for extended periods, however, vitamin A deficiency can be prevented by intramuscular injection with a commercially available vitamin A preparation or by the addition of preformed vitamin A to the diet as part of a salt mixture or as a pasture supplement.

Vitamin A is involved in a number of physiological functions in animals. It is essential for the stimulation of growth, the proper development of skeletal tissues, normal reproduction, vision, and the maintenance of normal epithelial tissue (Moore, 1957; Weber, 1983). Consequently, vitamin A deficiency results in clinical deficiency signs such as growth retardation; bone malformation; degeneration of the reproductive organs; night blindness; increased CSF pressure; and keratinization of the respiratory, alimentary, reproductive, urinary, and ocular epithelia (Moore, 1957; Weber, 1983). Also, a deficiency can result in the production of lambs that are weak, malformed, or dead at birth. Retained placenta also is encountered with ewes deficient in vitamin A.

Available high-potency vitamin A preparations and the common practice of vitamin A fortification of sheep diets necessitates caution because acute and chronic vitamin A toxicities have been reported for several animal species. For example, growing calves fed daily retinol intakes in excess of 2,200 μg/kg live weight (150 times the requirement) for 12 weeks exhibited changes in serum constituents and bone composition (Hazzard et al., 1964).

Vitamin D

Vitamin D activity is measured in international units (1 IU = 1 USP unit = antirachitic activity of 0.025 μg crystalline D_3) (Windholz et al., 1983). The vitamin D requirement for all classifications of sheep except early-weaned lambs is 555 IU/100 kg live weight per day; for early-weaned lambs, it is 666 IU/100 kg live weight per day. These are the same values used in the 1975 publication on sheep (NRC, 1975) and are based on the research of Andrews and Cunningham (1945). These values are only slightly higher than those proposed by ARC (1980) for all classes of sheep (520 IU/100 kg live weight).

Sheep use vitamin D_2 (ergocalciferol) and vitamin D_3 (cholecalciferol) equally well (Church and Pond, 1974). Recent research indicates that cholecalciferol is converted to active forms in the liver and kidney and acts in metabolism by affecting calcium absorption, deposition, and mobilization from bone (DeLuca, 1974; 1976). Vitamin D is fat soluble and stored in the body and therefore is less important in mature animals, except in the case of pregnancy, when demands are greater. Congenital malformations in the newborn may result from extreme vitamin D deficiencies. Vitamin D is required in addition to calcium and phosphorus for preventing rickets in young lambs and osteomalacia in older sheep, but newborn lambs are provided with enough vitamin D from their dams to prevent early rickets if their dams have adequate storage (Church and Pond, 1974).

Animals exposed to sunlight generally obtain sufficient vitamin D through ultraviolet irradiation. Animals with white skin or short wool receive more vitamin D activity through irradiation than animals with black skin or long wool. Sheep on pasture seldom need additional vitamin D, but under some conditions rickets has been observed (Fitch, 1943; Crowley, 1961; Nisbet et al., 1966). The question of adequacy arises if the weather is cloudy for long periods (Crowley, 1961) or if sheep are maintained indoors (Hidiroglou et al., 1979). Under these conditions, it is especially important that attention be given to the vitamin D content of diets of fast-growing lambs.

Sun-cured hays are good sources of vitamin D. Dehydrated hays, green feeds, seeds, and by-products of seeds are poor sources. Vitamin D is subject to loss by oxidation. Although it oxidizes more slowly than vitamin A, its stability is poor when it is mixed with minerals (and especially poor when it is mixed with calcium carbonate).

Use of high-potency vitamin D preparations in animal feeds requires caution. Excess vitamin D causes abnormal deposition of calcium in soft tissues and brittle bones subject to deformation and fractures (Church and Pond, 1974). Nevertheless, the amounts of vitamin D necessary to produce signs of toxicity are many times greater than the amounts required for nutritional purposes.

Vitamin E

Vitamin E is essential for all sheep, but unlike vitamin A, it does not appear to be stored in the body in appreciable concentrations (Rammell, 1983). On a practical basis, vitamin E fortification of the diet is more critical for young lambs than for older sheep. Recent estimates of the vitamin E requirements of ruminants vary from 10 to 60 mg/kg diet DM (NRC, 1975; ARC, 1980; NRC, 1984). This is not unexpected, since there are few studies specifically designed to determine requirements and actual requirements depend on the levels of selenium, polyunsaturated fatty acids, and (possibly) sulfur in the diet, as well as on the physiological status of the sheep and measurements used to assess deficiency (Muth et al., 1961; Hintz and Hogue, 1964; Rammell, 1983).

Rousseau et al. (1957) reported no signs of vitamin E deficiency in lambs fed 51.3 mg of d-α-tocopheryl acetate per kilogram DM. Ewan et al. (1968) found that 11.0 mg/kg live weight of dl-α-tocopherol added weekly to lamb diets containing 0.1 to 1.0 ppm selenium prevented deaths due to white muscle disease (WMD) and maintained serum enzymes within the normal range. For a 10-kg lamb consuming 0.6 kg of feed per day (DM basis), this is equivalent to a dietary tocopherol concentration of 26.2 mg/kg DM. Dietary supplementation with 20 IU of vitamin E/kg of feed was successful in preventing nutritional muscular dystrophy (NMD) in rapidly growing (> 300 g/d) early-weaned lambs fed a dystrophogenic diet (Sharman, 1973). Data summarized by ARC (1980) indicated that the minimum requirements for vitamin E in the diet of growing or pregnant sheep were between 10.0 and 15.0 mg/kg DM. If dietary selenium levels are below 0.05 ppm, however, even 15 to 30 mg of vitamin E/kg DM may prove inadequate. For young beef calves (NRC, 1984), 15 to 60 mg of dl-α-tocopheryl acetate per kilogram DM is suggested. In the absence of more definitive information on the vitamin E requirements of sheep, the following levels are recommended: lambs under 20 kg live weight should receive 20 IU/kg DM and lambs over 20 kg live weight and pregnant ewes should receive 15 IU/kg DM. (The IU is defined as 1 mg of dl-α-tocopheryl acetate; 1 mg dl-α-tocopherol has the biopotency of 1.5 IU of vitamin E activity.) The above recommendations assume that dietary selenium levels are > 0.05 ppm.

Vitamin E is now recognized as an important biological antioxidant. It functions in the body's intracellular defense against the adverse effects of reactive oxygen and free radicals (Rammell, 1983) and, as such, plays an important role in maintaining the integrity of biological cell membranes. Its mode of action is not well defined, but it is closely associated with selenium in metabolism. Some signs of vitamin E deficiency, such as WMD or NMD, may respond to either selenium or vitamin E or may require both (Hopkins et al., 1964; Ewan et al., 1968). Vitamin E and selenium also appear to have an additive effect on reducing serum levels of glutamic-oxalacetic transaminase (GOT), increasing survival time, and decreasing the level of urinary creatine excretion in deficient lambs less than 8 weeks old (Ewan et al., 1968).

The signs of WMD in nursing lambs are stiffness (especially in the rear quarters), tucked-up rear flanks, and arched back. On necropsy, the disease is shown as white striations in cardiac muscles and is characterized by bilateral lesions in skeletal muscles. Serum levels of the enzymes glutamic-oxalacetic transaminase and lactic dehydrogenase are elevated, indicating muscle damage. Blood levels of the selenium-containing enzyme glutathione peroxidase are reduced. Affected lambs often die of pneumonia, starvation, or heart failure (Suttle and Linklater, 1983). Vitamin E blood plasma levels of 0.3 mg α-tocopherol/dl are considered marginal in cattle, and similar values may apply to sheep (Adams, 1982).

Wheat germ meal, dehydrated alfalfa, some green feeds, and vegetable fat are good sources of vitamin E. Grains and grass hays are fair to good sources, but variations in levels are considerable. Protein-rich feeds such as fish and meat meal and solvent-extracted soybean and cottonseed meals are relatively poor sources. The level of vitamin E in ensiled forages is questionable (Bunnell et al., 1968; Kivimae and Carpena, 1973).

Reports by Bunnell et al. (1968) and Adams (1982) suggest that α-tocopherol levels in feedstuffs may be lower than previously reported. Furthermore, the extreme variations in α-tocopherol levels in the same kind of feeds as affected by stage of harvest, storage (oxidation may reduce levels 50 percent in 1 month), length of time between cutting and dehydrating, grinding of grains, stresses (such as adding minerals or fat in mixed feeds), and pelleting detract measurably from the reliability of book values for α-tocopherol content of rations. For example, the α-tocopherol content of 12 samples of 17 and 20 percent dehydrated alfalfa ranged from 28 to 141 mg/kg. Adams (1982) reported a range in plasma α-tocopherol values of 0.01 to 2.2 mg/dl among feedlot cattle. Of 286 plasma samples, 60 percent were below 0.3 mg α-tocopherol/dl, a level generally considered borderline between adequate and deficient.

Based on average α-tocopherol contents of feedstuffs (Bunnell et al., 1968) generally used in lamb growing-finishing rations (corn, soybean meal, and alfalfa hay), the typical ration may contain less than 15 mg α-tocopherol/kg, which could result in inadequate intake of vitamin E. In addition, preintestinal destruction of vitamin E increases from 8 to 42 percent of an orally administered dose as the corn content of the diet increases from 20 to 80 percent (Alderson et al., 1971). Many sheep rations, heretofore believed adequate in vitamin E, may be inadequate, explaining the sporadic outbreaks of WMD in areas considered adequate in selenium.

Values for the vitamin E requirements of sheep are presented in Tables 1, 2, and 9. The values presented in Table 1 were calculated from values per kilogram of dry feed consumed, given in Table 2. Table 9 presents daily vitamin E requirements for lambs and the suggested amounts of α-tocopheryl acetate to add to rations to provide 100 percent of these requirements.

Vitamin B Complex

The B vitamins are not required in the diet of sheep with functioning rumens, because the microorganisms synthesize these vitamins in adequate amounts. Lambs fed a niacin-deficient diet for 8 months have developed normally (Winegar et al., 1940). Mature sheep fed a diet low in thiamin, riboflavin, pyridoxine, and pantothenic acid have synthesized these vitamins in their rumens (McElroy and Goss, 1940 a,b; 1941 a,b). Cobalt is necessary for the synthesis of vitamin B_{12} (cyanocobalamin) in the rumen (see the section on Cobalt, p. 18).

There is no evidence that supplementation with the vitamin B complex affects the performance of ewes during breeding and pregnancy (Miller et al., 1942). Before their rumens are developed, young lambs (up to 2 months of age), if early weaned, have a dietary need for B vitamins.

A thiamin-responsive disease condition has been reported in feedlot lambs fed diets with high levels of grain and little roughage (see the section on Polioencephalomalacia, p. 27) (Barlow, 1983).

Vitamins K_1 and K_2

Vitamins K_1 (phylloquinone) and K_2 (menaquinone) are fat soluble, and one or the other is necessary in the blood-clotting mechanism. Green leafy materials of any kind, fresh or dry, are good sources of vitamin K_1 (Church and Pond, 1974). Vitamin K_2 is normally synthesized in large amounts in the rumen, and no need for dietary supplementation has been established (McElroy and Goss, 1940a; Matschiner, 1970).

3 Water

Sheep obtain water from snow and dew and by drinking; metabolic water is obtained from oxidation of nutrients in feed. The exact amount of water required by sheep is not known and varies considerably depending on body metabolism, ambient temperature, stage of production, size, wool covering, amount of feed consumed, and feed composition (Forbes, 1968).

Voluntary water consumption is two or three times dry matter consumption and increases with high-protein and salt-containing diets. Available snow, high-moisture feeds, and infrequent watering tend to reduce daily water consumption.

Forbes (1968) has confirmed that there is a significant relationship between total water intake (TWI) and dry matter intake (DMI) that can be represented by the formula

$$TWI = 3.86DMI - 0.99$$

Producers feeding pelleted rations note the obvious increase in water intake accompanied by increased urine output as a result of increased DMI. Conversely, sheep denied water for more than 24 hours ate little or no dry feed containing 15 percent protein, but intake was little affected when fed 2 percent protein hay (Forbes, 1968).

The relationship between water intake and mean temperature over 1°C also is significant (Forbes, 1968):

$$TWI/DMI = 0.18T + 1.25$$

where TWI/DMI is the average total water intake per unit of dry matter intake (kg/kg) and T is the average temperature in °C for each week.

Pregnancy and lactation also increase water intake. Water intake increases by the third month of gestation, is doubled by the fifth month, and is greater for twin-bearing ewes than for ewes carrying a single fetus. A lack of water accompanied by a severe depression in feed intake predisposes ewes to pregnancy toxemia. Forbes (1968) noted that water intake during early lactation is greater than the sum of water intake for nonpregnant ewes and the water in the milk, due to a higher metabolic rate and greater excretion. It is estimated that lactating ewes require 100 percent more water than nonlactating ewes.

Sheep may consume 12 times more water in summer than in winter; subsist on once-a-day watering when temperatures are below 40°C; and suffer no reduction in weight gains, feed intake, or digestibility of dry matter when snow is available and the temperature ranges between 0° and 21°C (Butcher, 1970). Lactating ewes would likely be stressed under a similar regime.

Adequate intake of good-quality water is essential for sheep to excrete excess toxic substances such as oxalates, ammonia, and mineral salts (phosphates that cause urinary calculi).

The effect of water temperature on rumen temperature, digestion, and rumen fermentation in sheep was studied by Brod et al. (1982), who reported that rumen temperatures were affected by temperature of water consumed, with 0°C water depressing rumen temperature more than 10°, 20°, or 30°C water. It required 108, 96, 96, and 72 minutes at water temperatures of 0°, 10°, 20°, and 30°C, respectively, to regain initial rumen temperature. Water temperature had no significant effect on nitrogen balance or on DM, protein, or crude fiber digestibility, although digestion coefficients tended to be lower with 0°C water. Water temperature had no significant effect on rumen pH, but water at all temperatures depressed rumen pH 2 to 4 hours postfeeding. Volatile fatty acids (VFA) and ammonia-nitrogen concentrations increased 1 to 4 hours postfeeding. Brod et al. concluded that 0°C water suppresses rumen microbial activity as evidenced by (1) elevated pH at 4 hours postfeeding for 0°C water compared with pH values for 10°, 20°, and 30°C water and (2) by depressed concentrations of VFA and ammonia-nitrogen and lower digestibility values compared with the other water-temperature treatments.

4 Nutrition Disorders

ENTEROTOXEMIA

Enterotoxemia (overeating disease, pulpy kidney disease) is a feed-related malady that causes sudden death in sheep due to a toxin produced by the bacterium *Clostridium perfringens* type D (although occasionally type C also occurs, particularly in 2- to 4-week-old suckling lambs). The organism appears to be widespread in nature and has been isolated from pastures, manure, and the gastrointestinal tract of healthy sheep (Jensen, 1974; Buxton, 1983).

Under conditions of high carbohydrate intake (high-grain diet; high milk intake; and rarely, high intake of immature forage) the causative bacteria multiply rapidly and produce a toxin. Thus, it is a disease that afflicts suckling lambs, creep-fed lambs, growing-finishing lambs, and ewes fed high levels of grain. Anything that interferes with the normal passage of feed through the gut, such as a heavy burden of parasites, exacerbates the situation (Jensen, 1974; Buxton, 1983).

Protection of lambs against enterotoxemia can be achieved by vaccinating twice (at least 10 days apart) with *Clostridium perfringens* type D toxoid. Approximately 2 to 4 weeks is required for the development of immunity after vaccination. Vaccinating pregnant ewes 2 to 4 weeks before parturition will transfer sufficient passive immunity to their lambs to protect them for the first 4 to 6 weeks postpartum. Lambs should receive a protective dose of antiserum at this age to protect them until market (Oxer et al., 1971; Jensen, 1974).

POLIOENCEPHALOMALACIA

Polioencephalomalacia (PEM), first described in the United States by Jensen et al. (1956), and cerebrocortical necrosis (CCN), first described in England by Terlecki and Markson (1959, 1961), are now considered synonymous terms for the same disease (Loew, 1972; Edwin and Jackman, 1982). Polioencephalomalacia has since been reported in most areas of the world and affects both cattle and sheep (Loew, 1972; Edwin, 1975). Clinical signs include disorientation, dullness, aimless wandering, loss of appetite, circling, progressive blindness, extensor spasms, and occasionally head pressing (Loew, 1972; Edwin, 1975; Edwin and Jackman, 1982). Final diagnosis is dependent on histopathological examination (Loew, 1972; Edwin et al., 1979; Spicer and Horton, 1981).

Following the finding that thiamin therapy could be used with marked success (Davies et al., 1965), it was established that affected animals were indeed thiamin deficient (Pill, 1967; Edwin, 1970). Although the precise etiology of the disease is still not known, it is now accepted that the thiamin deficiency, probably associated with cofactors and antimetabolites, is initiated by rumen-produced thiaminases (Roberts and Boyde, 1974; Mueller and Asplund, 1981; Edwin and Jackman, 1982; Edwin et al., 1982). The disease has been reported in most ages and classes of sheep, but it occurs most often in feedlot lambs (Loew, 1972; Mueller and Asplund, 1981). Animals affected with PEM can be successfully treated with 200 to 500 mg of thiamin injected intravenously, intramuscularly, or subcutaneously (McKenzie and Steele, 1980; Chick et al., 1981; Spicer and Horton, 1981; Edwin and Jackman, 1982). Although response is often dramatic, if significant brain damage has occurred the recovered animals rarely regain satisfactory levels of productivity. Therefore, very early treatment is critical. The thiamin injection can also be used to protect sheep at risk—for example, the remainder of a group in which PEM has been diagnosed (McKenzie and Steele, 1980; Chick et al., 1981).

PREGNANCY DISEASE

Pregnancy disease, also referred to as ketosis, acetonemia, and pregnancy toxemia, is associated with undernourishment and particularly with over-fat condition among ewes. It occurs in ewes in late pregnancy and usually is restricted to those carrying multiple fetuses. Stress factors such as shearing, transporting, severe weather exposure, and predator attacks, in addition to undernourishment, can precipitate outbreaks of the disease.

Clinical features of the disease include high blood levels of ketone bodies and hypoglycemia. The affected animals appear depressed, lack appetite, have a staggering gait, separate from the flock, and exhibit nervousness (Reid, 1968). In the final stages of the disease (prior to death), vision is impaired and ewes are unable to rise or stand because of weakness, stiffness, or partial paralysis. Ewes that give birth during the early stages of the syndrome usually recover.

During late pregnancy there are high glucose demands (about 1.5 times maintenance levels) placed on the ewe by the rapidly developing fetuses. With reduced rumen capacity due to increasing fetal size, feed intake is impaired. The ewe mobilizes adipose tissue in an attempt to meet glucose needs, the liver produces less glucose, a metabolic acidosis develops, and ketone bodies accumulate in the blood. The disease is not related to lack of exercise. It can be prevented by ensuring adequate nutrient intake in late pregnancy so that increases in weight occur. A drench of 200 to 300 ml of propylene glycol or glycerol can be used when signs first appear, as an energy source for ewes refusing to eat sufficient feed.

URINARY CALCULI

Urinary calculi (uroliths) are mineral deposits occurring in the urinary tract (Field, 1969). Although these deposits form in all breeds and sexes of sheep, blockage of the flow of urine generally only occurs in intact or castrated male sheep. The blockage may rupture the urinary bladder, resulting in a condition commonly called water belly, and cause death. Difficult or painful urination as evidenced by straining, slow urination, stomping of the feet, and kicking at the area of the penis are signs of calculi problems (Jensen, 1974).

Under feedlot conditions, this disease appears to have a nutritional or metabolic origin; affected animals excrete an alkaline urine that has a high phosphorus content (Crookshank, 1968; Jensen, 1974). Dietary intakes of calcium, phosphorus, magnesium, and potassium appear to play a major role in the incidence of calculosis in feedlot lambs, and an equation that uses intakes of these four minerals has been used to predict calculi formation in wethers (Lamprecht et al., 1969). The incidence of urinary calculi in growing-finishing lambs can be greatly reduced by preventing an excessive intake of phosphorus and by maintaining a calcium-to-phosphorus ratio greater than 2:1 (Emerick and Embry, 1963). Reducing the alkalinity of the urine by feeding acid-forming salts is also effective (Crookshank, 1968, 1970). Ammonium chloride or ammonium sulfate added to the complete diet at 0.5 percent has been used successfully; ammonium chloride appears to be more effective than ammonium sulfate (Crookshank, 1970). Ammonium chloride has also been used to drench sheep at a level of 7 to 14 g per sheep per day for 3 to 5 days. Reasonable success has been achieved with this procedure so long as animals were still able to pass a small amount of urine. Injection with a smooth muscle relaxant is helpful in these cases.

In range sheep, the disease is associated with the consumption of forages having a high silica content (Emerick et al., 1959; Bailey, 1978). Sodium chloride, fed at a level of 4 percent or more of the total diet, helps prevent urinary calculi, especially in range animals. Sodium chloride increases consumption of water and the amount of urine produced. It may be fed to range animals as a part of the protein supplement, provided adequate water is available.

Availability of a plentiful supply of clean water is important in minimizing calculi problems under range and feedlot conditions.

5 Other Aspects of Sheep Nutrition

PASTURES

Optimum utilization of pastures by sheep is very difficult to attain. As pasture forage matures, the protein content declines, fiber increases, and both forage intake and digestibility decline. The combination of internal parasites and the inability of young lambs to consume adequate dry matter invariably results in weight gains on pasture being 40 to 60 percent less than when lambs are grain-fed in drylot (Jordan and Marten, 1968a). Lambs 4 to 6 weeks old are particularly sensitive to heavy internal parasite infestation with which their dams normally infect the pasture. Pasture forage is best suited for maintenance of ewes who are significantly more tolerant of internal parasite infestation.

In some areas of the country, pastures are often underutilized and much forage is trampled and wasted. Limiting grazing time to a few hours a day or restricting grazing time to around 60 percent of normal (Jordan and Marten, 1968b) reduces selective grazing, reduces forage intake, increases pasture carrying capacity by 50 to 100 percent, and prolongs the period of available feed.

Legume forages rotationally grazed provide more nutrients over a longer growing period than nonlegume forages, although in some areas bloat precludes their use by sheep of any age. Where nonlegumes are the major forage they must be augmented with supplementary annual pastures.

Rape, a cool-season species, is an excellent summer and fall pasture for both ewes and lambs, resulting in an average daily gain of 0.20 to 0.25 kg. Forage peas have a low carrying capacity. Sudan grass or sudan-sorghum crosses produce high yield but result in very selective, spotty grazing and low lamb performance and are far better suited for mature sheep, in which maintenance rather than increases in weight is paramount (Wedin and Jordan, 1961).

Timothy, fescues, wheat grasses, and blue grass become unpalatable on reaching maturity in early summer. Orchard grass is less palatable than brome grass in midsummer but produces far more forage (Table 10). New varieties of low-alkaloid-containing canarygrass produce more digestible nutrients over a long grazing season than either orchard grass or brome grass and appear very promising (Marten et al., 1981).

RANGE SHEEP

Range sheep do not differ physiologically from pen-raised sheep; however, the nutrient needs of the two types differ widely.

Type and composition of plants at any one location on pasture or range is dependent on type and composition of the parent soil, as well as moisture, radiant energy available for growth, and previous and present management of the area. Soils inherently low in a given element often will produce plants low in that element, and thus, deficiencies of the element may occur. Where high levels of specific elements exist in soil (plants may accumulate these elements), it is likely that if they are toxic to sheep, toxicities will be seen. Although maps of states or of the United States are available that describe areas of mineral deficiencies and toxicities, it is important to understand that local environmental and topographical factors can influence the occurrence of toxicities and deficiencies.

Typically, range land is evaluated based on its stage of ecological succession toward climax vegetation for a specific type of vegetative community. Although range land classification is used in allocating forage for game and livestock, classification or score may not accurately predict animal performance. Important considerations for range use and expected animal performance on range are distribution of water, topography, season of use, presence of poisonous plants, occurrence of predation, and system of grazing management.

Range sheep must frequently be supplemented with phosphorus, protein, and energy for optimum performance. For example, forage available to range sheep during gestation (late fall, winter, and early spring) is often at its lowest concentration of nutrients (Cook et al., 1954; Huston, 1983; Huston et al., 1981). Ranges classified as fair to poor are unlikely to provide adequate energy, protein, or phosphorus. Excellent to good ranges generally supply adequate energy (except when snow covered), but sheep may need supplemental protein and usually are lacking in phosphorus (Bryant et al., 1979).

It has been estimated that maintenance requirements for energy of grazing sheep are 60 to 70 percent greater than for comparable pen-fed sheep (Young and Corbett, 1972). The greater need for energy by grazing sheep results largely from the impact of environmental factors and an increased activity increment. The environmental factors are discussed elsewhere in this publication and by NRC (1981). The higher energy requirement due to an increased activity increment for grazing sheep results from the energy costs of grazing, horizontal movement, vertical movement, and other activities such as rumination time. As range changes from essentially flat to rolling, the change in energy needs for travel will change because the energy cost of vertical travel is approximately 10 times the energy cost for horizontal travel (6.86 cal/m/kg body weight versus 0.59 cal/m/kg body weight; Clapperton, 1964). Also, as density of grazable forage decreases or distance to water increases, energy needs to satisfy daily requirements increase.

Because it is difficult to measure feed intake and selectivity by range sheep, management must rely on knowledge of nutrient composition of range forages at various stages of growth and during various seasons of the year, as well as on the ability of the sheep to achieve adequate quantity and quality of forages. Ewe condition in relation to previous condition and projected desired condition and the sheep's general vigor and activity are the usual criteria used to assess adequate feed intake. Although proper nutritional management may indicate supplementation, it is at times physically impossible to get sufficient supplemental feed to sheep; under these conditions sheep must rely on body stores to sustain them through periods of shortages. To be economically successful the range sheep operator must manage sheep so they meet their nutrient needs largely from grazing rather than from supplements, grain, and hay.

Formulating Supplements for Range Ewes

In formulating supplements for range ewes it is necessary to assess the composition of the available diet and the condition, status, and stage of production of the ewe. A diet consisting largely of dead grass will require a different supplement composition than one consisting of sage and browse.

Alfalfa hay, which may contain a good source of energy, protein, and β-carotene, discourages grazing. Its use is more suitable when the range is snow covered and there is a need for increased DM intake as well as for energy and protein. The usual supplement is fed as cubes that provide in a concentrated form whatever nutrients are deficient in the range forage (Weir and Torell, 1967). This type of supplement will generally encourage grazing and enhance the utilization of the nutrients provided by the range feed. The usual amount fed per ewe per day is 0.1 to 0.2 kg to provide 30 to 50 percent of the protein requirements, 75 percent of the vitamin A and phosphorus requirements, and 20 to 30 percent of the energy requirements. To avoid consumption of poisonous plants when trailing sheep or when feed is snow covered, the amount of supplement fed daily may be increased 2 to 4 times.

The usual supplements include 30 to 40 percent protein equivalent, 1.5 to 2.0 percent phosphorus, 3.5 to 4.0 Mcal DE/kg, and 15 to 20 mg carotene/kg.

Although range ewes must be managed quite differently than intensively raised sheep, their physiological needs and responses to nutrients are no different from those of confined sheep. Range ewes respond to flushing, are equally susceptible to pregnancy disease, and lactate at levels dictated by nutrient intake. Thus, they should be managed so that either grazing or a combination of grazing and supplementation will meet their needs during those critical periods. Table 11 presents formulas for range supplements for different ranges and nutrient needs.

FLUSHING

The practice of increasing nutrient intake or the dynamic effect that influences body weight (BW) change and condition prior to and during breeding is called flushing. Its purpose is to increase the rate of ovulation and, hence, the lambing rate. Although flushing is a husbandry practice used in major sheep-producing countries, the response to flushing is variable and an explanation for the response is not evident. A high level of hepatic steroid metabolizing enzymes (SME) is thought to be associated with an increased clearance rate of steroids, and a decrease in steroids is associated with an increase in gonadotropins and thus an increase in ovulation (Thomas et al., 1984). Increased intake of nutrients, particularly protein, effectively increases levels of hepatic SME. Phenobarbital is also an effective inducer of hepatic SME. Thomas et al. (1984) reported that 1 g phenobarbital daily per ewe increased the ovulation rate 0.24 ova per ewe, whereas 0.45 kg grain per ewe per day had no effect.

Lambing rate, as affected by nutritional alteration prior to and during breeding (flushing), is influenced not only by the number of ova fertilized but by embryo survival, which affects the number of ewes lambing. The first month after fertilization is very critical to embryo survival. Robinson (1983) divides that period into two, a preimplantation period of 15 days and a 14-day embryo implantation phase. During the first 15 days after conception, a balance in the distribution of embryos between the two horns of the uterus is accomplished and the implantation process is initiated linking the rapidly developing trophoblast and the epithelial cells of the maternal caruncles (Boshier, 1969). Loss of fertilized ova during this preimplantation period results in a high incidence of repeat estrous cycles occurring at normal intervals or a lowered lambing rate. Unless the ewes are subjected to severe undernutrition at this time, nutrition is likely to be only a minor factor affecting embryo survival (except very high levels of energy intake have detrimental effects on embryo survival) (Robinson, 1977; Doney, 1979). Nutrition does exert some effect on the concentration of progesterone in maternal plasma (Parr et al., 1982), and progesterone does influence embryo growth during this preimplantation period (Lawson, 1977).

During the implantation period (14 to 28 days), nutritionally related deaths have a wider range of effects on pregnancy. These include a higher-than-normal number of ewes returning to estrus at more than 19 days after a fertile mating, a reduced lambing rate, and reduced lamb birth weights. The last effect is due to embryo death in the third and fourth weeks of pregnancy disturbing the balance in the distribution of the fetuses between the two uterine horns. This increases within-litter variability in fetal growth as a result of the surviving embryos' inability to utilize the vacated maternal cotyledons and also reduces the birth weight of the fetuses that do survive (Robinson, 1983). Extremes in nutrition are detrimental to embryo survival, suggesting that ewes should be kept at maintenance levels of nutrition during the first month of pregnancy.

Another aspect of conditioning ewes for breeding is referred to as static effects or ewe size embracing metabolic mass and condition. Exceptionally poor body condition or severe undernutrition during the immediate premating period, irrespective of condition, may delay onset of seasonal estrus, lengthen the estrous cycle, cause ovulation failure, or result in ovulation unaccompanied by estrus (Doney and Gunn, 1981). Foote and Mathews (1983) reported a very high correlation between body weight and body size (0.999), prolificacy (0.992), and weight of lambs born per ewe lambing (0.998). Correlations between ewe body weight and weaning rate and

weight of lambs weaned were 0.336 and 0.672, respectively.

The response to flushing is affected by the age of the ewe (mature ewes show a greater response than yearlings), its breed, and the stage of the breeding season. Flushing during the seasonal peak in ovulation rate is less effective than during early or late in the breeding season. Ewes in fleshy condition during breeding have a significantly higher ovulation rate and greater follicle size but a lower embryonic survival rate (El-Sheikh et al., 1955). The lower embryonic survival rate is likely affected by and related to ovulation rate; that is, a higher ovulation rate would result in more ova subject to loss (Edey, 1969). Foote et al. (1959), however, found that maternal cotyledon weight increased when ewes were changed from full to limited feeding, probably to obtain a greater nutrient supply for the fetus from the mother, thereby protecting the fetus from a nutrient shortage imposed by the limited feeding. Ova loss is complicated by nutrition effects after mating and by interaction between pre- and postmating (Edey, 1976). Both severe undernourishment or overnourishment postmating may be associated with ova loss and may have more severe effects than a static intermediate level (Doney and Gunn, 1981).

The placenta generally attains 95 percent of its final weight during the first 90 days of gestation, whereas the fetus attains about 15 percent of its weight in 90 days (Russell, 1979). Thus, nutrition level during early gestation may have its greatest effect on maintenance of the integrity of fetal membranes, which in turn affect the retention of the fetus. Grain feeding and increased ewe weight also resulted in higher plasma glucose levels and greater adrenal and pituitary weight (Bellows et al., 1963; Howland et al., 1966; Memon et al., 1969) and consequently greater total follicle stimulating hormone and luteinizing hormone potency. Larger ewes, irrespective of fatness, had larger pituitaries and greater follicular fluid weight. Virtually all prenatal deaths occur within the first 25 days after breeding (Foote et al., 1959), and the integrity of the cotyledons and placental membranes are logically a contributing factor.

Doney (1979) suggests that the efficiency of reproduction depends on the average nutrient intake level over the year as well as on the actual level at different stages in the annual cycle. Ovulation rate is affected by factors operating up to the time of mating or during the recovery period between lactation and breeding, whereas ova loss or prenatal mortality is affected by nutrition during recovery and also during pregnancy. Thus, both the static (during the recovery period) and dynamic (flushing) aspects of nutrition influence lambing rate (Coop, 1966).

Changing nutrient intake from a high prebreeding level to a low postbreeding level appears to contribute more to prenatal mortality than if the ewes are maintained at a low level throughout the whole period. This suggests that extremes are to be avoided and that body condition throughout the year is as critical as during a short flushing period.

Flushing is usually accomplished by providing ewes with fresh pasture, supplemental harvested forage, or up to 0.50 kg of grain per ewe daily, depending on environmental stress, availability of forage, and body condition. This level of nutrient intake should approach the energy and protein levels normally provided during late gestation. Special feeding usually begins around 2 weeks prior to mating and continues 2 to 4 weeks into the breeding season. The practice is especially beneficial for thin ewes that have not recovered from previous lactation stress. It should not continue too long, because an extended period of high feeding is unnecessarily costly, and overconditioning during pregnancy should be avoided. Drastic or severe decreases in the plane of nutrition should be avoided.

CREEP FEEDING

The practice of providing supplemental feed to nursing lambs in an area that cannot be entered by their dams is called creep feeding. Lambs usually commence creep feeding around 10 to 14 days of age, and the amount consumed is inversely proportional to the amount of milk consumed.

Inadequate energy intake by suckling lambs is the major cause of slow weight gains. Greater efficiency and lamb weight gains occur if lambs are creep fed than if only the ewes are grain fed. Jordan and Gates (1961) fed hay to ewes but did not creep feed lambs, for a lamb ADG of 0.15 kg; fed hay plus grain to ewes but did not creep feed lambs, for a lamb ADG of 0.20 kg; gave hay to ewes and did creep feed lambs, for a lamb ADG of 0.30 kg; and gave hay plus grain to ewes and did creep feed lambs, for a lamb ADG of 0.33 kg. Creep feed consumption by the lambs approximated the amount of corn fed the ewes.

The amount of creep feed consumed by lambs 2 to 6 weeks of age is affected by the palatability of the ration (ration composition and ration form) and the location and environment of the creep area. A well-bedded, well-lighted area located close to where ewes congregate is preferred. Low milk yield tends to encourage creep consumption, but lamb size as affected by birth weight and milk consumption has a significant effect on daily creep feed consumption. Initially, lambs prefer ground creep rations to pelleted rations. After 4 or 5 weeks of age, lambs show a preference for pelleted rations, and after 5 to 6 weeks, lambs should be fed unground grains.

Ørskov (1983) reported that ground, pelleted barley,

corn, wheat, or oats versus whole grains did not affect weight gains or feed-conversion efficiency but did lower rumen pH approximately 1 point and increased the proportion of propionic acid to acetic acid to a level that exceeds the metabolic capacity of the liver, giving rise to odd- and branched-chain fatty acids resulting in soft fat and reduced carcass quality. Unprocessed grain alleviates these problems.

The deterrent to feeding whole grains is the separating out of various supplements that are usually finely ground. Pelleting only the supplement alleviates this problem.

Soybean meal is an important ingredient in creep diets because of its high protein content and palatability. Bran is well liked by lambs, as are most sweet feeds. Oats, while consumed readily, are less well liked than corn as the lambs get older. Acceptability of ground feed may be increased slightly by adding 2 to 5 percent molasses.

Typical creep diets are suggested in Table 12, but other formulations may perform equally well. For rapid weight gains, creep diets must be palatable and high in energy and must contain adequate protein (12 to 14 percent), minerals (especially calcium, since grains are low in calcium), and vitamins.

The most important physiological factor determining successful early weaning and ability to utilize solid food is the state of rumen development (Ørskov, 1983). Rumen development is stimulated by the intake of solid feed, which, on fermentation, yields volatile fatty acids. Lambs suckling heavy-milking dams are less inclined to eat solid feed. Restricting protein intake of the ewe reduces milk flow and thus encourages creep feed intake (Robinson et al., 1974).

To achieve satisfactory performance and encourage rumen growth, lambs should receive a diet that ferments rapidly and does not lead to an accumulation of indigestible fibrous material within the rumen. Corn satisfies both requirements, whereas oats are high in indigestible hulls and result in pot-bellied lambs (Ørskov, 1975). High-quality legumes degrade rapidly in the rumen and also stimulate rumen growth. Unless the transition from a stage of high milk-low creep feed intake to low milk-high creep feed intake is completed prior to weaning at 4 to 6 weeks, a check in growth will occur and lambs will not gain for 7 to 10 days (Ørskov, 1982; Frederiksen et al., 1980). Thus, the level of solid food intake is a better guide to weaning than lamb weight, since lambs suckling heavy-milking dams may meet the weight criteria but, because they have consumed little solid feed, may have less-developed rumens (Ørskov, 1983).

EARLY WEANING

Lactating ewes normally reach their peak in milk production around 3 to 4 weeks postpartum and produce 75 percent of their total milk yield during the first 8 weeks of lactation. While milk production during early lactation can be stimulated through proper selection of feeds, after 6 to 8 weeks milk production declines markedly and high nutrient intake fails to stimulate production (Jordan and Hanke, 1977).

Early weaning as used in this report refers to the practice of weaning lambs at 6 to 8 weeks of age. There is considerable interest in early weaning because of possible early marketing of lambs, out-of-season lambing, multiple lamb crops per year, and use of prolific breeds. Early weaning can be cost-effective because it enables higher and more-efficient gains while the lambs are young and also reduces ewe cost because the ewes can be maintained on a limited feed allowance for longer periods of time between parturitions.

Lambs to be early weaned should receive creep feed from the time they are old enough to eat solid feed (7 to 14 days of age). At weaning, stress on the lambs should be minimized by removing the ewes and leaving the lambs in familiar surroundings. The postweaning ration should be a high-concentrate ration with a minimum of 16 percent crude protein, 0.6 percent calcium, and 0.30 percent phosphorus.

Since their source of protein from milk has been removed, the level of protein in the dry diet of a 6- to 8-week-old weaned lamb should actually be higher than that for a 3- to 5-week-old suckling lamb (Jordan and Hanke, 1970) and certainly higher than for older lambs.

ARTIFICIAL REARING

The practice of removing lambs from their dams when they are 8 to 24 hours old and rearing them on milk replacer for 3 to 4 weeks is referred to as artificial rearing. Although milk replacers are expensive, artificial rearing is feasible in such cases as orphan lambs and ewes with insufficient milk supply because of mastitis and in cases of more prolific breeds that give birth to litters larger than can be adequately suckled (Frederiksen et al., 1980; Gorrill et al., 1982).

Lambs intended for artificial rearing should be allowed to obtain their mother's colostrum for a minimum of 8 hours after birth before being weaned. Frozen colostrum, warmed to body temperature and bottle fed, is an adequate alternative. At least 50 ml of colostrum per kilogram of lamb weight is necessary to provide an effective level of disease resistance (Frederiksen et al., 1980; Gorrill et al., 1982). Although frozen ewe colostrum is preferred, research has shown that frozen cow colostrum also provides adequate antibodies for rearing lambs (Larsen et al., 1974; Logan et al., 1978; Franken and Elving, 1982).

Maximum performance during artificial rearing is ob-

tained by feeding specially formulated lamb milk replacers containing at least 24 percent fat and 24 percent protein, with all of the protein provided by spray-dried milk products (Heaney et al., 1982a; Gorrill et al., 1982). Similar milk replacers in which part of the skim milk powder is replaced by casein and whey or cerelose are also being used successfully, but with this type of milk replacer it is recommended that lactose content be limited to 30 to 35 percent (Glimp, 1972; Frederiksen et al., 1980).

Lambs can also be successfully reared with a high-quality milk replacer designed for calves that contains at least 20 percent fat and 20 percent protein. It is very important that only a high-quality calf milk replacer with all the protein provided by skim milk powder be used. It is unlikely that lambs could adequately utilize lower-quality ingredients at the reduced protein level. Gains on calf milk replacer are around 90 percent of gains reported with lamb milk replacer. Nevertheless, such a system could be economical because the lower cost of calf milk replacer could offset the marginal reduction in performance (Heaney et al., 1982b).

During a 3- to 4-week artificial rearing program, a lamb will consume an average of 400 to 500 g of dry milk replacer per day when 1 part milk replacer is mixed with 4 to 5 parts water. Lambs should be fed the milk replacer ad libitum at 2° to 4°C to minimize digestive disturbances, particularly abomasal bloat (Large and Penning, 1967; Peters and Heaney, 1974; Frederiksen et al., 1980; Gorrill et al., 1982).

Lambs should be provided constant access to fresh water and high-quality, palatable solid feed to accustom them to eating dry feed and to minimize weight losses during the transition from a liquid to a solid feed diet at around 3 to 4 weeks. Weight gains should approximate 0.25 to 0.30 kg (0.55 to 0.66 lb) per lamb daily during the period that milk replacer is fed.

Because milk replacer is expensive, the liquid-feeding period should be as short as possible. Lambs can be successfully weaned from milk replacer at 3 weeks of age, although a growth check will occur in which the lambs lose some weight the first week before resuming normal gains (Heaney et al., 1982a,b, 1984). The growth check is primarily a reflection of reduced nutrient intake (Frederiksen et al., 1980). Delaying weaning to 4 weeks of age reduces the growth check and results in lamb weights approximately 1 kg (2.2 lb) heavier at 70 days of age. The extra weight is not sufficient, however, to offset the extra costs of the 3.0 to 3.5 kg of milk replacer required for the extra week of feeding (Heaney et al., 1984).

The postweaning diet should be high energy and should contain 18 to 20 percent protein (as-fed basis) for the first 3 weeks and then 14 to 17 percent protein thereafter. It is doubtful whether higher levels of protein will result in sufficiently better lamb performance to justify the cost (Meat and Livestock Commission, 1976; Frederiksen et al., 1980; Gorrill et al., 1982; Heaney et al., 1983).

FEED ADDITIVES

Antibiotics may improve performance when added to creep diets and growing-finishing diets for lambs (Ott, 1968). Responses to antibiotics seem to be markedly affected by differences in management and in the amount of stress to which animals are subjected (Hays, 1969). At present only chlortetracycline and oxytetracycline are approved by the Food and Drug Administration for nutritional uses in sheep diets (Anonymous, 1984a). Chlortetracycline can be used at levels varying from 22 to 55 mg/kg of feed to promote growth and improve feed efficiency. Oxytetracycline is approved for use at levels of 11 to 22 mg/kg of feed for the same purpose. The polyether antibiotic, lasalocid, which was recently approved for prevention of coccidiosis in sheep held in confinement (Anonymous, 1984b), has also been shown to improve rate of gain and feed efficiency in lambs (Foreyt et al., 1979; Horton and Stockdale, 1981). Lasalocid is approved for use at levels of 22 to 33 mg/kg of the total diet.

There is some evidence that antibiotics help reduce the incidence of enterotoxemia (Ott, 1968). Chlortetracycline can be used at a level of 22 mg/kg of feed for this purpose, and oxytetracycline can be used at a level of 25 mg per lamb per day. In addition to the above, a number of feed additives are approved for treatment of specific sheep diseases. Information for the approved usage of these antibiotics can be obtained by consulting the Feed Additive Compendium (Anonymous, 1984a).

POISONOUS PLANTS

Many poisonous plants grow on pastures and range areas in the United States (Kingsbury, 1964; Sperry et al., 1964; James et al., 1980). In some areas, such as the western states, poisonous plants are a major cause of economic loss to the sheep industry (Dwyer, 1978; Schuster, 1978). Most losses occur when desirable forage is scarce and poisonous plants are abundant (Binns, 1974). Losses result from death, abortions, photosensitization, decreased production, emaciation, and birth defects (James et al., 1980). Since there are no known specific treatments for animals poisoned by most poisonous plants, proper management of pastures and animals is the best approach to preventing losses (Merrill and Schuster, 1978). The best protection against poisonous plant problems is to become familiar with the poisonous plants that grow in pastures and learn under what conditions these plants

are dangerous to sheep. Sheep that have been under stress or that are overly hungry or thirsty should not be permitted to graze in areas infested with poisonous plants. Sheep introduced into a new area that contains poisonous plants with which they may not be familiar should be watched closely. Salt and supplemental feed should be provided to grazing animals as needed. Control of poisonous plants (spraying, grazing management, hand pulling) or of animal access to areas containing poisonous plants (fencing, pasture rotation) should be practiced where feasible. Effective treatment of poisoned sheep requires identification of the specific plant causing the problem, removal of sheep to a feed source free of the poisonous plant, and administration of an antidote if one is available. In cases where a specific treatment is unknown, the only course of action is to treat the signs.

RATION ALTERNATIVES

Although the daily nutrient requirements for ewes presented in Table 1 are specific, the sources of nutrients available to meet these requirements are many. Confinement feeding of diets low in energy to ewes on slotted floors at high density levels and often with inadequate feed bunk space makes it difficult to provide adequate nutrient intake to all sheep and to deal with the accumulation of refused feed under the slotted floor. Alternatives to the typical high-forage diets and various management approaches are available to circumvent these problems and to minimize labor and facility costs.

For example, feeding several groups of ewes at different times with one common feed bunk eliminates the problems of inadequate bunk space. Feeding gestating ewes on alternate days or 3 times weekly accommodates feeding groups of ewes at different times. Ewes fed three times weekly the same amount of feed per week were equal in weight gains and in lamb and wool production to ewes fed daily (Jordan and Hanke, 1963; Jordan, 1966).

Another ration alternative is to feed ewes higher-than-normal grain rations. The digestible energy (DE) values used for forages are overvalued in relation to the DE in grain, and since grains are often a lower-cost source of energy than hay, high-grain rations may offer advantages for intensively managed sheep. Gestating ewes fed rations consisting of equal parts of hay and corn (69 percent total digestible nutrients) in amounts equal to one-half the weight of an all-hay ration showed weight gains and lamb and wool production equal to ewes fed the all-hay diet (Jordan, 1966). However, dry matter or bulk is lacking, which results in wool picking. A more reasonable approach is to feed 3 parts of hay and 1 part of corn at 75 percent of an all-hay ration. This is more apt to provide adequate bulk, protein, and minerals and still reduce feeding costs.

It normally takes ewes 3 to 4 hours to eat enough long hay to meet their nutrient requirements, but when fed a 40 percent corn-60 percent hay ration, they can consume enough feed to meet their requirements in 20 to 30 minutes. The reduced time for feeding is particularly advantageous when feeding three or four different groups of ewes per day with one common feed bunk. To prevent esophageal choke, the corn should be mixed with the hay (or spread on top of long hay) to prevent too-rapid consumption. Also, hay must be of good quality with 15 to 18 percent protein so that protein and calcium deficiencies do not develop.

The composition of two important sheep feedstuffs, corn silage and haylage, are on a DM basis, but these feedstuffs contain 40 to 70 percent moisture on an as-fed basis. To compare the "as-fed" nutrient content of silage or haylage with the values presented in Table 13, multiply those values by the DM content in the silage or haylage being fed. Corn silage with 70 percent TDN, on a DM basis, × 35 percent DM contains 24.5 percent TDN on an as-fed basis. Haylage with 56 percent TDN, on a DM basis, × 50 percent DM contains 28 percent TDN on an as-fed basis.

There are numerous feedstuffs that can be used as ration alternatives to the conventional legume hay-grain feedstuffs generally used by producers. These include many grain, vegetable, fruit, and food industry by-products as well as damaged grains and roughages. The major consideration in using alternative feedstuffs is their cost relative to more conventional feeds. Frequent use of alternative feedstuffs requires careful attention to correcting whatever nutrient deficiencies may exist.

6 Formulating Diets for Sheep

Sheep should be fed an economical, nutritionally adequate diet. This is accomplished by combining the information given in Tables 1 and 2 on the nutritional requirements of sheep with the information in Tables 13 and 14 on the nutrients provided by various feedstuffs. The weight category is based on normal weight. If a ewe normally weighs 60 kg and gains 10 kg during early gestation, the weight category to use for late gestation in determining nutritional requirements is 60 kg, not 70 kg.

Rations can be formulated on the basis of (1) providing a complete diet containing the recommended composition shown in Table 2, which, when fed at recommended levels, will provide the daily requirements recommended in Table 1 or (2) providing the specific amount of nutrients per sheep daily as presented in Table 1.

Sheep rations usually are formulated by first selecting a major feed energy source, such as hay or silage. Next, determine what nutrients the source provides and compare these values with the requirements in Table 1 or 2. Finally, determine the composition and amount of supplement that must be fed with the hay or silage to compensate for nutrient shortages.

In the following examples rations will be formulated for a 60-kg ewe suckling twin lambs during the first 8 weeks lactation. Oat hay, barley, and soybean meal are the available feeds.

Complete diet formulation

Write down the recommended nutrient composition of the diet (from Table 2) and the nutrient content of the feeds (from Table A). In this example, feeds used were analyzed by a commercial laboratory; if analyzed values are not available, use average values from Table 13.

TABLE A Recommended Nutrient Concentration in Diets for 60-kg Ewes, First 6 to 8 Weeks Lactation Suckling Twins, and Nutrient Content of Feeds, Both on DM Basis

Item	DE (Mcal/kg)	Crude protein (%)	Ca (%)	P (%)	Carotene (mg/kg)	Vitamin A (IU/kg)
Diet concentration	2.9	15.0	0.39	0.29	—	2,500
Oat hay	2.38	9.2	0.26	0.24	101.0	
Barley	3.79	13.0	0.09	0.47	—	
Soybean meal	3.53	51.5	0.36	0.75	—	

Procedure

1. Compare the composition of oat hay with the ewe's requirements. The oat hay is inadequate in all nutrients except carotene (5 mg of carotene would supply the vitamin A requirement; see the section on Vitamin A on pp. 22).

2. Determine the substitution value of barley for oat hay: 3.79 Mcal DE (barley) − 2.38 Mcal DE (hay) = 1.41 Mcal DE/kg. The DE deficiency in an oat hay diet is 2.90 Mcal (required) − 2.38 Mcal (hay) = 0.52 Mcal DE. Determine the percent barley to substitute for part of the hay to provide the 0.52 Mcal DE/kg deficiency (0.52 Mcal ÷ 1.41 Mcal = 0.37). The diet at this stage becomes 37 percent barley and 63 percent oat hay.

3. Compare this combination of oat hay and barley with the dietary requirements for DM, DE, and protein (Table B).

TABLE B   Comparison of Dietary Requirements with Amount of Nutrients Provided in Hay-Barley Diet

Item	DM (% of diet)	DE (Mcal)	Protein (%)
Dietary requirement	100.0	2.9	15.0
Oat hay	63.0	1.5[a]	5.8[a]
Barley	37.0	1.4	4.8
Total	100.0	2.9	10.6
Difference	—	—	−4.4

[a]Values obtained by multiplying energy or protein content in feeds by percent of feeds in diet.

The diet is now adequate in digestible energy but is 4.4 percent deficient in protein.

4. Substitute soybean meal for barley to provide for the protein deficiency. Determine the difference in crude protein content of the two feeds: 51.5 percent (soybean meal) − 13.0 percent (barley) = 38.5 percent protein. Divide the amount of protein that is deficient (4.4 percent) by the amount provided when soybean meal is substituted for a unit of barley: 4.4 percent divided by 38.5 percent = 0.114, or 11.4 percent of the entire ration will be soybean meal. The diet becomes (Table C):

TABLE C   Comparison of Dietary Requirements with Energy and Protein Provided by the Oat Hay-Barley-Soybean Meal Diet

Item	DM (%)	DE (Mcal)	Protein (%)
Requirement	100.0	2.9	15.0
Oat hay	63.0	1.5	5.8
Barley	25.6	1.0	3.3
Soybean meal	11.4	0.4	5.9
Total	100.0	2.9	15.0

The diet is now adequate in both digestible energy and protein.

The Pearson square method may also be used for determining the amount of soybean meal to add to the barley. The hay contains 9.2 percent protein (see Table A) but constitutes only 63.0 percent of the ration (see Table C). Thus, the hay provides 5.8 percent (9.2 percent × 0.63) protein to the total ration. The dietary requirement of 15.0 percent protein (see Table C) − 5.8 percent protein from hay = 9.2 percent protein that must be provided in the 37.0 percent barley-soybean meal part of the ration. Thus, 9.2 percent ÷ 37.0 percent of the ration = 24.9 percent protein required in the barley-soybean meal mixture. The next step is to determine the parts of barley and soybean meal needed in the ration to provide the 24.9 percent protein requirement.

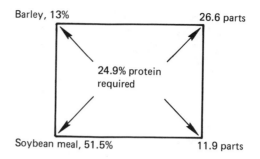

The parts of barley needed in the barley-soybean mixture can be calculated by subtracting diagonally the percent protein required (24.9) from the percent protein in the soybean meal (51.5), which equals 26.6 parts barley. The same method gives 11.9 parts soybean meal required. Then, 26.6 parts barley ÷ 38.5 total parts equals 69.1 percent barley required in the mixture; 11.9 parts soybean meal ÷ 38.5 total parts equals 30.9 percent soybean meal:

	Parts	Percent
Barley	26.6	69.1
Soybean meal	11.9	30.9
Total	38.5	100.0

If there is 30.9 percent soybean meal in the 37 percent portion of the ration that is provided by the barley-soybean meal mix, then in the entire hay-barley-soybean meal diet there is 0.37 × 30.9 = 0.114 = 11.4 percent soybean meal.

5. Write down the calcium and phosphorus requirements and compare these with the amounts provided by the hay-barley-soybean meal diet (Table D).

TABLE D   Comparison of Dietary Requirements with Calcium and Phosphorus Provided by the Oat Hay-Barley-Soybean Meal Diet

Item	DM (%)	Calcium (%)	Phosphorus (%)
Requirement	100.0	0.39	0.29
Oat hay	63.0	0.16	0.15
Barley	25.6	0.02	0.12
Soybean meal	11.4	0.04	0.08
Total	100.0	0.22	0.35
Difference	—	−0.17	+0.06

The diet is adequate in phosphorus but is 0.17 percent deficient in calcium. Limestone is a rich (34 percent) and inexpensive source of calcium (Table 14). Dividing the 0.17 percent deficiency by the 34 percent calcium in limestone gives 0.5 parts limestone that should be added to the diet.

The final diet now becomes as shown in Table E (parts, DM basis). When fed at the levels recommended in Table 1, it will satisfy the daily requirements for this category of sheep.

TABLE E   Complete Diet for 60-kg Ewes, First 6 to 8 Weeks Lactation Suckling Twins

Ingredient	DM (%)	Parts in Diet DM[a]	Air Dry or As-Fed Basis Parts[b]	Percent[c]
Oat hay	88.2	63.0	71.4	62.9
Barley	89.0	25.6	28.8	25.4
Soybean meal	89.0	11.4	12.8	11.3
Limestone	100.0	0.5	0.5	0.4
Total			113.5	100.0

[a]As determined in above steps.
[b]Calculated as 63.0/0.882 = 71.4.
[c]Calculated as 71.4/1.135 = 62.9.

Up to this point, all calculations have been made on a DM basis; however, few feeds are 100 percent dry matter. To convert the portions of feeds on a DM basis to an as-fed basis (Table E), divide the contribution of the feed in question by the percent of dry matter it contains (oat hay: 63 parts of the diet DM ÷ 88.2 percent dry matter = 71.4 parts, air dry). To convert the various component parts of the diet back to percentage values, divide the number of parts for each of the ration components by the total number of parts (oat hay: 71.4 parts air dry ÷ 113.5 total parts = 62.9 percent on an as-fed basis). Dry matter intake is converted to an as-fed basis by dividing the daily feed intake given in Table 1 (2.6 kg) by 0.89 (approximate DM in the total ration) = 2.92 kg (6.4 lb) of the complete diet per day. If the feeds were hand fed separately to the ewes, 62.9 percent or 1.84 kg (0.629 × 2.92) of the as-fed diet would be oat hay and 1.08 kg (2.92 − 1.84 kg) of the diet would consist of barley, soybean meal, and limestone.

The total air dry part of the barley-soybean meal-limestone portion of the diet is 42.1. Each feed part is divided by this value and multiplied by 100 to obtain the percent it contributes. The composition of this mixture becomes 68.4 percent barley, 30.4 percent soybean meal, and 1.2 percent limestone on an air dry basis.

Formulation to provide specific amounts of nutrients (same category of ewe and same feeds)

1. Write down the ewe's daily requirement (from Table 1) and the nutrient composition of the three feed ingredients (Table F). (Dry matter per se is not a nutrient, but it is an important indication of the amount of feed the ewe can and should consume.)

2. Determine the amount of energy that the designated DM intake of the major feed ingredient (oat hay) provides (2.6 kg DM × 2.38 Mcal DE/kg of hay = 6.19 Mcal DE). The ewe requires 7.4 Mcal DE and the oat hay provides 6.19 Mcal; thus, the diet is deficient by 1.21 Mcal DE.

TABLE F   Daily Nutrient Requirements and Feed Composition for 60-kg Ewes, First 6 to 8 Weeks Lactation Suckling Twins

Item	DM (kg)	DE (Mcal)	Crude protein (kg)	Ca (g)	P (g)	Carotene (mg/kg feed)	Vitamin A (IU)
			Daily Requirements				
	2.6	7.4	0.405	10.7	7.7		6,000
		Feed composition, dry matter basis					
Oat hay	88.2%	2.38	9.2%	0.26%	0.24%	101.0	
Barley	89.0%	3.79	13.0%	0.09%	0.47%	—	
Soybean meal	89.0%	3.53	51.5%	0.36%	0.75%	—	

3. Assume that 2.6 kg of dry matter is the maximum amount a 60-kg ewe can consume in a day. The shortage of digestible energy in the oat hay is provided by substituting barley for oat hay: 3.79 Mcal DE/kg (barley) − 2.38 Mcal DE/kg (hay) = 1.41 Mcal DE. Divide the 1.21 Mcal DE in which the hay is deficient (step 2) by the 1.41 Mcal of additional DE that one unit of barley provides to determine the amount of barley required in addition to hay (1.21 ÷ 1.41 = 0.86 kg of barley). Thus, the 2.6-kg ration of dry matter should comprise 0.86 kg of barley DM + 1.74 kg (i.e., 2.6 − 0.86 kg) of hay.

4. Determine whether the hay-barley ration provides sufficient protein (1.74 kg of hay DM × 9.2 percent protein [from Table A] = 0.160 kg of protein from hay; 0.86 kg barley DM × 13.0 percent = 0.112 kg protein from barley; total protein from the hay−barley ration is 0.272 kg). Thus, 0.405 kg required − 0.272 kg provided by the hay-barley ration gives a 0.133-kg protein deficiency in the hay-barley ration.

5. To determine the amount of soybean meal to substitute for barley to provide the required amount of protein, calculate the difference in the protein content of soybean meal and that of barley from Table F (0.515 − 0.13 = 0.385 percent). To compensate for the 0.133 kg protein lacking in the hay-barley ration, divide 0.133 by 0.385 = 0.345 kg DM from soybean meal. The ewe's ration becomes 1.74 kg DM from hay, 0.51 kg DM from barley, and 0.35 kg DM from soybean meal. The amount of soybean meal needed to substitute for part of the barley may also be determined by the Pearson square method.

6. The calcium provided by the hay (1.74 kg × 0.26 percent = 4.5 g), barley (0.51 kg × 0.09 percent = 0.5 g), and soybean meal (0.35 kg × 0.36 percent = 1.3 g) adds up to 6.3 g, leaving a deficiency of 4.4 g (10.7 − 6.3). To determine the amount of limestone to add to compensate for the calcium deficiency, divide 4.4 by 0.34 (calcium content of limestone) = 13 g or 0.013 kg. A similar comparison for phosphorus shows the diet to be adequate in this mineral. Therefore, the daily diet per ewe on a DM basis becomes 1.74 kg oat hay, 0.51 kg barley, 0.35 kg soybean meal, and 0.01 kg limestone.

To convert to an as-fed basis, divide each amount of dry matter by the percent dry matter in that feed. On an as-fed basis the daily diet per ewe is 1.97 kg oat hay, 0.57 kg barley, 0.39 kg soybean meal, and 0.01 kg limestone.

These are only two methods of formulating diets. Other methods include the use of simultaneous equations to algebraically arrive at a solution and the use of computers to solve more complex sets of equations. The procedures discussed in this section do not include all nutrients or effects of feed palatability, economics, and other factors that nutritionists and feed producers should consider.

7 Composition of Feeds

Tables 13 and 14 present the composition of certain sheep feeds and the composition of mineral supplements, respectively. In both tables, data are expressed on an as-fed and dry basis.

INTERNATIONAL NOMENCLATURE

In Tables 13 and 14 and in the *United States-Canadian Tables of Feed Composition* (NRC, 1982), which lists approximately 400 feeds, names of the feeds are based on a scheme proposed by Harris et al. (1980, 1981). The names are designed to give a qualitative description of each product where such information is available and pertinent. A complete name consists of as many as six facets, separated by commas and written in linear form. The facets are

1. Origin, consisting of scientific name (genus, species, variety) and common name (generic name, breed or kind, strain or chemical formula)
2. Part fed to animals as affected by process(es)
3. Process(es) and treatment(s) to which the part has been subjected
4. Stage of maturity or development of feed
5. Cutting (applicable to forages)
6. Grade (official grades with guarantees)

INTERNATIONAL FEED CLASSES

Feeds are grouped into eight classes:

1. Dry forages and roughages
2. Pasture, range plants, and forages fed fresh
3. Silages
4. Energy feeds

5. Protein supplements
6. Mineral supplements
7. Vitamin supplements
8. Additives

Feeds with more than 18 percent crude fiber or 35 percent cell wall (DM basis) are classified as forages or roughages; feeds with less than 20 percent protein and less than 18 percent crude fiber or less than 35 percent cell wall are classified as energy feeds; and those with 20 percent or more protein are considered protein supplements.

The feed class number precedes the international feed number in Tables 13 and 14.

INTERNATIONAL FEED NUMBER

Each international feed name is assigned a 5-digit international feed number (IFN) for identification and computer manipulation. The IFN is particularly useful as a tag to recall nutrient data for calculation of diets (Harris, 1963; Harris et al., 1968).

The following table shows how three feeds are described.

Descriptions of Three Feeds, Including Classification and IFN

Components of Name	Feed No. 1	Feed No. 2	Feed No. 3
Origin (or parent material)	Clover	Cotton	Wheat
Species, variety or kind	Red	—	—
Part eaten	Hay (foliage)	Seeds	Flour by-product
Process(es) and treatment(s) to which product has been subjected	Sun-cured	Meal mechanical extraced	—
Stage of maturity[a]	Early bloom	—	—

40

Descriptions of Three Feeds, Including Classification and IFN—
Continued

Components of Name	Feed No. 1	Feed No. 2	Feed No. 3
Grade or quality designation	—	41% Protein	< 4% Fiber (wheat) (red dog)
Classification (first digit in IFN)	Dry Forages and roughages	Protein supplements	Energy feeds
IFN	1-01-400	5-01-617	4-05-203

[a]See Table 15 for definitions of stages of maturity.

Thus, the names of the three feeds are written as follows:

Feed No. 1: Clover, red, hay, sun-cured, early bloom.

Feed No. 2: Cotton, seeds, meal mechanical extracted, 41 percent protein.

Feed No. 3: Wheat, flour by-product, less than 4 percent fiber (wheat, red dog).

DATA

The analytical data in Tables 13 and 14 are expressed in the metric system and are shown on an as-fed and dry basis. See Tables 16 and 17 for weight unit conversion factors and weight equivalents, respectively.

Analytical data may differ in the various NRC reports because the data are updated for each report. The feed names may also differ as feeds are more precisely described or as official definitions change. If the feed is the same, however, the International Feed Number will remain the same.

ENERGY VALUES OF FEEDS

Total digestible nutrients. Total digestible nutrients (TDN) were calculated from

(1) Average TDN *or*

(2) From digestion coefficients such as

digestible protein (%)	$\times$ 1
digestible crude fiber (%)	$\times$ 1
digestible nitrogen free extract (%)	$\times$ 1
digestible ether extract (%)	$\times$ 2.25
TDN (%)	Total *or*

(3) From regression equations of Harris et al. (1972).

Digestible energy. Digestible energy was calculated with the formula of Crampton et al. (1957) and Swift (1957):

DE (Mcal/kg DM) = % TDN for sheep $\times$ 0.04409

Metabolizable energy. ME was calculated from DE by the following formula:

ME (Mcal/kg DM) = 0.82 $\times$ DE (Mcal/kg DM)

Digestible protein. Digestible protein was calculated as follows:

$$(1) \quad \text{Digestible protein} = \frac{\% \text{ protein} \times \text{protein digestion coefficient}}{100} \quad or$$

(2) By equations of Knight and Harris (1966).

Tables

TABLE 1 Daily Nutrient Requirements of Sheep

Body Weight (kg)	(lb)	Weight Change/Day (g)	(lb)	Dry Matter per Animal[a] (kg)	(lb)	(% body weight)	Energy[b] TDN (kg)	(lb)	DE (Mcal)	ME (Mcal)	Crude protein (g)	(lb)	Ca (g)	P (g)	Vitamin A Activity (IU)	Vitamin E Activity (IU)
Ewes[c]																
Maintenance																
50	110	10	0.02	1.0	2.2	2.0	0.55	1.2	2.4	2.0	95	0.21	2.0	1.8	2,350	15
60	132	10	0.02	1.1	2.4	1.8	0.61	1.3	2.7	2.2	104	0.23	2.3	2.1	2,820	16
70	154	10	0.02	1.2	2.6	1.7	0.66	1.5	2.9	2.4	113	0.25	2.5	2.4	3,290	18
80	176	10	0.02	1.3	2.9	1.6	0.72	1.6	3.2	2.6	122	0.27	2.7	2.8	3,760	20
90	198	10	0.02	1.4	3.1	1.5	0.78	1.7	3.4	2.8	131	0.29	2.9	3.1	4,230	21
Flushing—2 Weeks prebreeding and first 3 weeks of breeding																
50	110	100	0.22	1.6	3.5	3.2	0.94	2.1	4.1	3.4	150	0.33	5.3	2.6	2,350	24
60	132	100	0.22	1.7	3.7	2.8	1.00	2.2	4.4	3.6	157	0.34	5.5	2.9	2,820	26
70	154	100	0.22	1.8	4.0	2.6	1.06	2.3	4.7	3.8	164	0.36	5.7	3.2	3,290	27
80	176	100	0.22	1.9	4.2	2.4	1.12	2.5	4.9	4.0	171	0.38	5.9	3.6	3,760	28
90	198	100	0.22	2.0	4.4	2.2	1.18	2.6	5.1	4.2	177	0.39	6.1	3.9	4,230	30
Nonlactating—First 15 weeks gestation																
50	110	30	0.07	1.2	2.6	2.4	0.67	1.5	3.0	2.4	112	0.25	2.9	2.1	2,350	18
60	132	30	0.07	1.3	2.9	2.2	0.72	1.6	3.2	2.6	121	0.27	3.2	2.5	2,820	20
70	154	30	0.07	1.4	3.1	2.0	0.77	1.7	3.4	2.8	130	0.29	3.5	2.9	3,290	21
80	176	30	0.07	1.5	3.3	1.9	0.82	1.8	3.6	3.0	139	0.31	3.8	3.3	3,760	22
90	198	30	0.07	1.6	3.5	1.8	0.87	1.9	3.8	3.2	148	0.33	4.1	3.6	4,230	24
Last 4 weeks gestation (130-150% lambing rate expected) or last 4-6 weeks lactation suckling singles[d]																
50	110	180 (45)	0.40 (0.10)	1.6	3.5	3.2	0.94	2.1	4.1	3.4	175	0.38	5.9	4.8	4,250	24
60	132	180 (45)	0.40 (0.10)	1.7	3.7	2.8	1.00	2.2	4.4	3.6	184	0.40	6.0	5.2	5,100	26
70	154	180 (45)	0.40 (0.10)	1.8	4.0	2.6	1.06	2.3	4.7	3.8	193	0.42	6.2	5.6	5,950	27
80	176	180 (45)	0.40 (0.10)	1.9	4.2	2.4	1.12	2.4	4.9	4.0	202	0.44	6.3	6.1	6,800	28
90	198	180 (45)	0.40 (0.10)	2.0	4.4	2.2	1.18	2.5	5.1	4.2	212	0.47	6.4	6.5	7,650	30
Last 4 weeks gestation (180-225% lambing rate expected)																
50	110	225	0.50	1.7	3.7	3.4	1.10	2.4	4.8	4.0	196	0.43	6.2	3.4	4,250	26
60	132	225	0.50	1.8	4.0	3.0	1.17	2.6	5.1	4.2	205	0.45	6.9	4.0	5,100	27
70	154	225	0.50	1.9	4.2	2.7	1.24	2.8	5.4	4.4	214	0.47	7.6	4.5	5,950	28
80	176	225	0.50	2.0	4.4	2.5	1.30	2.9	5.7	4.7	223	0.49	8.3	5.1	6,800	30
90	198	225	0.50	2.1	4.6	2.3	1.37	3.0	6.0	5.0	232	0.51	8.9	5.7	7,650	32
First 6-8 weeks lactation suckling singles or last 4-6 weeks lactation suckling twins[d]																
50	110	−25 (90)	−0.06 (0.20)	2.1	4.6	4.2	1.36	3.0	6.0	4.9	304	0.67	8.9	6.1	4,250	32
60	132	−25 (90)	−0.06 (0.20)	2.3	5.1	3.8	1.50	3.3	6.6	5.4	319	0.70	9.1	6.6	5,100	34
70	154	−25 (90)	−0.06 (0.20)	2.5	5.5	3.6	1.63	3.6	7.2	5.9	334	0.73	9.3	7.0	5,950	38
80	176	−25 (90)	−0.06 (0.20)	2.6	5.7	3.2	1.69	3.7	7.4	6.1	344	0.76	9.5	7.4	6,800	39
90	198	−25 (90)	−0.06 (0.20)	2.7	5.9	3.0	1.75	3.8	7.6	6.3	353	0.78	9.6	7.8	7,650	40

TABLE 1 Daily Nutrient Requirements of Sheep—*Continued*

Body Weight		Weight Change/Day		Dry Matter per Animal[a]			Nutrients per Animal							Ca	P	Vitamin A Activity	Vitamin E Activity
							Energy[b]				Crude protein						
							TDN		DE	ME							
(kg)	(lb)	(g)	(lb)	(kg)	(lb)	(% body weight)	(kg)	(lb)	(Mcal)	(Mcal)	(g)	(lb)	(g)	(g)	(IU)	(IU)
First 6-8 weeks lactation suckling twins																
50	110	−60	−0.13	2.4	5.3	4.8	1.56	3.4	6.9	5.6	389	0.86	10.5	7.3	5,000	36
60	132	−60	−0.13	2.6	5.7	4.3	1.69	3.7	7.4	6.1	405	0.89	10.7	7.7	6,000	39
70	154	−60	−0.13	2.8	6.2	4.0	1.82	4.0	8.0	6.6	420	0.92	11.0	8.1	7,000	42
80	176	−60	−0.13	3.0	6.6	3.8	1.95	4.3	8.6	7.0	435	0.96	11.2	8.6	8,000	45
90	198	−60	−0.13	3.2	7.0	3.6	2.08	4.6	9.2	7.5	450	0.99	11.4	9.0	9,000	48
Ewe lambs																
Nonlactating—First 15 weeks gestation																
40	88	160	0.35	1.4	3.1	3.5	0.83	1.8	3.6	3.0	156	0.34	5.5	3.0	1,880	21
50	110	135	0.30	1.5	3.3	3.0	0.88	1.9	3.9	3.2	159	0.35	5.2	3.1	2,350	22
60	132	135	0.30	1.6	3.5	2.7	0.94	2.0	4.1	3.4	161	0.35	5.5	3.4	2,820	24
70	154	125	0.28	1.7	3.7	2.4	1.00	2.2	4.4	3.6	164	0.36	5.5	3.7	3,290	26
Last 4 weeks gestation (100-120% lambing rate expected)																
40	88	180	0.40	1.5	3.3	3.8	0.94	2.1	4.1	3.4	187	0.41	6.4	3.1	3,400	22
50	110	160	0.35	1.6	3.5	3.2	1.00	2.2	4.4	3.6	189	0.42	6.3	3.4	4,250	24
60	132	160	0.35	1.7	3.7	2.8	1.07	2.4	4.7	3.9	192	0.42	6.6	3.8	5,100	26
70	154	150	0.33	1.8	4.0	2.6	1.14	2.5	5.0	4.1	194	0.43	6.8	4.2	5,950	27
Last 4 weeks gestation (130-175% lambing rate expected)																
40	88	225	0.50	1.5	3.3	3.8	0.99	2.2	4.4	3.6	202	0.44	7.4	3.5	3,400	22
50	110	225	0.50	1.6	3.5	3.2	1.06	2.3	4.7	3.8	204	0.45	7.8	3.9	4,250	24
60	132	225	0.50	1.7	3.7	2.8	1.12	2.5	4.9	4.0	207	0.46	8.1	4.3	5,100	26
70	154	215	0.47	1.8	4.0	2.6	1.14	2.5	5.0	4.1	210	0.46	8.2	4.7	5,950	27
First 6-8 weeks lactation suckling singles (wean by 8 weeks)																
40	88	−50	−0.11	1.7	3.7	4.2	1.12	2.5	4.9	4.0	257	0.56	6.0	4.3	3,400	26
50	110	−50	−0.11	2.1	4.6	4.2	1.39	3.1	6.1	5.0	282	0.62	6.5	4.7	4,250	32
60	132	−50	−0.11	2.3	5.1	3.8	1.52	3.4	6.7	5.5	295	0.65	6.8	5.1	5,100	34
70	154	−50	−0.11	2.5	5.5	3.6	1.65	3.6	7.3	6.0	301	0.68	7.1	5.6	5,450	38
First 6-8 weeks lactation suckling twins (wean by 8 weeks)																
40	88	−100	−0.22	2.1	4.6	5.2	1.45	3.2	6.4	5.2	306	0.67	8.4	5.6	4,000	32
50	110	−100	−0.22	2.3	5.1	4.6	1.59	3.5	7.0	5.7	321	0.71	8.7	6.0	5,000	34
60	132	−100	−0.22	2.5	5.5	4.2	1.72	3.8	7.6	6.2	336	0.74	9.0	6.4	6,000	38
70	154	−100	−0.22	2.7	6.0	3.9	1.85	4.1	8.1	6.6	351	0.77	9.3	6.9	7,000	40

Replacement ewe lambs[e]

30	66	227	0.50	1.2	2.6	4.0	0.78	1.7	3.4	2.8	185	0.41	6.4	2.6	1,410	18
40	88	182	0.40	1.4	3.1	3.5	0.91	2.0	4.0	3.3	176	0.39	5.9	2.6	1,880	21
50	110	120	0.26	1.5	3.3	3.0	0.88	1.9	3.9	3.2	136	0.30	4.8	2.4	2,350	22
60	132	100	0.22	1.5	3.3	2.5	0.88	1.9	3.9	3.2	134	0.30	4.5	2.5	2,820	22
70	154	100	0.22	1.5	3.3	2.1	0.88	1.9	3.9	3.2	132	0.29	4.6	2.8	3,290	22

Replacement ram lambs[e]

40	88	330	0.73	1.8	4.0	4.5	1.1	2.5	5.0	4.1	243	0.54	7.8	3.7	1,880	24
60	132	320	0.70	2.4	5.3	4.0	1.5	3.4	6.7	5.5	263	0.58	8.4	4.2	2,820	26
80	176	290	0.64	2.8	6.2	3.5	1.8	3.9	7.8	6.4	268	0.59	8.5	4.6	3,760	28
100	220	250	0.55	3.0	6.6	3.0	1.9	4.2	8.4	6.9	264	0.58	8.2	4.8	4,700	30

Lambs finishing—4 to 7 months old[f]

30	66	295	0.65	1.3	2.9	4.3	0.94	2.1	4.1	3.4	191	0.42	6.6	3.2	1,410	20
40	88	275	0.60	1.6	3.5	4.0	1.22	2.7	5.4	4.4	185	0.41	6.6	3.3	1,880	24
50	110	205	0.45	1.6	3.5	3.2	1.23	2.7	5.4	4.4	160	0.35	5.6	3.0	2,350	24

Early weaned lambs—Moderate growth potential[f]

10	22	200	0.44	0.5	1.1	5.0	0.40	0.9	1.8	1.4	127	0.38	4.0	1.9	470	10
20	44	250	0.55	1.0	2.2	5.0	0.80	1.8	3.5	2.9	167	0.37	5.4	2.5	940	20
30	66	300	0.66	1.3	2.9	4.3	1.00	2.2	4.4	3.6	191	0.42	6.7	3.2	1,410	20
40	88	345	0.76	1.5	3.3	3.8	1.16	2.6	5.1	4.2	202	0.44	7.7	3.9	1,880	22
50	110	300	0.66	1.5	3.3	3.0	1.16	2.6	5.1	4.2	181	0.40	7.0	3.8	2,350	22

Early weaned lambs—Rapid growth potential[f]

10	22	250	0.55	0.6	1.3	6.0	0.48	1.1	2.1	1.7	157	0.35	4.9	2.2	470	12
20	44	300	0.66	1.2	2.6	6.0	0.92	2.0	4.0	3.3	205	0.45	6.5	2.9	940	24
30	66	325	0.72	1.4	3.1	4.7	1.10	2.4	4.8	4.0	216	0.48	7.2	3.4	1,410	21
40	88	400	0.88	1.5	3.3	3.8	1.14	2.5	5.0	4.1	234	0.51	8.6	4.3	1,880	22
50	110	425	0.94	1.7	3.7	3.4	1.29	2.8	5.7	4.7	240	0.53	9.4	4.8	2,350	25
60	132	350	0.77	1.7	3.7	2.8	1.29	2.8	5.7	4.7	240	0.53	8.2	4.5	2,820	25

[a] To convert dry matter to an as-fed basis, divide dry matter values by the percentage of dry matter in the particular feed.

[b] One kilogram TDN (total digestible nutrients) = 4.4 Mcal DE (digestible energy); ME (metabolizable energy) = 82% of DE. Because of rounding errors, values in Table 1 and Table 2 may differ.

[c] Values are applicable for ewes in moderate condition. Fat ewes should be fed according to the next lower weight category and thin ewes at the next higher weight category. Once desired or moderate weight condition is attained, use that weight category through all production stages.

[d] Values in parentheses are for ewes suckling lambs the last 4-6 weeks of lactation.

[e] Lambs intended for breeding; thus, maximum weight gains and finish are of secondary importance.

[f] Maximum weight gains expected.

TABLE 2 Nutrient Concentration in Diets for Sheep (expressed on 100 Percent Dry Matter Basis[a])

Body Weight		Weight Change/Day		Energy[b]			Example Diet Proportions		Crude Protein	Cal-cium	Phos-phorus	Vitamin A Activity	Vitamin E Activity
				TDN[c]	DE	ME	Concentrate	Forage					
(kg)	(lb)	(g)	(lb)	(%)	(Mcal/kg)	(Mcal/kg)	%	%	(%)	(%)	(%)	(IU/kg)	(IU/kg)
Ewes[d]													
Maintenance													
70	154	10	0.02	55	2.4	2.0	0	100	9.4	0.20	0.20	2,742	15
Flushing—2 weeks prebreeding and first 3 weeks of breeding													
70	154	100	0.22	59	2.6	2.1	15	85	9.1	0.32	0.18	1,828	15
Nonlactating—First 15 weeks gestation													
70	154	30	0.07	55	2.4	2.0	0	100	9.3	0.25	0.20	2,350	15
Last 4 weeks gestation (130-150% lambing rate expected) or last 4-6 weeks lactation suckling singles[e]													
70	154	180 (0.45)	0.40 (0.10)	59	2.6	2.1	15	85	10.7	0.35	0.23	3,306	15
Last 4 weeks gestation (180-225% lambing rate expected)													
70	154	225	0.50	65	2.9	2.3	35	65	11.3	0.40	0.24	3,132	15
First 6-8 weeks lactation suckling singles or last 4-6 weeks lactation suckling twins[e]													
70	154	−25(90)	−0.06 (0.20)	65	2.9	2.4	35	65	13.4	0.32	0.26	2,380	15
First 6-8 weeks lactation suckling twins													
70	154	−60	−0.13	65	2.9	2.4	35	65	15.0	0.39	0.29	2,500	15
Ewe Lambs													
Nonlactating—First 15 weeks gestation													
55	121	135	0.30	59	2.6	2.1	15	85	10.6	0.35	0.22	1,668	15
Last 4 weeks gestation (100-120% lambing rate expected)													
55	121	160	0.35	63	2.8	2.3	30	70	11.8	0.39	0.22	2,833	15
Last 4 weeks gestation (130-175% lambing rate expected)													
55	121	225	0.50	66	2.9	2.4	40	60	12.8	0.48	0.25	2,833	15
First 6-8 weeks lactation suckling singles (wean by 8 weeks)													
55	121	−50	0.22	66	2.9	2.4	40	60	13.1	0.30	0.22	2,125	15
First 6-8 weeks lactation suckling twins (wean by 8 weeks)													
55	121	−100	−0.22	69	3.0	2.5	50	50	13.7	0.37	0.26	2,292	15
Replacement Ewe Lambs[f]													
30	66	227	0.50	65	2.9	2.4	35	65	12.8	0.53	0.22	1,175	15
40	88	182	0.40	65	2.9	2.4	35	65	10.2	0.42	0.18	1,343	15
50-70	110-154	115	0.25	59	2.6	2.1	15	85	9.1	0.31	0.17	1,567	15
Replacement Ram Lambs[f]													
40	88	330	0.73	63	2.8	2.3	30	70	13.5	0.43	0.21	1,175	15
60	132	320	0.70	63	2.8	2.3	30	70	11.0	0.35	0.18	1,659	15
80-100	176-220	270	0.60	63	2.8	2.3	30	70	9.6	0.30	0.16	1,979	15
Lambs Finishing—4 to 7 months old[g]													
30	66	295	0.65	72	3.2	2.5	60	40	14.7	0.51	0.24	1,085	15
40	88	275	0.60	76	3.3	2.7	75	25	11.6	0.42	0.21	1,175	15
50	110	205	0.45	77	3.4	2.8	80	20	10.0	0.35	0.19	1,469	15
Early Weaned Lambs—Moderate and rapid growth potential[g]													
10	22	250	0.55	80	3.5	2.9	90	10	26.2	0.82	0.38	940	20
20	44	300	0.66	78	3.4	2.8	85	15	16.9	0.54	0.24	940	20
30	66	325	0.72	78	3.3	2.7	85	15	15.1	0.51	0.24	1,085	15
40-60	88-132	400	0.88	78	3.3	2.7	85	15	14.5	0.55	0.28	1,253	15

[a]Values in Table 2 are calculated from daily requirements in Table 1 divided by DM intake. The exception, vitamin E daily requirements /head, are calculated from vitamin E/kg diet × DM intake.

[b]One kilogram TDN = 4.4 Mcal DE (digestible energy); ME (metabolizable energy) = 82% of DE. Because of rounding errors, values in Table 1 and Table 2 may differ.

[c]TDN calculated on following basis: hay DM, 55% TDN and on as-fed basis 50% TDN; grain DM, 83% TDN and on as-fed basis 75% TDN.

[d]Values are for ewes in moderate condition. Fat ewes should be fed according to the next lower weight category and thin ewes at the next higher weight category. Once desired or moderate weight condition is attained, use that weight category through all production stages.

[e]Values in parentheses are for ewes suckling lambs the last 4-6 weeks of lactation.

[f]Lambs intended for breeding; thus, maximum weight gains and finish are of secondary importance.

[g]Maximum weight gains expected.

TABLE 3 Net Energy Requirements for Lambs of Small, Medium, and Large Mature Weight Genotypes[a] (kcal/d)

Body Weight (kg)[b]:	10	20	25	30	35	40	45	50
NE$_m$ Requirements[c]:	315	530	626	718	806	891	973	1053
Daily Gain (g)[b]								
NE$_g$ Requirements								
Small mature weight lambs[d]								
100	178	300	354	406	456	504	551	596
150	267	450	532	610	684	756	826	894
200	357	600	708	812	912	1,008	1,102	1,192
250	446	750	886	1,016	1,140	1,261	1,377	1,490
300	535	900	1,064	1,219	1,368	1,513	1,652	1,788
Medium mature weight lambs[e]								
100	155	261	309	354	397	439	480	519
150	233	392	463	531	596	658	719	778
200	310	522	618	708	794	878	960	1,038
250	388	653	771	884	993	1,097	1,199	1,297
300	466	784	926	1,062	1,191	1,316	1,438	1,557
350	543	914	1,080	1,238	1,390	1,536	1,678	1,816
400	621	1,044	1,234	1,415	1,589	1,756	1,918	2,076
Large mature weight lambs[f]								
100	132	221	262	300	337	372	407	439
150	197	332	392	450	505	558	610	660
200	263	442	524	600	674	744	813	880
250	329	553	654	750	842	930	1,016	1,099
300	394	663	785	900	1,010	1,116	1,220	1,320
350	461	775	916	1,050	1,179	1,303	1,423	1,540
400	526	885	1,046	1,200	1,347	1,489	1,626	1,760
450	592	996	1,177	1,350	1,515	1,675	1,830	1,980

[a]Approximate mature ram weights of 95 kg, 115 kg, and 135 kg, respectively.
[b]Weights and gains include fill.
[c]NE$_m$ = 56 kcal · W$^{0.75}$ · d^{-1}.
[d]NE$_g$ = 317 kcal · W$^{0.75}$ · LWG, kg · d^{-1}.
[e]NE$_g$ = 276 kcal · W$^{0.75}$ · LWG, kg · d^{-1}.
[f]NE$_g$ = 234 kcal · W$^{0.75}$ · LWG, kg · d^{-1}.

TABLE 4 NE$_{preg}$ (NE$_y$) Requirements of Ewes Carrying Different Numbers of Fetuses at Various Stages of Gestation

Number of Fetuses Being Carried	Stage of Gestation (days)[a]					
	100	%[b]	120	%[b]	140	%[b]
	NE$_{preg}$ Required (kcal/day)					
1	70	100	145	100	260	100
2	125	178	265	183	440	169
3	170	243	345	238	570	219

[a]For gravid uterus (plus contents) and mammary gland development only.
[b]As a percentage of a single fetus's requirement.

TABLE 5   Crude Protein Requirements for Lambs of Small, Medium, and Large Mature Weight Genotypes[a] (g/d)

Body Weight (kg)[b]:	10	20	25	30	35	40	45	50
Daily Gain (g)[b]								
Small mature weight lambs								
100	84	112	122	127	131	136	135	134
150	103	121	137	140	144	147	145	143
200	123	145	152	154	156	158	154	151
250	142	162	167	168	168	169	164	159
300	162	178	182	181	180	180	174	168
Medium mature weight lambs								
100	85	114	125	130	135	140	139	139
150	106	132	141	145	149	153	151	149
200	127	150	158	160	163	166	163	160
250	147	167	174	175	177	179	175	171
300	168	185	191	191	191	191	186	181
350	188	203	207	206	205	204	198	192
400	209	221	224	221	219	217	210	202
Large mature weight lambs								
100	94	128	134	139	145	144	150	156
150	115	147	152	156	160	159	164	169
200	136	166	170	173	176	174	178	182
250	157	186	188	190	192	189	192	195
300	179	205	206	207	208	204	206	208
350	200	224	224	224	224	219	220	221
400	221	243	242	241	240	234	234	234
450	242	262	260	256	256	249	248	248

[a]Approximate mature ram weights of 95 kg, 115 kg, and 135 kg, respectively.
[b]Weights and gains include fill.

TABLE 6   Macromineral Requirements of Sheep (percentage of diet dry matter)[a]

Nutrient	Requirement
Sodium	0.09-0.18
Chlorine	—
Calcium	0.20-0.82
Phosphorus	0.16-0.38
Magnesium	0.12-0.18
Potassium	0.50-0.80
Sulfur	0.14-0.26

[a]Values are estimates based on experimental data.

TABLE 7   Micromineral Requirements of Sheep and Maximum Tolerable Levels (ppm, mg/kg of diet dry matter)[a]

Nutrient	Requirement	Maximum Tolerable Level[b]
Iodine	0.10-0.80[c]	50
Iron	30-50	500
Copper	7-11[d]	25[e]
Molybdenum	0.5	10[e]
Cobalt	0.1-0.2	10
Manganese	20-40	1,000
Zinc	20-33	750
Selenium	0.1-0.2	2
Fluorine	—	60-150

[a]Values are estimates based on experimental data.
[b]NRC (1980).
[c]High level for pregnancy and lactation in diets not containing goitrogens; should be increased if diets contain goitrogens.
[d]Requirement when dietary Mo concentrations are <1 mg/kg DM. See text for requirements under other circumstances.
[e]Lower levels may be toxic under some circumstances. See text.

TABLE 8   Composition of Ewe's Milk (2.5 weeks postpartum)[a]

Dry matter	18.2%
Fat (5-10%)	7.1 g/100 g milk
Protein (true)	$4.5 \times 5.49 = 24.7\%$ DM basis
Lactose	$4.8 \times 5.49 = 26.4\%$ DM basis
Ash	0.85 g/100 g milk
Fiber	0.0 g/100 g milk
Caloric value (GE)	110 kcal/100 g $\times$ 5.49 = 6.04 Mcal/kg milk DM basis
Principal salts (g/100 g)	
Na	0.040
K	0.150
Ca	0.200
Mg	0.016
P	0.150
Cl	0.075
Citrate	0.170
Trace minerals (mg/liter)	
Fe	0.60-0.70
Cu	0.05-0.15
Mn	0.06
Al	1.70
Zn	2.00-3.00
Vitamins (mg/liter, except where noted)	
A	1,450 IU/liter
E (α-tocopherol)	15
Thiamin	1.0
Riboflavin	4.0
Niacin	5.0
B_6	0.7
Pantothenic acid	4.0
Biotin	0.05-0.09
Folacin	0.05
B_{12}	0.006-0.010
Ascorbic acid	40-50

[a]Courtesy of Dr. Robert Jenness, Biochemistry Department, University of Minnesota.

TABLE 9   Vitamin E Requirements of Growing-Finishing Lambs and Suggested Levels of Feed Fortification to Provide 100 Percent of Requirements

Body Weight		α-Tocopheryl Acetate		Feed Intake per Lamb		Amount of Vitamin E Added to Concentrate			Amount of Vitamin E Added to Protein Supplement[b]		
(kg)	(lb)	(mg/lamb/day)[a]	(mg/kg diet)	(kg)	(lb)	(mg/kg)	(mg/lb)	(mg/ton)	(mg/kg)	(mg/lb)	(mg/ton)
10	22	5.0	20	0.23	0.50	20	9.1	18,200	133	60	120,000
20	44	10.0	20	0.45	1.00	20	9.1	18,200	133	60	120,000
30	66	15.0	15	0.96	2.10	15	6.8	13,600	100	45	90,000
40	88	20.0	15	1.30	2.86	15	6.8	13,600	100	45	90,000
50	110	25.0	15	1.60	3.50	15	6.8	13,600	100	45	90,000

[a]Rounded values based on approximate diet intake containing recommended vitamin E levels.

[b]Assumes the concentrate diet contains 15 percent protein supplement.

TABLE 10   Relative Ranking of Pasture Forages for Sheep

Species	Carrying Capacity	Lamb Performance	Lamb Production/ Acre	Sheep and Pasture Management Required
Alfalfa	High	High	High	Medium
Ladino clover	Low	High	Medium	Medium
Bird's-foot trefoil	Low	High	High	Medium
Blue grass	Low	Low	Low	Low
Brome grass	Medium	Medium	Medium	Low
Fescue	High	Low	Low	Low
Orchard grass	High	Medium	Medium	Low
Canarygrass	High	Low	Medium	Low
Timothy	Low	Low	Low	Low
Oats	Medium	Medium	Medium	Low
Barley	Medium	Medium	Medium	Low
Sudan	High	Low	Medium	High
Rape	High	High	High	Low
Turnips	High	Low	Medium	Low

TABLE 11   Range Supplements for Sheep (DM basis)[a]

Feeds[b]	Relative Protein Level (%)			
	High	Medium-High	Medium-Low	Low
Barley, grain or corn, dent yellow, grain, grade 2 US, min 54 lb/bu	5	40	75	65
Beet, sugar, molasses, or sugar cane molasses, 48% invert sugar, min 79.5° Brix	5	5	5	5
Cottonseed with some hulls, solvent extracted, ground, min 41% protein, max 14% fiber, min 0.5% fat (cottonseed meal)	66	36	—	16
Soybean, seeds, solvent extracted, ground, max 7% fiber, 44% protein (soybean meal)	10	10	10	10
Urea, technical, 282% protein equivalent	—	—	5	—
Alfalfa, aerial parts, dehydrated, ground, min 17% protein or alfalfa, hay, sun-cured, early bloom	10	5	—	—
Vitamin A (IU/kg)	—	4,000	8,000	8,000
Calcium phosphate, monobasic, commercial	1	1	2	1
Sodium phosphate, monobasic, technical	2	2	2	2
Salt or trace mineralized salt	1	1	1	1
Total	100	100	100	100
Composition[c]				
Protein ($N \times 6.25$) (%)	33.8	24.3	26.2	17.7
Digestible energy (Mcal/kg)	3.3	3.3	3.3	3.1
Phosphorus (%)	2.0	1.5	0.9	1.2
Carotene (mg/kg)	22.0	10.0	—	—
Vitamin A (IU/kg)	—	4,000.0	8,000.0	8,000.0
Rate of feeding[d] (kg/day)	0.1-0.2	0.1-0.2	0.1-0.2[e]	0.1-0.2[e]

[a]Feeds mixed and fed in meal or pellet form.
[b]See Table 16.
[c]Molasses and alfalfa hay, sun-cured, early bloom not included.
[d]Calculated on as-fed basis for mixing and feeding.
[e]In emergency situations, up to 0.5 kg may be fed.

TABLE 12   Suggested Creep Diets

Ingredient	Amount (as-fed basis, %)		
	Diet A	Diet B	Diet C
Simple Diets (grind for lambs under 6 weeks of age; feed whole thereafter; hand- or self-feed)[a]			
Barley, grain	38.5	—	—
Corn, dent yellow, grain, ground, grade 2 US, min 54 lb/bu	40.0	60.0	88.5
Oats, grain	—	28.5	—
Wheat, bran, dry milled	10.0	—	—
Linseed meal, soybean meal, or sunflower meal	10.0	10.0	10.0
Limestone, ground, min 33% calcium	1.0	1.0	1.0
Trace mineralized salt with selenium	0.5	0.5	0.5
Total	100.0	100.0	100.0

Alfalfa hay, sun-cured, early bloom should be fed free choice in conjunction with any of the above diets.

Commercially Mixed Diets (hand- or self-fed as meal, but usually as pellets)[b]			
Alfalfa, sun-cured, early bloom or dehydrated alfalfa	—	10.0	20.0
Barley, grain	20.0	—	—
Corn, dent yellow, grain, grade 2 US, min 54 lb/bu	54.5	34.5	44.5
Oats, grain	—	30.0	10.0
Linseed, soybean, or sunflower meal	10.0	10.0	10.0
Bran, wheat	10.0	10.0	10.0
Beet or cane molasses	4.0	4.0	4.0
Limestone, ground, min 33% calcium	1.0	1.0	1.0
Trace mineralized salt with selenium	0.5	0.5	0.5
Total	100.0	100.0	100.0
Chlortetracycline or oxytetracycline	15.0-25.0 mg/kg	15.0-25.0 mg/kg	15.0-25.0 mg/kg
Vitamin A, IU/kg	500.0	500.0	500.0
Vitamin D, IU/kg	50.0	50.0	50.0
Vitamin E, IU/kg	20.0	20.0	20.0

[a]Limestone will separate from whole grain, so a combination of protein supplement with 10% limestone may be top dressed on the whole grain. Equal parts of trace mineralized salt and limestone is an additional way to maintain adequate calcium intake and prevent urinary calculi.

[b]The addition of 0.25 to 0.50% ammonium chloride will minimize urinary calculi. Corn may be substituted for all the barley and oats. Weight gains are depressed when barley or oats exceed 40% of the ration.

TABLE 13   Composition of Some Sheep Feeds; Data Expressed on an As-Fed and Dry Basis (100% Dry Matter)

Entry Number	Feed Name Description[a]	International Feed Number	Dry Matter (%)	DE Sheep (Mcal/kg)	ME Sheep (Mcal/kg)	NE$_m$ (Mcal/kg)	NE$_g$ (Mcal/kg)	TDN Sheep (%)	Crude Protein (%)	Dig. Protein (%)	Cellulose (%)	Crude Fiber (%)	Lignin (%)
	ALFALFA *Medicago sativa*												
001	fresh	2-00-196	24	0.62	0.51	0.30	0.16	14	4.8	3.5	—	6.4	—
002			100	2.56	2.10	1.24	0.68	58	19.7	14.6	—	26.2	—
003	hay, sun-cured, late vegetative	1-00-054	90	2.29	1.88	1.12	0.61	52	17.9	14.3	21	19.7	6
004			100	2.56	2.10	1.24	0.68	58	20.0	15.9	23	22.0	7
005	hay, sun-cured, early bloom	1-00-059	90	2.22	1.82	1.06	0.55	51	16.2	12.7	22	20.7	7
006			100	2.47	2.03	1.18	0.61	56	18.0	14.1	24	23.0	8
007	hay, sun-cured, midbloom	1-00-063	90	2.22	1.82	1.06	0.55	51	15.3	11.6	23	23.4	8
008			100	2.47	2.03	1.18	0.61	56	17.0	12.9	26	26.0	9
009	hay, sun-cured, full bloom	1-00-068	90	2.10	1.72	0.96	0.47	47	13.5	9.4	25	26.1	9
010			100	2.34	1.92	1.07	0.52	53	15.0	10.5	28	29.0	10
011	hay, sun-cured, mature	1-00-071	91	2.17	1.78	1.01	0.50	49	11.7	7.7	26	34.4	13
012			100	2.38	1.95	1.11	0.55	54	12.9	8.5	29	37.7	14
013	meal dehydrated, 15% protein	1-00-022	90	2.27	1.86	1.09	0.58	52	15.6	10.9	26	26.6	11
014			100	2.51	2.06	1.21	0.64	57	17.3	12.1	29	29.4	12
015	meal dehydrated, 17% protein	1-00-023	92	2.43	1.99	1.23	0.71	55	17.3	11.6	22	24.0	10
016			100	2.65	2.17	1.34	0.77	60	18.9	12.7	24	26.2	11
017	silage	3-00-212	41	1.08	0.88	0.52	0.29	24	7.4	5.4	—	13.6	—
018			100	2.60	2.13	1.28	0.71	59	17.8	13.0	—	33.0	—
019	silage, < 30% dry matter	3-08-149	26	0.73	0.60	0.37	0.22	17	4.9	3.3	—	7.4	—
020			100	2.78	2.28	1.41	0.83	63	18.7	12.4	—	28.2	—
021	silage, 30-50% dry matter	3-08-150	43	1.11	0.91	0.53	0.29	25	7.8	5.5	—	15.0	—
022			100	2.56	2.10	1.24	0.68	58	17.9	12.7	—	34.6	—
023	silage, > 50% dry matter	3-08-151	57	1.42	1.17	0.69	0.36	32	9.8	6.7	—	19.3	—
024			100	2.51	2.06	1.21	0.64	57	17.3	11.9	—	34.0	—
	BARLEY *Hordeum vulgare*												
025	grain	4-00-549	88	3.35	2.74	1.87	1.28	76	11.9	9.8	4	5.0	2
026			100	3.79	3.11	2.12	1.45	86	13.5	11.1	5	5.7	2
027	grain, Pacific coast	4-07-939	89	3.46	2.84	1.94	1.36	79	9.6	6.3	—	6.3	—
028			100	3.88	3.18	2.18	1.50	88	10.8	7.1	—	7.1	—
029	hay, sun-cured	1-00-495	87	2.16	1.77	1.03	0.53	49	7.6	4.1	—	24.1	—
030			100	2.47	2.03	1.18	0.61	56	8.7	4.7	—	27.5	—
031	straw	1-00-498	91	1.93	1.58	0.82	0.32	43	4.0	0.7	34	38.3	10
032			100	2.12	1.74	0.90	0.35	48	4.3	0.8	37	42.0	11
	BEAN, NAVY *Phaseolus vulgaris*												
033	seeds	5-00-623	89	3.43	2.82	1.91	1.32	78	22.6	19.9	—	4.5	—
034			100	3.84	3.15	2.15	1.48	87	25.3	22.3	—	5.0	—
	BEET, MANGEL *Beta vulgaris macrorrhiza*												
035	roots, fresh	4-00-637	11	0.39	0.32	0.22	0.15	9	1.3	0.9	—	0.8	—
036			100	3.57	2.93	1.97	1.32	81	11.8	8.0	—	7.4	—
	BEET, SUGAR *Beta vulgaris altissima*												
037	pulp, dehydrated	4-00-669	91	2.96	2.43	1.60	1.04	67	8.8	4.5	—	18.0	2
038			100	3.26	2.68	1.76	1.14	74	9.7	5.0	—	19.8	2
039	pulp, wet	4-00-671	11	0.37	0.30	0.20	0.13	8	1.2	0.7	—	3.1	—
040			100	3.35	2.75	1.82	1.19	76	11.2	6.1	—	28.1	—
041	pulp with molasses, dehydrated	4-00-672	92	3.11	2.55	1.70	1.12	71	9.3	6.1	—	15.1	3
042			100	3.40	2.78	1.85	1.22	77	10.1	6.7	—	16.5	3
	BERMUDAGRASS *Cynodon dactylon*												
043	hay, sun-cured	1-00-703	91	1.97	1.62	0.85	0.35	45	8.9	4.6	—	27.8	—
044			100	2.16	1.77	0.93	0.39	49	9.8	5.0	—	30.4	—
045	hay, sun-cured, midbloom	1-00-700	93	2.21	1.81	1.03	0.51	50	8.8	4.7	—	25.9	—
046			100	2.38	1.95	1.11	0.55	54	9.5	5.1	—	27.9	—
047	hay, sun-cured, full bloom	1-00-701	92	2.11	1.73	0.96	0.45	48	7.5	3.5	—	26.3	—
048			100	2.29	1.88	1.04	0.49	52	8.1	3.8	—	28.5	—
	BERMUDAGRASS, COASTAL *Cynodon dactylon*												
049	hay, sun-cured	1-00-716	90	2.15	1.77	0.99	0.50	49	5.4	3.4	—	27.7	5
050			100	2.38	1.95	1.11	0.55	54	6.0	3.8	—	30.7	6
051	hay, sun-cured, early vegetative	1-00-713	94	2.49	2.04	1.23	0.70	57	15.0	10.3	—	25.2	4
052			100	2.65	2.17	1.31	0.74	60	16.0	10.9	—	26.8	4
053	hay, sun-cured, late vegetative	1-20-900	91	2.17	1.78	1.01	0.50	50	15.0	10.3	—	24.8	—
054			100	2.38	1.95	1.11	0.55	54	16.5	11.4	—	27.3	—
055	hay, sun-cured, early bloom	1-20-793	93	2.17	1.78	1.00	0.48	49	—	—	—	29.8	5
056			100	2.34	1.92	1.07	0.52	53	—	—	—	32.1	5
057	hay, sun-cured, full bloom	1-20-812	94	2.16	1.77	0.98	0.46	49	—	—	—	28.1	6
058			100	2.29	1.88	1.04	0.49	52	—	—	—	29.9	6
	BLOOD												
059	meal	5-00-380	92	2.70	2.22	1.42	0.86	61	79.8	65.0	—	1.0	—
060			100	2.95	2.42	1.54	0.94	67	87.2	71.0	—	1.1	—

Entry Number	Calcium (%)	Chlorine (%)	Cobalt (mg/kg)	Copper (mg/kg)	Fluorine (mg/kg)	Iodine (mg/kg)	Iron (mg/kg)	Magnesium (%)	Manganese (mg/kg)	Molybdenum (mg/kg)	Phosphorus (%)	Potassium (%)	Selenium (mg/kg)	Sodium (%)	Sulfur (%)	Zinc (mg/kg)	Provitamin A (Carotene) (mg/kg)	Vitamin E (mg/kg)	Vitamin D₂ (IU/g)
001	0.48	0.11	0.03	2	—	—	70	0.07	10	—	0.07	0.51	—	0.05	0.09	4	45	—	46
002	1.96	0.47	0.13	10	—	—	286	0.27	43	—	0.30	2.09	—	0.19	0.37	18	185	—	191
003	1.38	0.31	0.08	8	—	—	204	0.22	30	—	0.26	2.29	—	0.13	0.28	25	181	—	—
004	1.54	0.34	0.09	9	—	—	227	0.24	34	—	0.29	2.56	—	0.15	0.31	27	202	—	—
005	1.27	0.34	0.15	10	—	—	173	0.29	27	—	0.20	2.27	0.49	0.13	0.25	22	126	23	1,796
006	1.41	0.38	0.16	11	—	—	192	0.33	31	—	0.22	2.52	0.54	0.14	0.28	25	140	26	1,996
007	1.27	0.34	0.32	13	—	—	121	0.28	25	—	0.22	1.54	—	0.11	0.26	21	30	—	1,389
008	1.41	0.38	0.36	14	—	—	134	0.31	28	—	0.24	1.71	—	0.12	0.28	23	33	—	1,544
009	1.13	—	0.29	13	—	—	135	0.28	34	—	0.20	1.38	—	0.10	0.25	22	59	—	—
010	1.25	—	0.33	14	—	—	150	0.31	37	—	0.22	1.53	—	0.11	0.27	25	65	—	—
011	1.03	—	0.08	13	—	—	139	0.24	40	—	0.17	1.62	—	0.08	0.23	22	11	—	1,287
012	1.13	—	0.09	14	—	—	153	0.27	44	—	0.18	1.78	—	0.08	0.25	24	12	—	1,411
013	1.24	0.44	0.17	9	—	0.12	280	0.28	28	—	0.22	2.24	0.28	0.07	0.22	19	74	82	—
014	1.37	0.48	0.19	10	—	0.13	309	0.31	31	—	0.24	2.48	0.31	0.08	0.24	21	82	91	—
015	1.40	0.47	0.30	10	—	0.15	405	0.29	31	—	0.23	2.39	0.33	0.10	0.22	19	120	111	—
016	1.52	0.52	0.33	11	—	0.16	441	0.32	34	—	0.25	2.60	0.37	0.11	0.24	21	131	121	—
017	0.62	0.17	0.04	5	—	—	104	0.14	18	—	0.12	0.89	—	0.05	0.14	8	41	—	120
018	1.50	0.41	0.09	11	—	—	252	0.34	42	—	0.28	2.15	—	0.11	0.33	19	99	—	289
019	0.37	—	—	—	—	—	79	0.10	—	—	0.08	0.62	—	0.04	0.10	—	—	—	—
020	1.40	—	—	—	—	—	300	0.36	—	—	0.32	2.36	—	0.16	0.36	—	—	—	—
021	0.60	—	—	3	—	—	121	0.15	17	—	0.12	0.89	—	0.05	0.16	8	62	—	—
022	1.39	—	—	6	—	—	279	0.34	39	—	0.27	2.05	—	0.11	0.36	18	144	—	—
023	0.54	—	—	6	—	—	133	0.19	23	—	0.17	1.13	—	0.04	0.22	9	61	—	—
024	0.95	—	—	11	—	—	234	0.34	41	—	0.30	2.00	—	0.07	0.38	17	107	—	—
025	0.04	0.16	0.09	8	—	0.04	75	0.14	16	—	0.34	0.41	0.19	0.03	0.15	17	2	22	—
026	0.05	0.18	0.10	9	—	0.05	85	0.15	18	—	0.38	0.47	0.22	0.03	0.17	19	2	25	—
027	0.05	0.15	0.09	8	—	—	87	0.12	16	—	0.34	0.51	0.10	0.02	0.14	15	—	26	—
028	0.06	0.17	0.10	9	—	—	97	0.14	18	—	0.39	0.58	0.11	0.02	0.16	17	—	30	—
029	0.20	—	0.06	21	—	—	89	0.16	24	—	0.23	1.03	0.14	0.12	0.15	42	46	—	963
030	0.23	—	0.07	24	—	—	101	0.18	27	—	0.26	1.18	0.16	0.14	0.17	48	53	—	1,103
031	0.27	0.61	0.06	5	—	—	183	0.21	15	—	0.07	2.16	—	0.13	0.16	7	2	—	603
032	0.30	0.67	0.07	5	—	—	201	0.23	17	—	0.07	2.37	—	0.14	0.17	7	2	—	662
033	0.16	0.06	—	10	—	—	99	0.13	21	—	0.52	1.31	—	0.04	0.23	—	—	1	—
034	0.18	0.06	—	11	—	—	110	0.15	24	—	0.59	1.47	—	0.05	0.26	—	—	1	—
035	0.02	0.16	—	1	—	—	17	0.02	—	—	0.02	0.25	—	0.07	0.02	—	0	—	—
036	0.18	1.41	—	6	—	—	154	0.20	—	—	0.22	2.30	—	0.63	0.20	—	1	—	—
037	0.63	0.04	0.07	12	—	—	299	0.24	35	—	0.09	0.18	—	0.19	0.20	1	0	—	577
038	0.69	0.04	0.08	14	—	—	329	0.27	38	—	0.10	0.20	—	0.21	0.22	1	0	—	637
039	0.10	—	—	—	—	—	36	0.02	—	—	0.01	0.02	—	0.02	0.02	0	—	—	—
040	0.87	—	—	—	—	—	330	0.22	—	—	0.10	0.19	—	0.19	0.22	1	—	—	—
041	0.56	—	0.21	15	—	—	190	0.14	24	—	0.09	1.63	—	0.48	0.39	1	0	—	—
042	0.61	—	0.23	16	—	—	207	0.16	27	—	0.10	1.78	—	0.53	0.42	2	0	—	—
043	0.43	—	0.11	—	—	0.11	265	0.16	—	—	0.16	1.40	—	0.07	0.19	—	53	—	—
044	0.47	—	0.12	—	—	0.12	290	0.17	—	—	0.17	1.53	—	0.08	0.21	—	58	—	—
045	—	—	—	—	—	—	—	—	—	—	—	—	—	—	—	—	—	—	—
046	—	—	—	—	—	—	—	—	—	—	—	—	—	—	—	—	—	—	—
047	—	—	—	—	—	—	—	—	—	—	—	—	—	—	—	—	—	—	—
048	—	—	—	—	—	—	—	—	—	—	—	—	—	—	—	—	—	—	—
049	0.39	—	—	—	—	—	271	0.16	—	—	0.18	1.45	—	0.40	0.19	9	95	—	—
050	0.43	—	—	—	—	—	300	0.17	—	—	0.20	1.61	—	0.44	0.21	11	105	—	—
051	—	—	—	—	—	—	—	—	—	—	—	—	—	—	—	—	—	—	—
052	—	—	—	—	—	—	—	—	—	—	—	—	—	—	—	—	—	—	—
053	—	—	—	—	—	—	—	—	—	—	—	—	—	—	—	—	116	—	—
054	—	—	—	—	—	—	—	—	—	—	—	—	—	—	—	—	128	—	—
055	—	—	—	—	—	—	—	—	—	—	—	—	—	—	—	—	—	—	—
056	—	—	—	—	—	—	—	—	—	—	—	—	—	—	—	—	—	—	—
057	—	—	—	—	—	—	—	—	—	—	—	—	—	—	—	1	—	—	—
058	—	—	—	—	—	—	—	—	—	—	—	—	—	—	—	1	—	—	—
059	0.29	0.28	0.09	10	—	—	3719	0.22	5	—	0.24	0.09	0.73	0.32	0.34	4	—	—	—
060	0.32	0.30	0.10	11	—	—	4064	0.24	6	—	0.26	0.10	0.80	0.35	0.37	5	—	—	—

TABLE 13 Composition of Some Sheep Feeds; Data Expressed on an As-Fed and Dry Basis (100% Dry Matter)—*Continued*

Entry Number	Feed Name Description[a]	International Feed Number	Dry Matter (%)	DE Sheep (Mcal/kg)	ME Sheep (Mcal/kg)	NE$_m$ (Mcal/kg)	NE$_g$ (Mcal/kg)	TDN Sheep (%)	Crude Protein (%)	Dig. Protein (%)	Cellulose (%)	Crude Fiber (%)	Lignin (%)
	BLUEGRASS, CANADA *Poa compressa*												
061	fresh, early vegetative	2-00-763	26	0.76	0.62	0.39	0.24	17	4.9	3.7	—	6.6	—
062			100	2.91	2.39	1.51	0.91	66	18.7	14.4	—	25.5	—
063	hay, sun-cured	1-00-762	92	2.44	2.00	1.21	0.68	55	9.6	4.1	—	27.8	—
064			100	2.65	2.17	1.31	0.74	60	10.3	4.5	—	30.1	—
065	hay, sun-cured, early vegetative	1-00-760	91	2.41	1.97	1.19	0.67	54	15.7	11.0	—	23.5	—
066			100	2.65	2.17	1.31	0.74	60	17.3	12.1	—	25.8	—
	BLUEGRASS, KENTUCKY *Poa pratensis*												
067	fresh, early vegetative	2-00-777	31	0.88	0.72	0.46	0.27	20	5.4	4.1	8	7.8	1
068			100	2.87	2.35	1.47	0.88	65	17.4	13.2	26	25.3	3
069	fresh, early bloom	2-00-779	35	1.07	0.87	0.56	0.35	24	5.8	4.2	10	9.6	1
070			100	3.04	2.50	1.60	1.00	69	16.6	12.0	28	27.4	4
	BREWERS												
071	grains, dehydrated	5-02-141	92	2.84	2.33	1.50	0.95	65	27.1	19.8	—	13.2	6
072			100	3.09	2.53	1.63	1.03	70	29.4	21.5	—	14.4	6
	BROME *Bromus* spp												
073	fresh, early vegetative	2-00-892	34	1.20	0.98	0.66	0.44	27	6.1	5.0	9	8.1	1
074			100	3.53	2.89	1.94	1.30	80	18.0	14.8	27	24.0	3
075	fresh, mature	2-00-898	57	—	—	—	—	—	3.6	1.7	20	21.5	5
076			100	—	—	—	—	—	6.4	3.0	35	38.0	9
077	hay, sun-cured	1-00-890	91	2.20	1.80	1.04	0.53	49	8.8	4.8	—	30.1	4
078			100	2.43	1.99	1.14	0.58	55	9.7	5.3	—	33.3	5
	BUFFALOGRASS *Buchloe dactyloides*												
079	fresh	2-01-010	46	1.13	0.93	0.54	0.28	26	4.7	2.5	—	12.2	3
080			100	2.47	2.03	1.18	0.61	56	10.3	5.6	—	26.7	6
	CANARYGRASS, REED *Phalaris arundinacca*												
081	fresh	2-01-113	27	0.66	0.54	0.32	0.16	15	3.1	0.4	6	7.8	1
082			100	2.47	2.03	1.18	0.61	56	11.6	1.7	22	29.5	4
083	hay, sun-cured	1-01-104	91	1.97	1.61	0.85	0.35	45	9.4	5.8	24	30.1	3
084			100	2.16	1.77	0.93	0.39	49	10.3	6.4	26	33.0	4
	CANE MOLASSES—SEE MOLASSES												
	CATTLE MILK—SEE MILK												
	CITRUS *Citrus* spp												
085	pomace, silage (pulp)	4-01-234	21	0.81	0.67	0.46	0.32	18	1.5	0.8	—	3.3	—
086			100	3.88	3.18	2.18	1.50	88	7.3	3.7	—	15.6	—
087	pomace without fines, dehydrated	4-01-237	91	3.38	2.77	1.87	1.27	76	6.1	3.1	—	11.6	3
088	(pulp)		100	3.70	3.04	2.06	1.40	84	6.7	3.4	—	12.7	3
	CLOVER, ALSIKE *Trifolium hybridum*												
089	hay, sun-cured	1-01-313	88	2.25	1.84	1.09	0.60	51	13.1	8.7	—	26.5	—
090			100	2.56	2.10	1.24	0.68	58	14.9	9.9	—	30.1	—
	CLOVER, CRIMSON *Trifolium incarnatum*												
091	hay, sun-cured	1-01-328	87	2.12	1.73	0.99	0.50	48	16.1	11.0	—	26.3	—
092			100	2.43	1.99	1.14	0.58	55	18.4	12.7	—	30.1	—
	CLOVER, LADINO *Trifolium repens*												
093	hay, sun-cured	1-01-378	90	2.61	2.14	1.36	0.82	59	19.7	15.0	—	19.1	6
094			100	2.91	2.39	1.51	0.91	66	22.0	16.7	—	21.2	7
	CLOVER, RED *Trifolium pratense*												
095	fresh, early bloom	2-01-428	20	0.59	0.49	0.31	0.09	13	3.8	3.0	—	4.6	—
096			100	3.00	2.46	1.57	0.47	68	19.4	15.0	—	23.3	—
097	fresh, midbloom	2-07-725	26	0.80	0.66	0.42	0.27	18	4.0	2.9	—	6.6	—
098			100	3.09	2.53	1.63	1.03	70	15.3	11.0	—	25.4	—
099	fresh, full bloom	2-01-429	26	0.74	0.61	0.37	0.22	17	3.8	2.8	—	6.8	—
100			100	2.82	2.31	1.44	0.86	64	14.6	10.6	—	26.1	—
101	fresh, late bloom	2-07-724	23	0.67	0.55	0.34	0.20	15	3.6	2.6	—	5.5	—
102			100	2.87	2.35	1.47	0.88	65	15.2	11.2	—	23.4	—
103	hay, sun-cured	1-01-415	89	2.34	1.92	1.17	0.66	53	14.2	9.0	23	25.5	9
104			100	2.65	2.17	1.31	0.74	60	16.0	10.1	26	28.8	10
105	hay, sun-cured, early vegetative	1-01-394	87	2.50	2.05	1.28	0.77	57	18.7	13.8	—	17.8	—
106			100	2.87	2.35	1.47	0.88	65	21.4	15.8	—	20.4	—
107	hay, sun-cured, late vegetative	1-01-397	87	2.56	2.10	1.34	0.82	58	17.0	10.5	—	17.3	—
108			100	2.95	2.42	1.54	0.94	67	19.6	12.1	—	20.0	—
109	hay, sun-cured, early bloom	1-01-400	86	2.44	2.00	1.24	0.74	55	16.0	11.4	—	23.5	—
110			100	2.82	2.31	1.44	0.86	64	18.5	13.2	—	27.2	—
111	hay, sun-cured, midbloom	1-01-401	88	2.41	1.98	1.21	0.70	55	16.0	10.1	—	25.3	—
112			100	2.73	2.24	1.38	0.80	62	18.1	11.4	—	28.6	—
113	hay, sun-cured, full bloom	1-01-403	86	2.38	1.96	1.21	0.71	54	13.1	8.5	—	25.6	—
114			100	2.78	2.28	1.41	0.83	63	15.3	9.9	—	29.8	—

Entry Number	Calcium (%)	Chlorine (%)	Cobalt (mg/kg)	Copper (mg/kg)	Fluorine (mg/kg)	Iodine (mg/kg)	Iron (mg/kg)	Magnesium (%)	Manganese (mg/kg)	Molybdenum (mg/kg)	Phosphorus (%)	Potassium (%)	Selenium (mg/kg)	Sodium (%)	Sulfur (%)	Zinc (mg/kg)	Provitamin A (Carotene) (mg/kg)	Vitamin E (mg/kg)	Vitamin D₂ (IU/g)
061	0.10	—	—	—	—	—	78	0.04	—	—	0.10	0.53	—	0.04	0.04	—	104	—	—
062	0.39	—	—	—	—	—	300	0.16	—	—	0.39	2.04	—	0.14	0.17	—	400	—	—
063	0.28	—	—	—	—	—	277	0.31	85	—	0.25	1.65	—	0.10	0.12	—	270	—	—
064	0.30	—	—	—	—	—	300	0.33	93	—	0.27	1.78	—	0.11	0.13	—	293	—	—
065	0.27	—	—	—	—	—	273	0.30	—	—	0.26	1.45	—	0.10	0.12	—	—	—	—
066	0.30	—	—	—	—	—	300	0.33	—	—	0.29	1.59	—	0.11	0.13	—	—	—	—
067	0.15	—	—	—	—	—	92	0.05	—	—	0.14	0.70	—	0.04	0.05	—	149	48	—
068	0.50	—	—	—	—	—	300	0.18	—	—	0.44	2.27	—	0.14	0.17	—	482	156	—
069	0.16	—	—	—	—	—	105	0.04	—	—	0.14	0.70	—	0.05	0.06	—	98	—	—
070	0.46	—	—	—	—	—	300	0.11	—	—	0.39	2.01	—	0.14	0.17	—	280	—	—
071	0.30	0.15	0.08	21	—	0.07	245	0.15	37	—	0.51	0.08	0.70	0.21	0.30	27	0	26	—
072	0.33	0.17	0.08	23	—	0.07	266	0.16	40	—	0.55	0.09	0.76	0.23	0.32	30	1	29	—
073	0.17	—	—	—	—	—	68	0.06	—	—	0.10	0.78	—	0.01	0.07	—	156	—	—
074	0.50	—	—	—	—	—	200	0.18	—	—	0.30	2.30	—	0.02	0.20	—	459	—	—
075	0.11	—	—	—	—	—	113	0.10	—	—	0.15	0.71	—	0.01	0.11	—	47	—	—
076	0.20	—	—	—	—	—	200	0.18	—	—	0.26	1.25	—	0.02	0.20	—	83	—	—
077	0.31	—	—	—	—	—	181	0.09	—	—	0.17	1.74	—	0.02	0.18	—	31	—	948
078	0.35	—	—	—	—	—	200	0.09	—	—	0.19	1.93	—	0.02	0.20	—	34	—	1,407
079	0.26	—	—	—	—	—	—	0.06	—	—	0.09	0.33	—	—	—	—	43	—	—
080	0.57	—	—	—	—	—	—	0.14	—	—	0.21	0.71	—	—	—	—	94	—	—
081	0.11	—	—	—	—	—	—	—	—	—	0.09	0.97	—	—	—	—	—	—	—
082	0.41	—	—	—	—	—	—	—	—	—	0.35	3.64	—	—	—	—	—	—	—
083	0.35	—	0.02	11	—	—	137	0.27	108	—	0.23	2.51	—	0.13	—	—	23	—	—
084	0.38	—	0.02	12	—	—	150	0.29	118	—	0.25	2.76	—	0.14	—	—	26	—	—
085	0.43	—	—	—	—	—	33	0.03	—	—	0.03	0.13	—	0.02	0.00	3	—	—	—
086	2.04	—	—	—	—	—	160	0.16	—	—	0.15	0.62	—	0.09	0.02	16	—	—	—
087	1.67	—	0.14	6	—	—	345	0.16	7	—	0.11	0.72	—	0.08	0.08	14	0	—	—
088	1.84	—	0.16	6	—	—	378	0.17	7	—	0.12	0.79	—	0.09	0.08	15	0	—	—
089	1.13	0.69	—	5	—	—	228	0.36	61	—	0.23	2.17	—	0.40	0.17	—	164	—	—
090	1.29	0.78	—	6	—	—	260	0.41	69	—	0.26	2.46	—	0.46	0.19	—	187	—	—
091	1.22	0.55	—	—	—	0.06	610	0.24	149	—	0.19	2.09	—	0.34	0.24	—	20	—	—
092	1.40	0.63	—	—	—	0.07	700	0.28	171	—	0.22	2.40	—	0.39	0.28	—	23	—	—
093	1.21	0.27	0.15	9	—	0.27	370	0.43	85	—	0.28	2.35	—	0.12	0.19	15	75	—	—
094	1.35	0.30	0.16	10	—	0.30	413	0.48	95	—	0.31	2.62	—	0.13	0.21	17	83	—	—
095	0.45	—	—	—	—	—	59	0.10	—	—	0.08	0.49	—	0.04	0.03	—	49	—	—
096	2.26	—	—	—	—	—	300	0.51	—	—	0.38	2.49	—	0.20	0.17	—	248	—	—
097	0.46	—	—	—	—	—	—	0.13	—	—	0.09	0.52	—	—	0.05	—	—	—	—
098	1.76	—	—	—	—	—	—	0.51	—	—	0.33	1.98	—	—	0.18	—	—	—	—
099	0.27	—	—	—	—	—	79	0.13	—	—	0.07	0.51	—	0.05	0.05	—	54	—	—
100	1.01	—	—	—	—	—	300	0.51	—	—	0.27	1.96	—	0.20	0.17	—	208	—	—
101	—	—	—	—	—	—	—	—	—	—	—	—	—	—	—	—	—	—	—
102	—	—	—	—	—	—	—	—	—	—	—	—	—	—	—	—	—	—	—
103	1.35	0.28	0.14	10	—	0.22	163	0.38	65	—	0.22	1.44	—	0.16	0.15	15	18	—	1,694
104	1.53	0.32	0.16	11	—	0.25	184	0.43	73	—	0.25	1.62	—	0.19	0.17	17	20	—	1,914
105	1.35	—	0.20	18	—	—	629	0.34	76	—	0.32	2.82	—	—	—	45	—	—	—
106	1.55	—	0.23	21	—	—	721	0.39	87	—	0.37	3.24	—	—	—	52	—	—	—
107	1.29	—	0.15	18	—	—	315	0.33	72	—	0.29	2.54	—	—	—	37	—	—	—
108	1.49	—	0.17	20	—	—	363	0.38	83	—	0.33	2.93	—	—	—	43	—	—	—
109	1.24	—	0.14	15	—	—	213	0.19	69	—	0.30	2.59	—	—	—	35	—	—	—
110	1.44	—	0.16	18	—	—	246	0.22	80	—	0.35	3.00	—	—	—	40	—	—	—
111	1.48	—	—	—	—	—	—	—	—	—	0.26	1.28	—	—	—	—	—	—	—
112	1.67	—	—	—	—	—	—	—	—	—	0.29	1.45	—	—	—	—	—	—	—
113	1.25	—	0.11	13	—	—	137	0.33	66	—	0.23	2.00	—	0.17	0.15	35	—	—	1,643
114	1.46	—	0.13	15	—	—	159	0.39	77	—	0.27	2.33	—	0.20	0.18	41	—	—	1,914

TABLE 13   Composition of Some Sheep Feeds; Data Expressed on an As-Fed and Dry Basis (100% Dry Matter)—*Continued*

Entry Number	Feed Name Description[a]	International Feed Number	Dry Matter (%)	DE Sheep (Mcal/kg)	ME Sheep (Mcal/kg)	NE$_m$ (Mcal/kg)	NE$_g$ (Mcal/kg)	TDN Sheep (%)	Crude Protein (%)	Dig. Protein (%)	Cellulose (%)	Crude Fiber (%)	Lignin (%)
	CORN, DENT YELLOW *Zea mays indentata*												
115	aerial part with ears, sun-cured	1-28-231	81	2.26	1.85	1.14	0.67	51	7.2	3.8	23	20.5	2
116	(fodder)		100	2.78	2.28	1.41	0.83	63	8.9	4.7	28	25.2	3
117	aerial part without ears without	1-28-233	85	2.21	1.82	1.09	0.60	50	5.6	2.5	21	29.3	9
118	husks, sun-cured (stover) (straw)		100	2.60	2.13	1.28	0.71	59	6.6	2.9	25	34.4	11
119	cobs, ground	1-28-234	90	2.03	1.66	0.96	0.41	46	2.8	−0.5	25	32.7	6
120			100	2.25	1.84	1.07	0.45	51	3.2	−0.5	28	36.2	7
121	distillers grains, dehydrated	5-28-235	94	3.59	2.94	2.02	1.39	82	21.5	15.6	—	11.3	—
122			100	3.84	3.15	2.12	1.48	87	23.0	16.7	—	12.1	—
123	distillers grains with solubles,	5-28-236	92	3.52	2.89	1.98	1.36	80	23.0	11.2	13	9.1	4
124	dehydrated		100	3.84	3.15	2.15	1.48	87	25.0	12.3	14	9.9	4
125	distillers solubles, dehydrated	5-28-237	93	3.48	2.85	1.94	1.33	79	27.6	21.8	6	4.6	1
126			100	3.75	3.07	2.09	1.43	85	29.7	23.5	6	5.0	1
127	ears, ground (corn and cob meal)	4-28-238	87	3.17	2.60	1.77	1.19	71	7.8	4.8	—	8.2	—
128			100	3.66	3.00	2.03	1.37	83	9.0	5.5	—	9.4	—
129	ears with husks, silage	4-28-239	44	1.43	1.17	0.77	0.50	32	3.9	2.1	—	5.1	—
130			100	3.26	2.68	1.76	1.14	74	8.9	4.8	—	11.6	—
131	gluten, meal	5-28-241	91	3.54	2.90	1.98	1.37	80	42.7	36.3	7	4.4	1
132			100	3.88	3.18	2.18	1.50	88	46.8	39.8	8	4.8	1
133	gluten with bran (corn gluten feed)	5-28-243	90	3.29	2.70	1.83	1.23	75	23.0	—	—	8.7	—
134			100	3.66	3.00	2.03	1.37	83	25.6	—	—	9.7	—
135	grain, grade 2 69.5 kg/hl (54	4-02-931	88	3.39	2.78	1.89	1.30	77	8.9	5.7	—	2.0	—
136	lb/bushel)		100	3.84	3.15	2.15	1.48	87	10.1	6.5	—	2.2	—
137	grain, grade 3 66.9 kg/hl (52	4-02-932	86	3.30	2.71	1.85	1.27	75	8.7	5.6	—	2.0	—
138	lb/bushel)		100	3.84	3.15	2.15	1.48	87	10.1	6.5	—	2.4	—
139	silage, aerial part without ears	3-28-251	31	0.72	0.59	0.33	0.16	16	1.9	0.5	8	9.6	2
140	without husks (stalklage) (stover)		100	2.34	1.92	1.07	0.52	53	6.3	1.7	25	31.3	7
141	silage, well eared	3-28-250	33	1.03	0.85	0.54	0.34	23	2.7	1.2	—	7.9	—
142			100	3.09	2.53	1.63	1.03	70	8.1	3.6	—	23.7	—
	CORN SWEET *Zea mays saccharata*												
143	process residue, silage (cannery	3-07-955	32	0.88	0.72	0.45	0.27	20	2.4	1.0	—	11.2	—
144	residue)		100	2.78	2.28	1.41	0.83	63	7.7	3.2	—	35.5	—
	COTTON *Gossypium* spp												
145	gin by-product	1-08-413	90	1.83	1.50	0.75	0.26	42	6.6	2.9	—	30.7	—
146			100	2.03	1.66	0.83	0.29	46	7.4	3.2	—	34.1	—
147	hulls	1-01-599	91	1.96	1.60	0.85	0.35	44	3.7	−0.5	53	43.3	22
148			100	2.16	1.77	0.93	0.39	49	4.1	−0.5	59	47.8	24
149	seeds, ground	5-01-608	92	3.98	3.27	2.27	1.60	90	21.8	16.1	—	18.2	—
150			100	4.32	3.54	2.47	1.74	98	23.6	17.5	—	19.8	—
151	seeds, meal mechanical extracted	5-01-609	93	2.58	2.12	1.31	0.77	59	37.9	27.3	—	13.3	—
152			100	2.78	2.28	1.41	0.83	63	40.8	29.3	—	14.3	—
153	seeds, meal mechanical extracted, 41%	5-01-617	93	3.06	2.51	1.66	1.08	70	41.0	—	12	11.9	6
154	protein		100	3.31	2.71	1.79	1.16	75	44.3	—	13	12.8	6
155	seeds, meal solvent extracted, 41%	5-01-621	91	2.86	2.34	1.52	0.96	65	41.2	—	11	12.1	—
156	protein		100	3.13	2.57	1.67	1.06	71	45.2	—	12	13.3	—
	DISTILLERS GRAINS—SEE CORN; SEE RYE; SEE SORGHUM												
	FESCUE, KENTUCKY 31 *Festuca arundinacea*												
157	fresh	2-01-902	29	0.85	0.69	0.44	0.26	19	4.2	2.8	—	7.1	—
158			100	2.91	2.39	1.51	0.91	66	14.5	9.6	—	24.6	—
159	fresh, early vegetative	2-01-900	28	0.89	0.73	0.48	0.31	20	6.1	4.9	—	5.9	—
160			100	3.22	2.64	1.73	1.11	73	22.1	17.6	—	21.4	—
161	fresh, early bloom	2-01-901	29	0.85	0.69	0.45	0.27	19	4.8	3.6	—	7.1	—
162			100	2.95	2.42	1.54	0.94	67	16.7	12.6	—	24.7	—
163	hay, sun-cured	1-20-800	92	2.43	1.99	1.20	0.68	55	16.7	12.0	—	22.9	4
164			100	2.65	2.17	1.31	0.74	60	18.2	13.1	—	24.9	4
165	hay, sun-cured, early vegetative	1-09-184	92	3.09	2.53	1.67	1.09	70	18.9	14.1	—	21.2	3
166			100	3.35	2.75	1.82	1.19	76	20.6	15.3	—	23.0	3
167	hay, sun-cured, late vegetative	1-09-185	91	3.05	2.50	1.66	1.08	70	19.4	14.9	—	22.4	—
168			100	3.35	2.75	1.82	1.19	76	21.3	16.3	—	24.6	—
169	hay, sun-cured, early bloom	1-09-186	91	2.49	2.04	1.26	0.73	56	18.4	13.9	26	22.8	3
170			100	2.73	2.24	1.38	0.80	62	20.2	15.3	29	25.0	3
171	hay, sun-cured, midbloom	1-09-187	92	2.44	2.00	1.21	0.68	55	15.2	10.3	28	24.4	3
172			100	2.65	2.17	1.31	0.74	60	16.4	11.2	30	26.5	4
173	hay, sun-cured, full bloom	1-09-188	92	2.34	1.92	1.14	0.63	53	11.1	7.1	29	25.1	5
174			100	2.56	2.10	1.24	0.68	58	12.1	7.7	32	27.4	5

Entry Number	Calcium (%)	Chlorine (%)	Cobalt (mg/kg)	Copper (mg/kg)	Fluorine (mg/kg)	Iodine (mg/kg)	Iron (mg/kg)	Magnesium (%)	Manganese (mg/kg)	Molybdenum (mg/kg)	Phosphorus (%)	Potassium (%)	Selenium (mg/kg)	Sodium (%)	Sulfur (%)	Zinc (mg/kg)	Provitamin A (Carotene) (mg/kg)	Vitamin E (mg/kg)	Vitamin D₂ (IU/g)
115	0.41	0.15	—	6	—	—	81	0.24	55	—	0.20	0.76	—	0.02	0.11	—	4	—	1,074
116	0.50	0.19	—	8	—	—	100	0.29	68	—	0.25	0.93	—	0.03	0.14	—	4	—	1,323
117	0.49	—	—	4	—	—	179	0.34	116	—	0.08	1.24	—	0.06	0.15	—	4	—	938
118	0.57	—	—	5	—	—	210	0.40	136	—	0.10	1.45	—	0.07	0.17	—	4	—	1,103
119	0.11	—	0.12	7	—	—	208	0.06	6	—	0.04	0.79	—	0.42	0.42	—	1	—	—
120	0.12	—	0.13	7	—	—	230	0.07	6	—	0.04	0.87	—	0.47	0.47	—	1	—	—
121	0.10	0.07	0.08	45	—	0.04	209	0.07	22	—	0.40	0.17	0.45	0.09	0.43	33	3	—	—
122	0.11	0.08	0.09	48	—	0.05	223	0.07	23	—	0.43	0.18	0.48	0.10	0.46	35	3	—	—
123	0.14	0.17	0.17	53	—	—	237	0.16	23	—	0.65	0.40	0.39	0.53	0.31	—	3	40	551
124	0.15	0.18	0.18	58	—	—	259	0.18	25	—	0.71	0.44	0.42	0.57	0.33	—	3	43	600
125	0.33	0.26	0.20	83	—	0.11	566	0.60	74	—	1.27	1.67	0.33	0.23	0.37	85	1	46	—
126	0.35	0.28	0.21	89	—	0.12	610	0.65	80	—	1.37	1.80	0.36	0.25	0.40	92	1	49	—
127	0.06	0.04	0.27	7	—	0.02	79	0.12	12	—	0.24	0.46	0.07	0.02	0.14	12	3	18	—
128	0.07	0.05	0.31	8	—	0.03	91	0.14	14	—	0.27	0.53	0.09	0.02	0.16	14	4	20	—
129	0.04	—	—	—	—	—	35	0.05	—	—	0.13	0.22	—	0.00	0.06	—	3	—	—
130	0.10	—	—	—	—	—	80	0.12	—	—	0.29	0.49	—	0.01	0.13	—	8	—	—
131	0.15	0.06	0.08	28	—	—	386	0.06	8	—	0.45	0.03	1.01	0.09	0.35	174	16	31	—
132	0.16	0.07	0.08	30	—	—	423	0.06	8	—	0.50	0.03	1.11	0.10	0.39	190	18	34	—
133	0.33	0.22	0.09	47	—	0.07	424	0.33	23	—	0.74	0.57	0.27	0.94	0.21	65	6	12	—
134	0.36	0.25	0.10	52	—	0.07	471	0.36	26	—	0.82	0.64	0.30	1.05	0.23	72	7	14	—
135	0.02	0.04	0.03	4	—	—	23	0.12	5	—	0.31	0.33	—	0.02	0.12	14	2	22	—
136	0.02	0.05	0.04	4	—	—	26	0.13	6	—	0.35	0.37	—	0.02	0.14	16	2	25	—
137	0.02	—	—	—	—	—	22	0.15	5	—	0.25	0.33	—	0.01	0.12	—	—	—	—
138	0.02	—	—	—	—	—	25	0.17	6	—	0.29	0.38	—	0.01	0.14	—	—	—	—
139	0.12	—	—	—	—	—	—	0.10	—	—	0.09	0.47	—	0.01	0.03	—	5	—	—
140	0.38	—	—	—	—	—	—	0.31	—	—	0.31	1.54	—	0.03	0.11	—	15	—	—
141	0.08	—	0.02	3	—	—	87	0.06	10	—	0.07	0.32	—	0.00	0.05	7	15	—	40
142	0.23	—	0.06	10	—	—	260	0.19	30	—	0.22	0.96	—	0.01	0.15	21	45	—	119
143	0.10	—	—	—	—	—	63	0.08	—	—	0.29	0.36	—	0.01	0.04	—	4	—	—
144	0.30	—	—	—	—	—	200	0.24	—	—	0.90	1.15	—	0.03	0.11	—	13	—	—
145	0.75	—	—	—	—	—	—	—	—	—	0.20	—	—	—	—	—	—	—	—
146	0.83	—	—	—	—	—	—	—	—	—	0.22	—	—	—	—	—	—	—	—
147	0.13	0.02	0.02	12	—	—	119	0.13	108	—	0.09	0.79	—	0.02	0.08	20	—	—	—
148	0.15	0.02	0.02	13	—	—	131	0.14	119	—	0.09	0.87	—	0.02	0.09	22	—	—	—
149	0.14	—	—	50	—	—	139	0.32	9	—	0.67	1.11	—	0.29	0.24	—	—	—	—
150	0.15	—	—	55	—	—	151	0.35	10	—	0.73	1.20	—	0.31	0.26	—	—	—	—
151	0.20	0.02	0.15	21	—	—	139	0.53	22	—	0.90	1.26	—	0.04	0.24	—	—	—	—
152	0.21	0.02	0.16	23	—	—	150	0.57	24	—	0.97	1.35	—	0.04	0.26	—	—	—	—
153	0.19	0.04	0.16	19	—	—	182	0.54	22	—	1.08	1.34	—	0.04	0.40	64	0	32	—
154	0.21	0.05	0.17	20	—	—	197	0.58	24	—	1.16	1.45	—	0.05	0.43	69	0	35	—
155	0.17	0.05	0.15	20	—	—	208	0.54	21	—	1.10	1.39	—	0.04	0.26	62	—	16	—
156	0.18	0.05	0.17	22	—	—	228	0.59	23	—	1.21	1.52	—	0.05	0.28	68	—	17	—
157	0.15	—	—	—	—	—	—	—	—	—	0.11	—	—	—	—	—	64	—	—
158	0.51	—	—	—	—	—	—	—	—	—	0.37	—	—	—	—	—	219	—	—
159	0.15	—	—	—	—	—	—	—	—	—	0.11	—	—	—	—	—	84	—	—
160	0.53	—	—	—	—	—	—	—	—	—	0.39	—	—	—	—	—	306	—	—
161	0.15	—	—	—	—	—	—	—	—	—	0.11	—	—	—	—	—	63	—	—
162	0.52	—	—	—	—	—	—	—	—	—	0.37	—	—	—	—	—	221	—	—
163	0.41	—	—	25	—	—	157	0.19	114	—	0.37	2.57	—	0.01	—	35	—	—	—
164	0.44	—	—	28	—	—	171	0.21	124	—	0.40	2.80	—	0.01	—	38	—	—	—
165	0.62	—	—	17	—	—	451	0.22	153	—	0.47	2.17	—	0.01	—	53	—	—	—
166	0.67	—	—	18	—	—	490	0.24	166	—	0.51	2.36	—	0.01	—	57	—	—	—
167	0.45	—	—	16	—	—	294	0.18	139	—	0.38	2.37	—	0.01	—	38	—	—	—
168	0.50	—	—	17	—	—	323	0.19	153	—	0.42	2.61	—	0.01	—	42	—	—	—
169	0.35	—	—	15	—	—	221	0.11	74	—	0.24	1.78	—	0.02	—	32	—	—	—
170	0.38	—	—	17	—	—	243	0.12	81	—	0.26	1.96	—	0.02	—	35	—	—	—
171	0.42	—	—	23	—	—	144	0.16	96	—	0.27	1.90	—	0.01	—	33	—	—	—
172	0.45	—	—	25	—	—	156	0.17	104	—	0.29	2.06	—	0.01	—	36	—	—	—
173	0.39	—	—	26	—	—	174	0.16	94	—	0.29	2.16	—	—	—	35	—	—	—
174	0.43	—	—	28	—	—	190	0.17	103	—	0.32	2.36	—	—	—	38	—	—	—

TABLE 13 Composition of Some Sheep Feeds; Data Expressed on an As-Fed and Dry Basis (100% Dry Matter)—*Continued*

Entry Number	Feed Name Description[a]	International Feed Number	Dry Matter (%)	DE Sheep (Mcal/kg)	ME Sheep (Mcal/kg)	NE$_m$ (Mcal/kg)	NE$_g$ (Mcal/kg)	TDN Sheep (%)	Crude Protein (%)	Dig. Protein (%)	Cellulose (%)	Crude Fiber (%)	Lignin (%)
	FESCUE, MEADOW *Festuca elatior*												
175	hay, sun-cured	1-01-912	88	2.29	1.87	1.13	0.62	52	8.0	4.4	33	29.1	6
176			100	2.60	2.13	1.28	0.71	59	9.1	5.1	38	33.1	7
	FISH, MENHADEN *Brevoortia tyrannus*												
177	meal mechanical extracted	5-02-009	92	2.83	2.32	1.50	0.95	64	61.1	49.5	—	0.9	—
178			100	3.09	2.53	1.63	1.03	70	66.7	54.0	—	1.0	—
179	meal mechanical extracted, 60%	5-20-969	91	3.11	2.55	1.68	1.11	71	60.9	—	—	0.8	—
180	protein		100	3.40	2.78	1.85	1.22	77	66.6	—	—	0.9	—
181	solubles, condensed	5-02-007	50	1.87	1.53	1.03	0.70	42	31.6	—	—	—	—
182			100	3.70	3.04	2.06	1.40	84	62.7	—	—	—	—
183	solubles, dehydrated	5-02-008	93	3.39	2.78	1.89	1.27	77	62.0	—	—	—	—
184			100	3.66	3.00	2.03	1.37	83	66.9	—	—	—	—
	FLAX, COMMON *Linum usitatissimum*												
185	seeds, meal mechanical extracted	5-02-045	91	3.32	2.72	1.85	1.25	75	34.3	28.9	—	8.8	6
186	(linseed meal)		100	3.66	3.00	2.03	1.37	83	37.9	31.8	—	9.6	7
187	seeds, meal solvent extracted	5-02-048	90	3.14	2.58	1.72	1.14	72	34.6	29.5	—	9.1	5
188	(linseed meal)		100	3.48	2.86	1.91	1.27	79	38.3	32.8	—	10.1	6
	GRAMA *Boutelous* spp												
189	fresh, early vegetative	2-02-163	41	1.09	0.89	0.54	0.30	25	5.4	3.8	—	11.2	—
190			100	2.65	2.17	1.31	0.74	60	13.1	9.2	—	27.2	—
191	fresh, mature	2-02-166	63	1.57	1.28	0.74	0.43	35	4.1	1.9	—	20.7	—
192			100	2.47	2.03	1.18	0.68	56	6.5	3.0	—	32.7	—
	GRASS-LEGUME												
193	aerial part molasses added, silage	3-02-309	28	0.74	0.61	0.36	0.20	17	3.4	2.0	—	9.1	—
194			100	2.60	2.13	1.28	0.71	59	11.8	6.9	—	32.0	—
195	silage	3-02-303	29	0.81	0.66	0.40	0.23	18	3.3	1.9	—	9.4	—
196			100	2.73	2.24	1.38	0.80	62	11.3	6.5	—	31.8	—
	HOP, COMMON *Humulus lupulus*												
197	fruit (hops), spent dehydrated	5-02-396	93	1.40	1.15	0.34	—	32	23.1	6.9	—	22.7	—
198			100	1.50	1.23	0.37	—	34	24.8	7.4	—	24.3	—
	KOCHIA—SEE SUMMERCYPRESS												
	LESPEDEZA, COMMON *Lespedeza striata*												
199	fresh	2-02-568	28	0.71	0.58	0.35	0.19	16	4.2	3.1	—	10.0	—
200			100	2.56	2.10	1.24	0.68	58	15.3	11.3	—	36.1	—
201	fresh, late vegetative	2-07-093	25	0.65	0.53	0.32	0.18	15	4.0	3.0	—	8.0	—
202			100	2.60	2.13	1.28	0.71	59	16.0	11.9	—	32.0	—
203	hay, sun-cured	1-08-591	88	1.95	1.60	0.85	0.37	44	14.8	6.4	—	27.2	—
204			100	2.21	1.81	0.97	0.42	50	16.8	7.2	—	30.8	—
205	hay, sun-cured, early vegetative	1-20-886	89	2.40	1.97	1.19	0.69	54	14.3	9.7	—	22.7	—
206			100	2.69	2.21	1.34	0.77	61	16.0	10.9	—	25.5	—
207	hay, sun-cured, late vegetative	1-20-881	90	2.18	1.79	1.03	0.52	50	14.4	9.8	—	23.0	—
208			100	2.43	1.99	1.14	0.58	55	16.0	10.9	—	25.6	—
209	hay, sun-cured, midbloom	1-02-554	92	2.30	1.89	1.11	0.59	52	13.8	9.2	—	26.4	—
210			100	2.51	2.06	1.21	0.64	57	15.1	10.1	—	28.8	—
211	hay, sun-cured, full bloom	1-20-887	89	2.28	1.87	1.10	0.61	52	12.8	8.4	—	27.4	—
212			100	2.56	2.10	1.24	0.68	58	14.3	9.4	—	30.7	—
	LINSEED—SEE FLAX												
	MEADOW PLANTS, INTERMOUNTAIN												
213	hay, sun-cured	1-03-181	95	2.43	1.99	1.18	0.65	55	8.3	5.0	—	30.7	—
214			100	2.56	2.10	1.24	0.68	58	8.7	5.2	—	32.3	—
215	hay, sun-cured, early vegetative	1-08-464	90	2.78	2.28	—	—	63	—	—	—	—	—
216			100	3.09	2.53	—	—	70	—	—	—	—	—
217	hay, sun-cured, late bloom, cut 1	1-09-176	94	1.90	1.56	0.78	0.27	43	7.6	3.6	—	—	—
218			100	2.03	1.66	0.83	0.29	46	8.1	3.8	—	—	—
219	hay, sun-cured, mature	1-08-465	91	1.64	1.35	0.58	0.10	37	5.1	1.5	—	30.0	—
220			100	1.81	1.48	0.64	0.11	41	5.6	1.6	—	33.0	—
	MILK *Bos taurus*												
221	fresh (cattle)	5-01-168	12	0.69	0.65	0.46	0.46	8	3.3	3.1	—	—	—
222			100	5.60	5.43	3.80	3.80	150	26.7	25.4	—	—	—
223	skimmed, fresh (cattle)	5-01-170	10	0.39	0.39	0.28	0.28	11	3.0	—	—	—	—
224			100	4.06	3.94	2.76	2.76	109	31.2	—	—	—	—
	MILK *Ovis aries*												
225	fresh (sheep)	5-08-510	19	1.15	1.11	0.77	0.77	31	4.7	—	—	0	—
226			100	6.00	5.82	4.07	4.07	161	24.7	—	—	0	—
	MOLASSES *Beta vulgaris altissima*												
	beet, sugar, molasses, more than 48%												
227	invert sugar more than 79.5 degrees	4-00-668	78	2.64	2.16	1.44	0.95	60	6.6	3.4	—	—	—
228	brix		100	3.40	2.78	1.85	1.22	77	8.5	4.4	—	—	—

Entry Number	Calcium (%)	Chlorine (%)	Cobalt (mg/kg)	Copper (mg/kg)	Fluorine (mg/kg)	Iodine (mg/kg)	Iron (mg/kg)	Magnesium (%)	Manganese (mg/kg)	Molybdenum (mg/kg)	Phosphorus (%)	Potasium (%)	Selenium (mg/kg)	Sodium (%)	Sulfur (%)	Zinc (mg/kg)	Pro-vitamin A (Carotene) (mg/kg)	Vitamin E (mg/kg)	Vitamin D2 (IU/g)
175	0.35	—	0.12	—	—	—	—	0.44	22	—	0.27	1.61	—	—	—	—	64	119	—
176	0.40	—	0.14	—	—	—	—	0.50	25	—	0.31	1.84	—	—	—	—	73	136	—
177	5.18	0.55	0.15	11	—	1.09	480	0.14	34	—	2.89	0.70	2.19	0.39	0.45	148	—	12	—
178	5.65	0.60	0.17	12	—	1.19	524	0.16	37	—	3.16	0.76	2.40	0.43	0.49	162	—	13	—
179	5.21	0.32	0.14	11	—	1.20	423	0.13	30	—	3.00	0.60	—	0.32	0.34	134	—	9	—
180	5.70	0.35	0.16	12	—	1.31	462	0.14	33	—	3.28	0.65	—	0.35	0.38	146	—	10	—
181	0.06	—	—	2	—	—	839	0.12	12	—	0.58	1.79	2.14	1.80	—	17	—	—	—
182	0.11	—	—	4	—	—	1663	0.24	24	—	1.15	3.55	4.24	3.57	—	35	—	—	—
183	0.13	—	—	7	—	—	736	0.22	14	—	1.19	3.82	3.93	4.91	—	26	—	—	—
184	0.14	—	—	7	—	—	794	0.24	15	—	1.28	4.12	4.24	5.30	—	28	—	—	—
185	0.41	0.04	0.41	26	—	0.07	176	0.58	38	—	0.87	1.22	0.81	0.11	0.37	33	0	8	—
186	0.45	0.04	0.46	29	—	0.07	194	0.64	42	—	0.96	1.34	0.89	0.12	0.41	36	0	9	—
187	0.39	0.04	0.19	26	—	—	319	0.60	38	—	0.80	1.38	0.82	0.14	0.39	—	—	14	—
188	0.43	0.04	0.21	29	—	—	354	0.66	42	—	0.89	1.53	0.91	0.15	0.43	—	—	15	—
189	0.22	—	—	2	—	—	—	—	18	—	0.08	—	—	—	—	—	—	—	—
190	0.53	—	—	6	—	—	—	—	44	—	0.19	—	—	—	—	—	—	—	—
191	0.22	—	0.12	8	—	—	824	—	30	—	0.08	0.22	—	—	—	—	19	—	—
192	0.34	—	0.18	13	—	—	1300	—	47	—	0.12	0.35	—	—	—	—	30	—	—
193	0.30	—	—	—	—	—	148	0.09	—	—	0.10	0.55	—	0.04	0.07	—	—	—	—
194	1.07	—	—	—	—	—	520	0.32	—	—	0.34	1.92	—	0.13	0.24	—	—	—	—
195	0.25	0.31	0.04	—	—	—	153	0.09	16	—	0.08	0.53	—	0.04	0.16	—	68	—	85
196	0.85	1.06	0.13	—	—	—	520	0.32	55	—	0.27	1.80	—	0.13	0.54	—	230	—	289
197	—	—	—	—	—	—	—	—	—	—	—	—	—	—	—	—	—	—	—
198	—	—	—	—	—	—	—	—	—	—	—	—	—	—	—	—	—	—	—
199	0.31	—	—	—	—	—	88	0.08	49	—	0.08	0.32	—	—	—	—	—	—	—
200	1.13	—	—	—	—	—	320	0.27	178	—	0.27	1.16	—	—	—	—	—	—	—
201	—	—	—	—	—	—	—	—	—	—	—	—	—	—	—	—	—	—	—
202	—	—	—	—	—	—	—	—	—	—	—	—	—	—	—	—	—	—	—
203	0.78	—	—	7	—	—	187	0.20	99	—	0.25	1.21	—	—	0.21	21	44	—	—
204	0.88	—	—	8	—	—	211	0.23	112	—	0.29	1.37	—	—	0.24	24	50	—	—
205	1.09	—	—	—	—	—	285	0.23	145	—	0.26	0.95	—	—	—	—	—	—	—
206	1.22	—	—	—	—	—	320	0.26	163	—	0.29	1.07	—	—	—	—	—	—	—
207	—	—	—	—	—	—	—	—	—	—	—	—	—	—	—	—	—	—	—
208	—	—	—	—	—	—	—	—	—	—	—	—	—	—	—	—	—	—	—
209	1.08	—	—	—	—	—	284	0.24	204	—	0.22	0.92	—	—	—	—	—	—	—
210	1.18	—	—	—	—	—	310	0.26	223	—	0.24	1.01	—	—	—	—	—	—	—
211	1.02	—	—	—	—	—	268	0.20	102	—	0.19	0.93	—	—	—	36	—	—	—
212	1.14	—	—	—	—	—	300	0.23	114	—	0.21	1.04	—	—	—	41	—	—	—
213	0.58	—	—	—	—	—	—	0.16	—	—	0.17	1.50	—	0.11	—	—	32	—	—
214	0.61	—	—	—	—	—	—	0.17	—	—	0.18	1.58	—	0.12	—	—	33	—	—
215	—	—	—	—	—	—	—	—	—	—	—	—	—	—	—	—	—	—	—
216	—	—	—	—	—	—	—	—	—	—	—	—	—	—	—	—	—	—	—
217	—	—	—	—	—	—	—	—	—	—	—	—	—	—	—	—	—	—	—
218	—	—	—	—	—	—	—	—	—	—	—	—	—	—	—	—	—	—	—
219	—	—	—	—	—	—	—	—	—	—	—	—	—	—	—	—	—	—	—
220	—	—	—	—	—	—	—	—	—	—	—	—	—	—	—	—	—	—	—
221	0.12	0.11	0.00	0	—	—	1	0.01	—	—	0.09	0.14	—	0.05	0.04	3	—	—	—
222	0.95	0.92	0.01	1	—	—	10	0.10	—	—	0.76	1.12	—	0.38	0.32	23	—	—	—
223	0.13	0.09	0.01	—	—	—	1	0.01	0	—	0.10	0.18	—	0.04	0.03	5	—	—	—
224	1.31	0.96	0.11	—	—	—	10	0.12	2	—	1.04	1.90	—	0.47	0.32	51	—	—	—
225	0.20	0.04	—	—	—	—	—	0.02	—	—	0.15	—	—	0.04	—	—	—	15	—
226	—	—	—	—	—	—	—	—	—	—	—	—	—	0	—	—	—	—	—
227	0.13	1.28	0.36	17	—	—	68	0.23	4	—	0.03	4.72	—	1.15	0.46	14	—	4	—
228	0.17	1.64	0.46	22	—	—	87	0.29	6	—	0.03	6.07	—	1.48	0.60	18	—	5	—

TABLE 13 Composition of Some Sheep Feeds; Data Expressed on an As-Fed and Dry Basis (100% Dry Matter)—*Continued*

Entry Number	Feed Name Description[a]	International Feed Number	Dry Matter (%)	DE Sheep (Mcal/kg)	ME Sheep (Mcal/kg)	NE$_m$ (Mcal/kg)	NE$_g$ (Mcal/kg)	TDN Sheep (%)	Crude Protein (%)	Dig. Protein (%)	Cellulose (%)	Crude Fiber (%)	Lignin (%)
	MOLASSES *Saccharum officinarum*												
229	sugarcane, molasses, dehydrated	4-04-695	94	3.16	2.60	1.71	1.12	71	9.7	6.3	—	6.3	—
230			100	3.35	2.75	1.83	1.19	76	10.3	6.7	—	6.7	—
	sugarcane, molasses > 46%												
231	invert sugars > 79.5°	4-04-696	75	2.60	2.13	1.43	0.95	59	4.4	-1.3	—	0.4	0
232	Brix (black strap)		100	3.48	2.86	1.91	1.27	79	5.8	-1.7	—	0.5	0
	NEEDLEANDTHREAD *Stipa comata*												
233	fresh, early vegetative	2-03-195	29	0.75	0.62	0.37	0.21	17	3.1	2.0	9	8.4	1
234			100	2.60	2.13	1.28	0.71	59	10.6	6.9	30	29.0	4
235	fresh, early bloom	2-03-196	33	0.86	0.70	0.42	0.23	19	3.1	1.9	11	10.3	2
236			100	2.60	2.13	1.28	0.71	59	9.5	5.8	33	31.1	5
237	fresh, midbloom	2-03-197	35	0.90	0.73	0.43	0.24	20	3.1	1.9	—	11.5	—
238			100	2.56	2.10	1.24	0.68	58	8.9	5.3	—	32.9	—
239	fresh, full bloom	2-03-198	38	0.94	0.77	0.45	0.23	21	3.2	1.8	—	14.2	—
240			100	2.47	2.03	1.18	0.61	56	8.4	4.8	—	37.3	—
241	fresh, mature	2-03-199	57	1.13	0.93	0.45	0.14	26	3.0	0.9	19	20.6	4
242			100	1.98	1.63	0.79	0.25	45	5.2	1.5	33	36.2	7
243	fresh, stem cured	2-07-989	92	1.74	1.43	0.66	0.17	40	3.7	1.0	33	—	6
244			100	1.90	1.56	0.72	0.18	43	4.1	1.1	36	—	6
	OATS *Avena sativa*												
245	cereal by-product, less than 4% fiber	4-03-303	91	3.88	3.18	2.23	1.57	88	14.8	11.9	—	3.5	—
246	(feeding oat meal) (oat middlings)		100	4.28	3.51	2.45	1.73	97	16.4	13.1	—	3.9	—
247	grain	4-03-309	89	3.02	2.47	1.65	1.09	68	11.8	9.3	10	10.8	2
248			100	3.40	2.78	1.85	1.22	77	13.3	10.4	11	12.1	3
249	grain, grade 1 heavy 46.3 kg/hl	4-03-312	89	3.18	2.61	1.75	1.17	72	12.6	11.1	—	8.9	—
250			100	3.57	2.93	1.97	1.32	81	14.2	12.5	—	10.0	—
251	grain, grade 2 41.2 kg/hl	4-03-316	89	2.98	2.44	1.62	1.06	68	11.4	8.0	—	10.8	—
252			100	3.35	2.75	1.82	1.19	76	12.8	9.0	—	12.2	—
253	grain, light less than 34.7 kg/hl	4-03-318	91	2.64	2.16	1.37	0.83	59	11.9	8.2	—	14.4	—
254			100	2.91	2.39	1.51	0.91	66	13.1	9.1	—	15.9	—
255	grain, Pacific coast	4-07-999	91	3.13	2.56	1.71	1.13	71	9.1	5.8	—	11.2	—
256			100	3.44	2.82	1.88	1.24	78	10.0	6.4	—	12.3	—
257	groats	4-03-331	90	4.03	3.30	2.12	1.49	91	15.8	12.0	—	2.5	—
258			100	4.50	3.69	2.35	1.65	102	17.7	13.4	—	2.8	—
259	hay, sun-cured	1-03-280	91	2.13	1.75	1.04	0.53	49	8.5	5.2	—	27.8	5
260			100	2.34	1.92	1.14	0.58	53	9.3	5.7	—	30.4	6
261	silage	3-03-298	31	0.84	0.69	0.43	0.25	19	3.0	1.5	—	9.7	—
262			100	2.73	2.24	1.38	0.80	62	9.6	4.9	—	31.5	—
263	straw	1-03-283	92	1.91	1.57	0.73	0.23	44	4.1	0.3	37	37.3	13
264			100	2.07	1.70	0.79	0.25	47	4.4	0.3	40	40.5	14
	ONION, GARDEN *Allium cepa*												
265	aerial part, fresh	2-03-417	91	2.66	2.18	1.37	0.83	60	11.5	8.0	—	20.7	—
266			100	2.91	2.39	1.51	0.91	66	12.6	8.7	—	22.6	—
267	bulbs, fresh, mature	4-03-418	10	—	—	—	—	—	1.0	0.7	—	—	—
268			100	—	—	—	—	—	10.1	6.5	—	—	—
	ORCHARDGRASS *Dactylis glomerata*												
269	fresh, early vegetative	2-03-439	23	0.69	0.57	0.35	0.22	16	4.3	3.1	6	5.8	1
270		270	100	2.95	2.42	1.54	0.94	67	18.4	13.3	25	24.7	3
271	fresh, late vegetative	2-08-476	24	0.70	0.57	0.36	0.22	16	4.1	3.1	4	6.4	1
272		272	100	2.91	2.39	1.51	0.91	66	17.0	12.8	19	26.5	4
273	fresh, early bloom	2-03-442	25	0.67	0.55	0.34	0.19	15	4.0	2.2	7	7.4	1
274		274	100	2.69	2.21	1.34	0.77	61	16.0	8.9	28	30.0	4
275	fresh, midbloom	2-03-443	31	0.79	0.65	0.40	0.22	18	3.9	2.7	10	10.2	2
276		276	100	2.60	2.13	1.28	0.71	59	12.8	8.9	33	33.5	6
277	fresh, full bloom	2-03-445	30	0.79	0.65	0.39	0.22	18	3.2	2.0	8	9.9	2
278		278	100	2.65	2.17	1.31	0.74	60	10.6	6.8	28	33.1	8
279	hay, sun-cured	1-03-438	91	2.33	1.91	1.13	0.62	53	10.2	6.5	31	31.9	4
280		280	100	2.56	2.10	1.24	0.68	58	11.2	7.1	35	35.1	4
281	hay, sun-cured, early vegetative	1-03-423	90	2.45	2.01	1.24	0.72	56	—	—	—	—	3
282		282	100	2.73	2.24	1.38	0.80	62	—	—	—	—	3
283	hay, sun-cured, late vegetative	1-03-424	89	2.20	1.80	1.05	0.54	50	14.5	10.0	31	25.4	3
284		284	100	2.47	2.03	1.18	0.61	56	16.3	11.2	35	28.5	3
285	hay, sun-cured, early bloom	1-03-425	89	2.04	1.68	0.93	0.44	47	13.4	7.3	26	27.6	4
286		286	100	2.29	1.88	1.04	0.49	52	15.0	8.2	29	31.0	5
287	hay, sun-cured, full bloom	1-03-427	93	2.00	1.64	0.86	0.36	45	11.5	6.6	—	30.7	4
288		288	100	2.16	1.77	0.93	0.39	49	12.4	7.1	—	33.1	5

Entry Number	Calcium (%)	Chlorine (%)	Cobalt (mg/kg)	Copper (mg/kg)	Fluorine (mg/kg)	Iodine (mg/kg)	Iron (mg/kg)	Magnesium (%)	Manganese (mg/kg)	Molybdenum (mg/kg)	Phosphorus (%)	Potassium (%)	Selenium (mg/kg)	Sodium (%)	Sulfur (%)	Zinc (mg/kg)	Provitamin A (Carotene) (mg/kg)	Vitamin E (mg/kg)	Vitamin D₂ (IU/g)
229	1.04	—	1.15	75	—	1.98	236	0.44	54	—	0.14	3.40	—	0.19	0.43	31	—	5	—
230	1.10	—	1.21	79	—	2.10	250	0.47	57	—	0.15	3.60	—	0.20	0.46	33	—	6	—
231	0.75	2.31	0.90	59	—	1.57	186	0.32	42	—	0.08	2.86	—	0.16	0.35	22	—	5	—
232	1.00	3.10	1.21	79	—	2.10	250	0.43	56	—	0.11	3.84	—	0.22	0.47	30	—	7	—
233	0.27	—	0.02	—	—	—	—	—	—	—	0.05	—	—	—	—	—	26	—	—
234	0.93	—	0.05	—	—	—	—	—	—	—	0.16	—	—	—	—	—	88	—	—
235	—	—	—	—	—	—	—	—	—	—	—	—	—	—	—	—	—	—	—
236	—	—	—	—	—	—	—	—	—	—	—	—	—	—	—	—	—	—	—
237	—	—	—	—	—	—	—	—	—	—	—	—	—	—	—	—	—	—	—
238	—	—	—	—	—	—	—	—	—	—	—	—	—	—	—	—	—	—	—
239	0.22	—	—	2	—	—	—	0.06	23	—	0.04	0.32	—	0.00	0.05	5	—	—	—
240	0.58	—	—	6	—	—	—	0.16	59	—	0.11	0.83	—	0.01	0.12	14	—	—	—
241	0.28	—	—	—	—	—	—	—	—	—	0.05	—	—	—	—	—	0	—	—
242	0.49	—	—	—	—	—	—	—	—	—	0.09	—	—	—	—	—	0	—	—
243	0.99	—	—	—	—	—	—	—	—	—	0.06	—	—	—	—	—	—	—	—
244	1.08	—	—	—	—	—	—	—	—	—	0.06	—	—	—	—	—	—	—	—
245	0.07	0.05	0.05	4	—	—	382	0.14	44	—	0.44	0.50	—	0.09	0.22	139	—	24	—
246	0.08	0.06	0.05	5	—	—	421	0.16	48	—	0.49	0.55	—	0.10	0.24	154	—	26	—
247	0.07	0.09	0.06	6	—	0.10	76	0.13	37	—	0.33	0.39	0.23	0.07	0.21	37	0	14	—
248	0.07	0.11	0.06	7	—	0.11	85	0.14	42	—	0.38	0.44	0.26	0.08	0.23	41	0	15	—
249	—	—	—	—	—	—	—	—	—	—	—	—	—	—	—	—	—	—	—
250	—	—	—	—	—	—	—	—	—	—	—	—	—	—	—	—	—	—	—
251	0.06	—	—	—	—	—	—	—	—	—	0.27	—	—	—	—	—	—	—	—
252	0.07	—	—	—	—	—	—	—	—	—	0.30	—	—	—	—	—	—	—	—
253	—	—	—	—	—	—	—	—	—	—	—	—	—	—	—	—	—	—	—
254	—	—	—	—	—	—	—	—	—	—	—	—	—	—	—	—	—	—	—
255	0.10	0.12	—	—	—	—	73	0.17	38	—	0.31	0.38	0.08	0.06	0.20	—	—	20	—
256	0.11	0.13	—	—	—	—	80	0.19	42	—	0.34	0.42	0.08	0.07	0.22	—	—	22	—
257	0.08	0.08	—	6	—	0.11	73	0.11	28	—	0.43	0.35	—	0.05	0.20	0	—	15	—
258	0.08	0.09	—	7	—	0.12	82	0.13	31	—	0.48	0.39	—	0.06	0.22	0	—	16	—
259	0.22	0.48	0.07	14	—	—	142	0.24	59	—	0.20	1.38	0.16	0.17	0.22	36	25	—	1,410
260	0.24	0.52	0.07	15	—	—	155	0.26	64	—	0.22	1.51	0.17	0.18	0.25	39	28	—	1,544
261	0.10	—	0.02	2	—	—	65	0.09	13	—	0.07	0.84	0.03	0.07	0.09	11	14	—	—
262	0.34	—	0.06	6	—	—	211	0.30	43	—	0.24	2.74	0.08	0.23	0.29	35	45	—	—
263	0.22	0.71	—	9	—	—	161	0.17	34	—	0.06	2.37	—	0.39	0.21	6	4	—	609
264	0.24	0.78	—	10	—	—	175	0.18	37	—	0.06	2.57	—	0.42	0.23	6	4	—	662
265	1.65	—	—	—	—	—	—	0.15	—	—	0.19	1.61	—	—	—	—	—	—	—
266	1.80	—	—	—	—	—	—	0.16	—	—	0.21	1.76	—	—	—	—	—	—	—
267	—	—	—	—	—	—	—	—	—	—	0.04	—	—	—	—	—	—	—	—
268	—	—	—	—	—	—	—	—	—	—	0.40	—	—	—	—	—	—	—	—
269	0.13	0.02	—	2	—	—	39	0.07	22	—	0.13	0.84	—	0.01	0.05	—	112	—	—
270	0.58	0.08	—	7	—	—	169	0.31	96	—	0.54	3.58	—	0.04	0.21	—	482	—	—
271	0.10	—	—	—	—	—	48	0.07	—	—	0.10	0.81	—	0.01	0.06	—	—	—	—
272	0.42	—	—	—	—	—	200	0.31	—	—	0.42	3.38	—	0.04	0.26	—	—	—	—
273	0.06	—	—	8	—	—	194	0.08	26	—	0.10	0.84	—	0.01	0.06	—	—	—	—
274	0.25	—	—	33	—	—	785	0.31	104	—	0.39	3.38	—	0.04	0.26	—	—	—	—
275	0.07	—	—	—	—	—	—	—	—	—	0.07	—	—	—	—	—	—	—	—
276	0.23	—	—	—	—	—	—	—	—	—	0.23	—	—	—	—	—	—	—	—
277	0.07	—	—	—	—	—	—	—	—	—	0.07	—	—	—	—	—	73	—	—
278	0.23	—	—	—	—	—	—	—	—	—	0.22	—	—	—	—	—	245	—	—
279	0.35	0.37	0.42	12	—	—	90	0.15	109	—	0.32	3.06	—	0.05	0.24	23	20	174	—
280	0.39	0.41	0.46	13	—	—	99	0.17	120	—	0.35	3.36	—	0.05	0.26	26	22	191	—
281	0.34	—	0.49	16	—	—	276	0.11	141	—	0.39	3.41	—	0.02	—	42	—	—	—
282	0.38	—	0.55	18	—	—	308	0.12	157	—	0.43	3.80	—	0.02	—	47	—	—	—
283	0.31	—	0.52	15	—	—	191	0.12	122	—	0.45	3.48	—	0.02	—	36	—	—	—
284	0.35	—	0.58	17	—	—	214	0.14	137	—	0.50	3.91	—	0.03	—	40	—	—	—
285	0.24	—	0.38	17	—	—	83	0.10	141	—	0.30	2.59	—	0.01	—	36	33	—	—
286	0.27	—	0.43	19	—	—	93	0.11	158	—	0.34	2.91	—	0.01	—	40	38	—	—
287	—	—	—	—	—	—	—	—	—	—	—	—	—	—	—	—	—	—	—
288	—	—	—	—	—	—	—	—	—	—	—	—	—	—	—	—	—	—	—

TABLE 13 Composition of Some Sheep Feeds; Data Expressed on an As-Fed and Dry Basis (100% Dry Matter)—*Continued*

Entry Number	Feed Name Description[a]	International Feed Number	Dry Matter (%)	DE Sheep (Mcal/kg)	ME Sheep (Mcal/kg)	NE$_m$ (Mcal/kg)	NE$_g$ (Mcal/kg)	TDN Sheep (%)	Crude Protein (%)	Dig. Protein (%)	Cellulose (%)	Crude Fiber (%)	Lignin (%)
	PEANUT *Arachis hypogaea*												
289	kernels, meal mechanical extracted	5-03-649	93	3.84	3.15	2.19	1.53	87	48.1	43.8	4	6.9	—
290	(peanut meal)		100	4.14	3.40	2.35	1.65	94	52.0	47.3	5	7.5	—
291	kernels, meal solvent extracted	5-03-650	92	3.12	2.56	1.70	1.12	71	48.1	—	—	9.9	—
292	(peanut meal)		100	3.40	2.78	1.85	1.22	77	52.3	—	—	10.8	—
293	pods (hulls)	1-08-028	91	0.80	0.66	—	—	19	7.1	1.7	36	57.3	21
294		294	100	0.88	0.72	—	—	20	7.8	1.9	40	62.9	23
	PRAIRIE PLANTS, MIDWEST												
295	hay, sun-cured, early vegetative	1-03-183	90	2.50	2.05	1.27	0.75	57	7.8	3.9	—	28.3	—
296		296	100	2.78	2.28	1.41	0.83	63	8.7	4.4	—	31.4	—
297	hay, sun-cured, midbloom	1-07-956	95	2.26	1.86	1.05	0.52	51	6.7	2.7	—	30.5	—
298		298	100	2.38	1.95	1.11	0.55	54	7.0	2.8	—	32.1	—
299	hay, sun-cured, full bloom	1-03-184	89	2.03	1.67	0.93	0.40	46	5.4	1.8	—	29.9	—
300		300	100	2.29	1.88	1.04	0.45	52	6.1	2.0	—	33.7	—
301	hay, sun-cured, mature	1-03-187	91	1.92	1.58	0.82	0.32	44	4.6	2.2	—	32.2	—
302		302	100	2.12	1.74	0.90	0.35	48	5.1	2.4	—	35.4	—
	PRICKLYPEAR *Opuntia* spp												
303	fresh	2-01-061	17	0.42	0.35	0.21	0.11	9	0.8	0.4	—	2.3	1
304		304	100	2.51	2.06	1.21	0.64	57	4.8	2.1	—	13.5	8
	RAPE *Brassica napus*												
305	fresh	2-03-867	17	0.58	0.48	0.32	0.22	13	2.9	2.4	—	2.4	—
306		306	100	3.48	2.86	1.91	1.27	79	17.6	14.5	—	14.7	—
307	fresh, early vegetative	2-03-865	18	0.65	0.53	0.35	0.24	15	4.6	3.7	—	2.4	—
308		308	100	3.57	2.93	1.97	1.32	81	25.0	20.3	—	13.0	—
309	fresh, early bloom	2-03-866	11	0.37	0.31	0.20	0.13	8	2.7	2.3	—	1.8	—
310		310	100	3.31	2.71	1.79	1.16	75	23.5	20.2	—	15.8	—
311	seeds, meal mechanical extracted	5-03-870	92	3.04	2.49	1.65	1.07	69	35.6	30.1	—	12.0	—
312		312	100	3.31	2.71	1.79	1.16	75	38.7	32.8	—	13.1	—
313	seeds, meal solvent extracted	5-03-871	91	2.97	2.44	1.60	1.04	67	37.0	—	—	12.0	—
314		314	100	3.26	2.68	1.76	1.14	74	40.6	—	—	13.2	—
	REDTOP *Agrostis alba*												
315	fresh, midbloom	2-03-890	39	1.02	0.83	0.50	0.28	23	2.9	1.8	—	11.3	—
316		316	100	2.60	2.13	1.28	0.71	59	7.4	4.5	—	29.0	—
317	fresh, full bloom	2-03-891	26	0.67	0.55	0.32	0.18	15	2.1	1.2	—	7.9	—
318		318	100	2.56	2.10	1.24	0.68	58	8.1	4.5	—	30.0	—
319	hay, sun-cured	1-03-885	92	2.19	1.80	1.02	0.51	50	7.4	3.5	—	28.4	—
320		320	100	2.38	1.95	1.11	0.55	54	8.1	3.8	—	30.9	—
321	hay, sun-cured, early vegetative	1-03-880	92	2.31	1.90	1.11	0.59	52	12.7	8.2	—	29.3	—
322		322	100	2.51	2.06	1.21	0.64	57	13.8	8.9	—	31.9	—
323	hay, sun-cured, early bloom	1-05-683	91	2.29	1.88	1.10	0.58	52	11.4	7.1	—	25.0	—
324		324	100	2.51	2.06	1.21	0.64	57	12.5	7.8	—	27.5	—
325	hay, sun-cured, midbloom	1-03-886	94	2.33	1.91	1.11	0.57	53	11.0	6.9	—	29.0	—
326		326	100	2.47	2.03	1.18	0.61	56	11.7	7.3	—	30.7	—
327	hay, sun-cured, full bloom	1-03-882	91	2.16	1.77	1.01	0.50	49	8.5	5.3	—	28.2	—
328		328	100	2.38	1.95	1.11	0.55	54	9.4	5.8	—	31.1	—
	RICE *Oryza sativa*												
329	bran with germs (rice, bran)	4-03-928	91	2.96	2.43	1.60	1.04	67	12.7	8.7	10	11.6	4
330		330	100	3.26	2.68	1.76	1.14	74	14.1	9.6	11	12.8	4
331	groats, polished (rice, polished)	4-03-942	89	3.56	2.92	2.03	1.41	81	7.2	3.9	—	0.4	—
332		332	100	4.01	3.29	2.28	1.58	91	8.2	4.5	—	0.4	—
	RYE *Secale cereale*												
333	distillers grains, dehydrated	5-04-023	92	2.59	2.13	1.32	0.79	59	21.6	12.9	—	12.3	—
334		334	100	2.82	2.31	1.44	0.86	64	23.5	14.1	—	13.4	—
335	grain	4-04-047	88	3.28	2.69	1.84	1.26	75	12.1	9.5	—	2.2	—
336		336	100	3.75	3.07	2.09	1.43	85	13.8	10.9	—	2.5	—
337	straw	1-04-007	90	1.78	1.46	0.71	0.23	41	2.7	-0.6	—	38.7	—
338		338	100	1.98	1.63	0.79	0.25	45	3.0	-0.7	—	43.1	—
	RYEGRASS, ITALIAN *Lolium multiflorum*												
339	fresh	2-04-073	25	0.64	0.52	0.45	0.18	14	3.5	1.5	—	5.8	—
340		340	100	2.60	2.13	1.28	0.71	59	14.5	6.2	—	23.8	—
341	fresh, early bloom	2-04-071	35	0.93	0.77	0.46	0.26	21	5.3	3.9	—	10.6	—
342		342	100	2.65	2.17	1.31	0.74	60	15.0	11.0	—	30.1	—
343	fresh, mature	2-04-072	35	0.90	0.74	0.43	0.24	21	2.0	0.8	—	10.6	—
344		344	100	2.56	2.10	1.24	0.68	58	5.8	2.4	—	30.1	—
345	hay, sun-cured	1-04-069	86	2.24	1.84	1.00	0.61	51	6.5	2.7	—	26.6	—
346		346	100	2.60	2.13	1.28	0.71	59	7.6	3.1	—	30.9	—
347	hay, sun-cured, early vegetative	1-04-064	89	2.36	1.94	1.17	0.66	54	13.6	9.1	—	17.6	—
348		348	100	2.65	2.17	1.31	0.74	60	15.2	10.2	—	19.7	—
349	hay, sun-cured, early bloom	1-04-066	88	2.21	1.81	1.06	0.56	50	11.4	7.1	—	25.4	—
350		350	100	2.51	2.06	1.21	0.64	57	12.9	8.1	—	28.9	—
351	hay, sun-cured, full bloom	1-04-067	86	2.08	1.71	0.98	0.50	48	5.7	1.5	—	26.5	—
352		352	100	2.43	1.99	1.14	0.58	55	6.6	1.7	—	30.9	—

Entry Number	Calcium (%)	Chlorine (%)	Cobalt (mg/kg)	Copper (mg/kg)	Fluorine (mg/kg)	Iodine (mg/kg)	Iron (mg/kg)	Magnesium (%)	Manganese (mg/kg)	Molybdenum (mg/kg)	Phosphorus (%)	Potassium (%)	Selenium (mg/kg)	Sodium (%)	Sulfur (%)	Zinc (mg/kg)	Provitamin A (Carotene) (mg/kg)	Vitamin E (mg/kg)	Vitamin D$_2$ (IU/g)
289	0.19	0.03	0.11	15	—	0.07	156	0.29	26	—	0.57	1.16	0.29	0.21	0.27	21	0	2	—
290	0.20	0.03	0.12	16	—	0.07	169	0.31	28	—	0.61	1.25	0.31	0.23	0.29	22	0	3	—
291	0.27	0.03	0.11	15	—	0.07	142	0.15	27	—	0.62	1.13	—	0.07	0.30	20	—	3	—
292	0.29	0.03	0.12	17	—	0.07	154	0.17	29	—	0.68	1.23	—	0.08	0.33	22	—	3	—
293	0.24	—	0.11	16	—	—	285	0.15	63	—	0.06	0.87	—	0.12	0.09	22	1	—	—
294	0.26	—	0.12	18	—	—	312	0.17	69	—	0.07	0.95	—	0.13	0.10	24	1	—	—
295	0.44	—	—	—	—	—	81	0.22	—	—	0.21	0.97	—	—	—	—	—	—	—
296	0.49	—	—	—	—	—	90	0.24	—	—	0.23	1.08	—	—	—	—	—	—	—
297	—	—	0.07	—	—	—	95	—	—	—	—	—	—	—	—	28	—	—	—
298	—	—	0.07	—	—	—	100	—	—	—	—	—	—	—	—	29	—	—	—
299	0.34	—	—	9	—	—	80	0.21	109	—	0.12	0.96	—	—	—	30	—	—	879
300	0.38	—	—	10	—	—	90	0.24	123	—	0.14	1.08	—	—	—	34	—	—	992
301	0.34	—	—	21	—	—	101	0.26	45	—	0.14	—	—	—	—	—	9	—	—
302	0.38	—	—	23	—	—	111	0.29	49	—	0.16	—	—	—	—	—	10	—	—
303	1.61	0.04	—	—	—	—	—	0.23	—	—	0.02	0.37	—	0.05	0.04	—	—	—	—
304	9.61	0.21	—	—	—	—	—	1.38	—	—	0.12	2.21	—	0.30	0.23	—	—	—	—
305	0.22	0.08	—	1	—	—	30	0.01	8	—	0.07	0.50	—	0.01	0.10	—	—	—	—
306	1.33	0.45	—	8	—	—	182	0.07	46	—	0.39	2.98	—	0.05	0.58	—	—	—	—
307	—	—	—	—	—	—	—	—	—	—	—	—	—	—	—	—	28	—	—
308	—	—	—	—	—	—	—	—	—	—	—	—	—	—	—	—	155	—	—
309	—	—	—	—	—	—	—	—	—	—	—	—	—	—	—	—	—	—	—
310	—	—	—	—	—	—	—	—	—	—	—	—	—	—	—	—	—	—	—
311	0.66	—	—	7	—	—	175	0.50	55	—	1.04	0.83	0.96	0.46	—	43	—	19	—
312	0.72	—	—	7	—	—	190	0.54	60	—	1.14	0.90	1.04	0.50	—	47	—	20	—
313	0.61	0.10	—	—	—	—	—	0.55	—	—	0.95	1.24	0.97	0.09	1.14	—	—	—	—
314	0.67	0.11	—	—	—	—	—	0.60	—	—	1.04	1.36	1.07	0.10	1.25	—	—	—	—
315	0.13	—	—	—	—	—	—	0.07	—	—	0.09	0.83	—	—	0.10	—	—	—	—
316	0.33	—	—	—	—	—	—	0.18	—	—	0.23	2.13	—	—	0.26	—	—	—	—
317	0.16	—	—	—	—	—	53	0.07	—	—	0.10	0.62	—	0.01	0.04	—	40	—	—
318	0.62	—	—	—	—	—	200	0.25	—	—	0.37	2.35	—	0.05	0.16	—	153	—	—
319	0.39	0.06	0.13	4	—	0.09	141	0.20	208	—	0.20	1.74	—	0.06	0.23	—	4	—	—
320	0.43	0.07	0.15	4	—	0.10	154	0.22	226	—	0.22	1.89	—	0.07	0.25	—	4	—	—
321	—	—	—	—	—	—	—	—	—	—	—	—	—	—	—	—	—	—	—
322	—	—	—	—	—	—	—	—	—	—	—	—	—	—	—	—	—	—	—
323	—	—	—	—	—	—	—	—	—	—	—	—	—	—	—	—	—	—	—
324	—	—	—	—	—	—	—	—	—	—	—	—	—	—	—	—	—	—	—
325	0.60	—	—	—	—	—	—	—	—	—	0.33	1.60	—	—	—	—	5	—	—
326	0.63	—	—	—	—	—	—	—	—	—	0.35	1.69	—	—	—	—	5	—	—
327	—	—	—	—	—	—	—	—	—	—	—	—	—	—	—	—	—	—	—
328	—	—	—	—	—	—	—	—	—	—	—	—	—	—	—	—	—	—	—
329	0.07	0.07	—	13	—	—	190	0.94	376	—	1.54	1.74	0.40	0.03	0.18	29	—	60	—
330	0.08	0.08	—	15	—	—	210	1.04	415	—	1.70	1.92	0.44	0.04	0.20	32	—	66	—
331	0.02	0.04	—	3	—	—	14	0.02	11	—	0.11	0.11	—	0.02	0.08	2	—	4	—
332	0.03	0.04	—	3	—	—	16	0.02	12	—	0.13	0.12	—	0.02	0.09	2	—	4	—
333	0.05	0.15	—	—	—	—	—	0.17	18	—	0.48	0.07	—	0.17	0.44	—	—	—	—
334	0.16	0.05	—	—	—	—	—	0.18	20	—	0.52	0.08	—	0.18	0.48	—	—	—	—
335	0.06	0.03	—	7	—	—	60	0.12	58	—	0.32	0.46	0.38	0.02	0.15	31	0	15	—
336	0.07	0.03	—	8	—	—	69	0.14	66	—	0.37	0.52	0.44	0.03	0.17	36	0	17	—
337	0.22	0.21	—	4	—	—	—	0.07	6	—	0.08	0.87	—	0.12	0.10	—	—	—	—
338	0.24	0.24	—	4	—	—	—	0.08	7	—	0.09	0.97	—	0.13	0.11	—	—	—	—
339	0.16	—	—	—	—	—	160	0.09	—	—	0.10	0.49	—	0.00	0.03	—	98	—	—
340	0.65	—	—	—	—	—	650	0.35	—	—	0.41	2.00	—	0.01	0.10	—	401	—	—
341	—	—	—	—	—	—	—	—	—	—	—	—	—	—	—	—	—	—	—
342	—	—	—	—	—	—	—	—	—	—	—	—	—	—	—	—	—	—	—
343	—	—	—	—	—	—	—	—	—	—	—	—	—	—	—	—	—	—	—
344	—	—	—	—	—	—	—	—	—	—	—	—	—	—	—	—	—	—	—
345	0.53	—	—	—	—	—	275	0.28	—	—	0.29	1.34	—	—	—	—	250	—	—
346	0.62	—	—	—	—	—	320	0.32	—	—	0.34	1.56	—	—	—	—	290	—	—
347	—	—	—	—	—	—	—	—	—	—	—	—	—	—	—	—	—	—	—
348	—	—	—	—	—	—	—	—	—	—	—	—	—	—	—	—	—	—	—
349	—	—	—	—	—	—	—	—	—	—	—	—	—	—	—	—	—	—	—
350	—	—	—	—	—	—	—	—	—	—	—	—	—	—	—	—	—	—	—
351	—	—	—	—	—	—	—	—	—	—	—	—	—	—	—	—	—	—	—
352	—	—	—	—	—	—	—	—	—	—	—	—	—	—	—	—	—	—	—

TABLE 13 Composition of Some Sheep Feeds; Data Expressed on an As-Fed and Dry Basis (100% Dry Matter)—*Continued*

Entry Number	Feed Name Description[a]	International Feed Number	Dry Matter (%)	DE Sheep (Mcal/kg)	ME Sheep (Mcal/kg)	NE$_m$ (Mcal/kg)	NE$_g$ (Mcal/kg)	TDN Sheep (%)	Crude Protein (%)	Dig. Protein (%)	Cellulose (%)	Crude Fiber (%)	Lignin (%)
	SAFFLOWER *Carthamus tinctorius*												
353	seeds, meal mechanical extracted	5-04-109	91	2.50	2.05	1.26	0.73	57	20.2	17.0	—	32.4	—
354			100	2.73	2.24	1.38	0.80	62	22.1	18.6	—	35.4	—
355	seeds, meal solvent extracted	5-04-110	92	2.28	1.87	1.09	0.56	52	23.4	—	—	30.0	13
356			100	2.47	2.03	1.18	0.61	56	25.4	—	—	32.5	14
	SAGE, BLACK *Salvia mellifera*												
357	browse, fresh, stem cured	2-05-564	65	1.40	1.15	0.60	0.25	32	5.5	2.9	—	—	—
358			100	2.16	1.77	0.93	0.39	49	8.5	4.5	—	—	—
	SAGEBRUSH, BIG *Artemisia tridentata*												
359	browse, fresh, stem cured	2-07-992	65	1.43	1.18	0.63	0.27	33	6.1	3.2	—	—	8
360			100	2.21	1.81	0.97	0.42	50	9.3	4.9	—	—	12
	SAGEBRUSH, BUD *Artemisia spinescens*												
361	browse, fresh, early vegetative	2-07-991	23	0.52	0.42	0.23	0.10	12	4.0	3.1	—	—	—
362			100	2.25	1.84	1.00	0.45	51	17.3	13.7	—	—	—
363	browse, fresh, late vegetative	2-04-124	32	0.79	0.65	0.38	0.20	18	5.6	4.3	—	7.3	—
364			100	2.47	2.03	1.18	0.61	56	17.5	13.3	—	22.7	—
	SAGEBRUSH, FRINGED *Artemisia frigida*												
365	browse, fresh, midbloom	2-04-129	43	1.12	0.92	0.55	0.31	26	4.0	2.5	—	14.3	—
366			100	2.60	2.13	1.28	0.71	59	9.4	5.8	—	33.2	—
367	browse, fresh, mature	2-04-130	60	1.43	1.17	0.67	0.33	33	4.3	2.2	—	19.1	6
368			100	2.38	1.95	1.11	0.55	54	7.1	3.6	—	31.8	10
	SALTBUSH, NUTTALL *Atriplex nuttallii*												
369	browse, fresh, stem cured	2-07-993	55	0.87	0.72	0.25	—	20	4.0	1.8	—	—	—
370			100	1.59	1.30	0.45	—	36	7.2	3.4	—	—	—
	SALTBUSH, SHADSCALE *Atriplex confertifolia*												
371	browse, fresh, stem cured	2-05-565	80	1.09	0.90	0.21	—	25	6.1	3.5	—	—	—
372			100	1.37	1.12	0.26	—	31	7.7	4.4	—	—	—
	SALTGRASS *Distichlis spp*												
373	fresh	2-04-170	74	1.87	1.53	0.90	0.47	42	4.8	0.7	—	22.5	—
374			100	2.51	2.06	1.21	0.64	57	6.5	0.9	—	30.3	—
375	fresh, post ripe	2-04-169	74	1.87	1.53	0.90	0.47	42	3.1	0.7	—	26.0	—
376			100	2.51	2.06	1.21	0.64	57	4.2	0.9	—	34.9	—
377	hay, sun-cured	1-04-168	89	2.01	1.65	0.89	0.41	45	8.0	4.1	—	28.3	—
378			100	2.25	1.84	1.00	0.45	51	8.9	4.6	—	31.6	—
	SALTGRASS, DESERT *Distichlia stricta*												
379	fresh	2-04-171	29	0.77	0.63	0.38	0.21	17	1.7	0.7	—	8.6	—
380			100	2.65	2.17	1.31	0.74	60	5.9	2.5	—	29.7	—
	SHEEP MILK—SEE MILK												
	SORGHUM *Sorghum bicolor*												
381	aerial part, sun-cured, early vegetative	1-04-299	92	—	—	—	—	—	14.7	10.0	25	25.8	4
382			100	—	—	—	—	—	16.0	10.9	27	28.0	4
383	aerial part, sun-cured, full bloom	1-04-371	90	2.21	1.81	1.06	0.55	50	5.7	2.1	—	21.3	—
384			100	2.47	2.03	1.18	0.61	56	6.4	2.3	—	23.8	—
385	aerial part, sun-cured, mature	1-04-301	90	2.11	1.73	0.96	0.47	48	6.1	2.3	—	25.2	—
386			100	2.34	1.92	1.07	0.52	53	6.7	2.6	—	28.0	—
387	aerial part, sun-cured	1-07-960	89	2.28	1.87	1.10	0.61	52	6.7	2.8	—	23.9	—
388			100	2.56	2.10	1.24	0.68	58	7.5	3.1	—	26.9	—
389	aerial part without heads, sun-cured, mature	1-07-961	88	—	—	—	—	—	3.9	0.5	—	28.4	—
390			100	—	—	—	—	—	4.4	0.5	—	32.3	—
391	distillers grains, dehydrated	5-04-374	94	3.51	2.88	1.96	1.34	79	32.2	—	—	11.9	—
392			100	3.75	3.07	2.09	1.43	85	34.4	—	—	12.7	—
393	grain	4-04-383	90	3.48	2.85	1.96	1.35	79	11.1	8.2	3	2.4	—
394			100	3.88	3.18	2.18	1.50	88	12.4	9.1	3	2.6	—
395	grain, less than 9% protein	4-08-138	89	3.36	2.75	1.89	1.29	76	8.9	5.7	—	2.2	—
396			100	3.79	3.11	2.12	1.45	86	10.1	6.5	—	2.5	—
397	grain, 9–12% protein	4-08-139	89	3.36	2.76	1.89	1.29	76	10.2	6.9	—	2.2	—
398			100	3.79	3.11	2.12	1.45	86	11.5	7.7	—	2.4	—
399	grain, > 12% protein	4-08-140	89	—	—	—	—	—	11.6	8.1	—	1.8	—
400			100	—	—	—	—	—	13.0	9.1	—	2.0	—
401	silage	3-04-323	30	0.74	0.61	0.36	0.12	17	2.2	0.6	—	8.2	2
402			100	2.51	2.06	1.21	0.64	57	7.5	2.2	—	27.9	6
403	silage, milk stage	3-09-092	25	0.64	0.52	0.30	0.16	14	2.4	1.0	8	7.5	2
404			100	2.51	2.06	1.21	0.64	57	9.6	3.8	31	29.5	7
405	silage, dough stage	3-04-321	28	0.64	0.52	0.28	0.13	14	1.7	0.3	9	·8.1	2
406			100	2.25	1.84	1.00	0.45	51	6.0	0.9	31	28.5	7
407	silage, mature	3-04-322	32	0.71	0.58	0.31	0.13	16	2.4	0.7	9	8.0	2
408			100	2.21	1.81	0.97	0.42	50	7.5	2.3	28	24.9	7

Entry Number	Calcium (%)	Chlorine (%)	Cobalt (mg/kg)	Copper (mg/kg)	Fluorine (mg/kg)	Iodine (mg/kg)	Iron (mg/kg)	Magnesium (%)	Manganese (mg/kg)	Molybdenum (mg/kg)	Phosphorus (%)	Potassium (%)	Selenium (mg/kg)	Sodium (%)	Sulfur (%)	Zinc (mg/kg)	Provitamin A (Carotene) (mg/kg)	Vitamin E (mg/kg)	Vitamin D$_2$ (IU/g)
353	0.25	—	—	10	—	—	471	0.33	18	—	0.71	0.72	—	0.05	—	40	—	1	—
354	0.27	—	—	11	—	—	515	0.36	20	—	0.78	0.79	—	0.05	—	44	—	1	—
355	0.34	—	—	10	—	—	495	0.35	18	—	0.75	0.76	—	0.05	0.13	41	—	1	—
356	0.37	—	—	11	—	—	537	0.37	20	—	0.81	0.82	—	0.05	0.14	44	—	1	—
357	0.53	—	—	—	—	—	—	—	—	—	0.11	—	—	—	—	—	—	—	—
358	0.81	—	—	—	—	—	—	—	—	—	0.17	—	—	—	—	—	—	—	—
359	0.46	—	—	—	—	—	—	—	—	—	0.12	—	—	—	—	—	10	—	—
360	0.71	—	—	—	—	—	—	—	—	—	0.18	—	—	—	—	—	16	—	—
361	0.22	—	—	—	—	—	—	—	—	—	0.08	—	—	—	—	—	5	—	—
362	0.97	—	—	—	—	—	—	—	—	—	0.33	—	—	—	—	—	24	—	—
363	0.19	—	—	—	—	—	—	0.16	—	—	0.13	—	—	—	—	—	—	—	—
364	0.60	—	—	—	—	—	—	0.49	—	—	0.42	—	—	—	—	—	—	—	—
365	—	—	—	—	—	—	—	—	—	—	—	—	—	—	—	—	—	—	—
366	—	—	—	—	—	—	—	—	—	—	—	—	—	—	—	—	—	—	—
367	—	—	—	—	—	—	—	—	—	—	—	—	—	—	—	—	—	—	—
368	—	—	—	—	—	—	—	—	—	—	—	—	—	—	—	—	—	—	—
369	1.22	—	—	—	—	—	—	—	—	—	0.06	—	—	—	—	—	10	—	—
370	2.21	—	—	—	—	—	—	—	—	—	0.12	—	—	—	—	—	19	—	—
371	1.78	—	—	—	—	—	—	—	—	—	0.07	—	—	—	—	—	14	—	—
372	2.23	—	—	—	—	—	—	—	—	—	0.08	—	—	—	—	—	18	—	—
373	0.16	—	—	—	—	—	141	0.22	115	—	0.06	0.18	—	—	—	—	—	—	—
374	0.22	—	—	—	—	—	190	0.30	155	—	0.08	0.24	—	—	—	—	—	—	—
375	0.17	—	—	—	—	—	—	0.22	—	—	0.05	—	—	—	—	—	—	—	—
376	0.23	—	—	—	—	—	—	0.30	—	—	0.07	—	—	—	—	—	—	—	—
377	—	—	—	—	—	—	—	—	—	—	—	—	—	—	—	—	—	—	—
378	—	—	—	—	—	—	—	—	—	—	—	—	—	—	—	—	—	—	—
379	0.05	—	—	—	—	—	—	—	—	—	0.03	—	—	—	—	—	—	—	—
380	0.16	—	—	—	—	—	—	—	—	—	0.09	—	—	—	—	—	—	—	—
381	0.46	—	—	—	—	—	—	0.46	—	—	0.17	2.39	—	—	—	—	—	—	—
382	0.50	—	—	—	—	—	—	0.50	—	—	0.18	2.60	—	—	—	—	—	—	—
383	0.56	—	—	—	—	—	—	0.27	—	—	0.17	1.11	—	0.02	—	—	—	—	—
384	0.62	—	—	—	—	—	—	0.30	—	—	0.19	1.24	—	0.02	—	—	—	—	—
385	0.56	—	—	—	—	—	181	0.27	—	—	0.17	1.12	—	0.02	—	—	—	—	—
386	0.62	—	—	—	—	—	200	0.30	—	—	0.19	1.24	—	0.02	—	—	—	—	—
387	0.35	—	—	—	—	—	—	0.26	—	—	0.18	1.31	—	0.02	—	—	—	46	—
388	0.40	—	—	—	—	—	—	0.29	—	—	0.21	1.47	—	0.02	—	—	—	52	—
389	0.46	—	—	—	—	—	1,761	0.24	—	—	0.10	0.72	—	0.06	—	—	—	—	—
390	0.52	—	—	—	—	—	2,000	0.28	—	—	0.12	0.82	—	0.07	—	—	—	—	—
391	0.15	—	—	—	—	—	47	0.18	—	—	0.69	0.36	—	0.05	0.17	—	—	—	—
392	0.16	—	—	—	—	—	50	0.19	—	—	0.74	0.38	—	0.05	0.18	—	—	—	—
393	0.03	0.09	0.16	10	—	0.04	45	0.16	16	—	0.29	0.35	0.44	0.03	0.13	17	1	10	26
394	0.04	0.10	0.18	11	—	0.04	51	0.18	18	—	0.33	0.39	0.50	0.03	0.15	19	1	12	29
395	0.03	—	0.07	10	—	0.02	18	—	15	—	0.27	0.35	—	0.04	—	14	—	2	—
396	0.03	—	0.08	11	—	0.03	20	—	17	—	0.31	0.40	—	0.05	—	15	—	2	—
397	0.03	—	0.07	10	—	0.02	31	0.17	15	—	0.28	0.34	—	0.03	0.16	14	—	1	—
398	0.03	—	0.07	11	—	0.03	35	0.19	17	—	0.31	0.39	—	0.03	0.18	15	—	1	—
399	0.03	—	—	—	—	—	45	0.17	—	—	0.29	0.34	—	0.05	0.16	—	—	—	—
400	0.03	—	—	—	—	—	50	0.19	—	—	0.32	0.38	—	0.05	0.18	—	—	—	—
401	0.10	0.04	0.09	10	—	—	84	0.09	22	—	0.06	0.40	0.06	0.01	0.03	9	5	—	196
402	0.35	0.13	0.30	35	—	—	285	0.29	73	—	0.21	1.37	0.22	0.02	0.11	32	15	—	662
403	—	—	—	—	—	—	—	—	—	—	—	—	—	—	—	—	—	—	—
404	—	—	—	—	—	—	—	—	—	—	—	—	—	—	—	—	—	—	—
405	—	—	—	—	—	—	—	—	—	—	—	—	—	—	—	—	—	—	—
406	—	—	—	—	—	—	—	—	—	—	—	—	—	—	—	—	—	—	—
407	—	—	—	—	—	—	—	—	—	—	—	—	—	—	—	—	—	—	—
408	—	—	—	—	—	—	—	—	—	—	—	—	—	—	—	—	—	—	—

TABLE 13   Composition of Some Sheep Feeds; Data Expressed on an As-Fed and Dry Basis (100% Dry Matter)—*Continued*

Entry Number	Feed Name Description[a]	International Feed Number	Dry Matter (%)	DE Sheep (Mcal/kg)	ME Sheep (Mcal/kg)	NE$_m$ (Mcal/kg)	NE$_g$ (Mcal/kg)	TDN Sheep (%)	Crude Protein (%)	Dig. Protein (%)	Cellulose (%)	Crude Fiber (%)	Lignin (%)
	SORGHUM, JOHNSONGRASS *Sorghum halepense*												
409	fresh	2-04-412	24	0.66	0.54	0.33	0.19	15	3.7	2.7	—	7.0	—
410			100	2.73	2.24	1.38	0.80	62	15.4	11.3	—	29.0	—
411	fresh, early vegetative	2-04-409	20	0.54	0.44	0.28	0.16	12	3.1	2.3	—	5.6	—
412			100	2.73	2.24	1.38	0.80	62	15.5	11.4	—	28.5	—
413	fresh, midbloom	2-08-516	35	0.91	0.75	0.45	0.25	21	3.1	1.9	—	10.9	—
414			100	2.60	2.13	1.28	0.71	59	8.9	5.3	—	31.0	—
415	fresh, full bloom	2-04-410	35	0.90	0.73	0.43	0.24	20	2.8	1.6	—	11.4	—
416			100	2.56	2.10	1.24	0.68	58	8.1	4.5	—	32.7	—
417	hay, sun-cured	1-04-407	89	2.21	1.81	1.05	0.54	50	8.5	3.7	—	29.9	—
418			100	2.47	2.03	1.18	0.61	56	9.5	4.2	—	33.5	—
419	hay, sun-cured, early vegetative	1-04-401	92	2.23	1.83	1.05	0.53	51	13.8	9.2	—	26.6	—
420			100	2.43	1.99	1.14	0.58	55	15.0	10.0	—	29.0	—
421	hay, sun-cured, late vegetative	1-09-257	88	2.02	1.65	0.92	0.43	46	10.6	6.4	—	27.5	—
422			100	2.29	1.88	1.04	0.49	52	12.0	7.3	—	31.3	—
423	hay, sun-cured, midbloom	1-04-403	92	2.06	1.69	0.92	0.41	47	7.9	3.9	—	29.9	—
424			100	2.25	1.84	1.00	0.45	51	8.6	4.3	—	32.6	—
425	hay, sun-cured, post ripe	1-04-405	93	2.05	1.68	0.90	0.39	46	5.3	1.6	—	31.8	—
426			100	2.21	1.81	0.97	0.42	50	5.7	1.7	—	34.2	—
	SORGHUM, KAFIR *Sorghum bicolor caffrorum*												
427	grain	4-04-428	89	3.34	2.74	1.86	1.27	75	10.9	8.8	—	2.0	—
428			100	3.75	3.07	2.09	1.43	85	12.3	9.9	—	2.3	—
	SORGHUM, MILO *Sorghum bicolor subglabrescens*												
429	grain	4-04-444	89	3.44	2.82	1.94	1.34	78	10.0	7.8	3	2.2	—
430			100	3.88	3.18	2.18	1.50	88	11.3	8.8	3	2.5	—
431	heads	4-04-446	90	3.33	2.73	1.85	1.26	76	9.0	6.9	—	8.0	—
432			100	3.70	3.04	2.06	1.40	84	10.0	7.6	—	8.9	—
	SORGHUM, SORGO *Sorghum bicolor saccharatum*												
433	silage	3-04-468	27	0.73	0.60	0.30	0.20	16	1.7	0.4	—	7.8	—
434			100	2.65	2.17	1.31	0.74	60	6.2	1.4	—	28.3	—
	SORGHUM, SUDANGRASS *Sorghum bicolor sudanense*												
435	fresh, early vegetative	2-04-484	18	0.49	0.41	0.25	0.15	11	3.0	2.3	5	4.1	1
436			100	2.78	2.28	1.41	0.83	63	16.8	12.6	26	23.0	3
437	fresh, midbloom	2-04-485	23	0.56	0.46	0.27	0.14	13	2.0	1.2	8	6.8	1
438			100	2.47	2.03	1.18	0.61	56	8.8	5.2	34	30.0	5
439	hay, sun-cured	1-04-480	91	2.21	1.81	1.04	0.53	50	7.3	4.0	32	32.8	5
440			100	2.43	1.99	1.14	0.58	55	8.0	4.3	35	36.0	6
441	silage	3-04-499	28	0.67	0.55	0.30	0.15	15	3.1	1.9	11	9.4	1
442			100	2.34	1.92	1.07	0.52	53	10.8	6.6	38	33.1	5
	SOYBEAN *Glycine max*												
443	hay, sun-cured	1-04-558	89	2.25	1.84	1.08	0.57	51	14.3	10.1	—	30.1	—
444			100	2.51	2.06	1.21	0.64	57	16.0	11.3	—	33.7	—
445	seed coats (hulls)	1-04-560	91	2.17	1.78	1.01	0.50	49	11.0	6.7	42	36.4	2
446			100	2.38	1.95	1.11	0.55	54	12.1	7.3	46	40.1	2
447	seeds	5-04-610	92	3.79	3.11	2.16	1.52	86	39.2	35.1	—	5.3	—
448			100	4.14	3.40	2.35	1.65	94	42.8	38.3	—	5.8	—
449	seeds, meal mechanical extracted	5-04-600	90	3.37	2.77	1.88	1.29	77	42.9	36.8	—	5.9	—
450			100	3.75	3.07	2.09	1.43	85	47.7	40.9	—	6.6	—
451	seeds, meal solvent extracted	5-04-604	90	3.48	2.85	1.96	1.35	79	44.8	41.6	—	5.8	—
452			100	3.88	3.18	2.18	1.50	88	49.9	46.4	—	6.5	—
453	straw	1-04-567	88	1.66	1.36	0.63	0.16	38	4.6	1.3	33	38.9	14
454			100	1.90	1.56	0.72	0.18	43	5.2	1.5	38	44.3	16
	SUGARCANE MOLASSES—SEE MOLASSES												
	SUMMERCYPRESS, GRAY *Kochia vestita*												
455	fresh, stem-cured	2-08-843	85	1.87	1.54	0.82	0.36	42	7.7	5.3	—	18.7	—
456			100	2.21	1.81	0.97	0.42	50	9.0	6.2	—	22.0	—
	SUNFLOWER, COMMON *Helianthus annuus*												
457	fresh	2-10-697	15	0.40	0.33	0.20	0.11	9	1.4	0.8	—	4.4	—
458			100	2.65	2.17	1.31	0.74	60	9.2	5.6	—	29.3	—
459	seeds, meal solvent extracted	5-09-340	90	1.79	1.46	0.68	0.23	41	23.3	18.9	—	31.6	11
460			100	1.98	1.63	0.75	0.25	45	25.9	21.0	—	35.1	12
461	seeds without hulls, meal solvent extracted	5-04-739	93	3.12	2.56	1.69	1.11	70	46.3	—	—	11.4	—
462			100	3.35	2.75	1.82	1.19	76	49.8	—	—	12.2	—

Entry Number	Calcium (%)	Chlorine (%)	Cobalt (mg/kg)	Copper (mg/kg)	Fluorine (mg/kg)	Iodine (mg/kg)	Iron (mg/kg)	Magnesium (%)	Manganese (mg/kg)	Molybdenum (mg/kg)	Phosphorus (%)	Potassium (%)	Selenium (mg/kg)	Sodium (%)	Sulfur (%)	Zinc (mg/kg)	Provitamin A (Carotene) (mg/kg)	Vitamin E (mg/kg)	Vitamin D$_2$ (IU/g)
409	0.22	—	—	—	—	—	—	0.06	—	—	0.06	0.75	—	—	—	—	48	—	—
410	0.91	—	—	—	—	—	—	0.25	—	—	0.26	3.12	—	—	—	—	198	—	—
411	0.18	—	—	—	—	—	—	—	—	—	0.06	—	—	—	—	—	—	—	—
412	0.93	—	—	—	—	—	—	—	—	—	0.31	—	—	—	—	—	—	—	—
413	0.29	—	—	—	—	—	—	—	—	—	0.06	—	—	—	—	—	—	—	—
414	0.83	—	—	—	—	—	—	—	—	—	0.17	—	—	—	—	—	—	—	—
415	0.29	—	—	—	—	—	—	—	—	—	0.06	—	—	—	—	—	—	—	—
416	0.83	—	—	—	—	—	—	—	—	—	0.17	—	—	—	—	—	—	—	—
417	0.75	—	—	—	—	—	527	0.31	—	—	0.25	1.21	—	0.01	0.09	—	35	—	—
418	0.84	—	—	—	—	—	590	0.35	—	—	0.28	1.35	—	0.01	0.10	—	39	—	—
419	0.63	—	—	—	—	—	—	—	—	—	0.45	—	—	—	—	—	—	—	—
420	0.69	—	—	—	—	—	—	—	—	—	0.49	—	—	—	—	—	—	—	—
421	—	—	—	—	—	—	—	—	—	—	—	—	—	—	—	—	—	—	—
422	—	—	—	—	—	—	—	—	—	—	—	—	—	—	—	—	—	—	—
423	0.58	—	—	—	—	—	—	—	—	—	0.21	—	—	—	—	—	—	—	—
424	0.63	—	—	—	—	—	—	—	—	—	0.23	—	—	—	—	—	—	—	—
425	—	—	—	—	—	—	—	—	—	—	—	—	—	—	—	—	—	—	—
426	—	—	—	—	—	—	—	—	—	—	—	—	—	—	—	—	—	—	—
427	0.03	0.10	0.39	7	—	—	63	0.15	16	—	0.31	0.34	0.80	0.05	0.16	14	0	—	—
428	0.04	0.11	0.43	8	—	—	71	0.17	18	—	0.35	0.38	0.89	0.06	0.18	15	0	—	—
429	0.04	0.08	0.47	4	—	0.06	49	0.13	16	—	0.30	0.31	0.20	0.04	0.11	17	0	12	25
430	0.05	0.09	0.53	5	—	0.07	55	0.14	18	—	0.34	0.35	0.23	0.04	0.12	20	0	13	29
431	0.12	—	—	—	—	—	—	0.15	—	—	0.22	0.50	—	—	0.12	—	1	—	—
432	0.13	—	—	—	—	—	—	0.17	—	—	0.25	0.56	—	—	0.13	—	1	—	—
433	0.09	0.02	—	9	—	—	54	0.08	17	—	0.05	0.31	—	0.04	0.03	—	10	—	—
434	0.34	0.06	—	31	—	—	198	0.27	61	—	0.17	1.12	—	0.15	0.10	—	36	—	—
435	0.08	—	—	—	—	—	36	0.06	—	—	0.07	0.38	—	0.00	0.02	—	35	—	—
436	0.43	—	—	—	—	—	200	0.35	—	—	0.41	2.14	—	0.01	0.11	—	198	—	—
437	0.10	—	—	—	—	—	46	0.08	—	—	0.08	0.49	—	0.00	0.03	—	42	—	—
438	0.43	—	—	—	—	—	200	0.35	—	—	0.36	2.14	—	0.01	0.11	—	183	—	—
439	0.50	—	0.12	34	—	—	176	0.47	83	—	0.28	1.70	—	0.02	0.06	35	54	—	—
440	0.55	—	0.13	37	—	—	193	0.51	91	—	0.30	1.87	—	0.02	0.06	38	59	—	—
441	0.13	—	0.09	11	—	—	36	0.13	28	—	0.06	0.64	—	0.01	0.02	—	30	—	—
442	0.46	—	0.31	37	—	—	127	0.44	99	—	0.21	2.25	—	0.02	0.06	—	105	—	—
443	0.15	1.13	0.08	8	—	0.22	261	0.71	95	—	0.25	0.96	—	0.08	0.21	22	41	26	947
444	1.29	0.15	0.09	9	—	0.24	292	0.79	106	—	0.28	1.07	—	0.09	0.24	24	45	30	1059
445	0.45	—	0.11	16	—	—	295	—	10	—	0.19	1.16	—	0.01	0.08	22	—	6	—
446	0.49	—	0.12	18	—	—	324	—	11	—	0.21	1.27	—	0.01	0.09	24	—	7	—
447	0.25	0.03	—	18	—	—	84	0.26	36	—	0.60	1.66	0.11	0.02	0.22	57	1	33	—
448	0.27	0.03	—	20	—	—	91	0.29	39	—	0.65	1.82	0.12	0.02	0.24	62	1	37	—
449	0.26	0.07	0.18	22	—	—	157	0.25	31	—	0.61	1.79	0.10	0.03	0.33	60	0	7	—
450	0.29	0.08	0.20	24	—	—	175	0.28	35	—	0.68	1.98	0.11	0.03	0.37	66	0	7	—
451	0.30	0.04	0.09	23	—	0.13	119	0.27	29	—	0.63	1.97	0.30	0.04	0.43	43	0	3	—
452	0.34	0.04	0.10	25	—	0.15	133	0.30	32	—	0.70	2.20	0.34	0.04	0.47	48	0	3	—
453	1.40	—	—	—	—	—	263	0.81	45	—	0.05	0.49	—	0.11	0.23	—	—	—	—
454	1.59	—	—	—	—	—	300	0.92	51	—	0.06	0.56	—	0.12	0.26	—	—	—	—
455	2.01	—	—	—	—	—	—	—	—	—	0.10	—	—	—	—	—	15	—	—
456	2.36	—	—	—	—	—	—	—	—	—	0.12	—	—	—	—	—	18	—	—
457	—	—	—	—	—	—	—	—	—	—	—	—	—	—	—	—	—	—	—
458	—	—	—	—	—	—	—	—	—	—	—	—	—	—	—	—	—	—	—
459	—	—	—	—	—	—	—	0.68	—	—	0.93	0.96	—	—	0.30	—	—	—	—
460	0.23	—	—	—	—	—	—	0.75	—	—	1.03	1.06	—	—	0.33	—	—	—	—
461	0.41	0.10	—	4	—	—	31	0.71	19	—	0.91	1.06	—	0.22	—	—	—	11	—
462	0.44	0.11	—	4	—	—	33	0.77	20	—	0.98	1.14	—	0.24	—	—	—	12	—

TABLE 13 Composition of Some Sheep Feeds; Data Expressed on an As-Fed and Dry Basis (100% Dry Matter)—*Continued*

Entry Number	Feed Name Description[a]	International Feed Number	Dry Matter (%)	DE Sheep (Mcal/kg)	ME Sheep (Mcal/kg)	NE$_m$ (Mcal/kg)	NE$_g$ (Mcal/kg)	TDN Sheep (%)	Crude Protein (%)	Dig. Protein (%)	Cellulose (%)	Crude Fiber (%)	Lignin (%)
	SWEETCLOVER, YELLOW *Melilotus officinalis*												
463	hay, sun-cured	1-04-754	87	2.04	1.67	0.93	0.45	46	13.7	10.0	—	29.2	—
464			100	2.34	1.92	1.07	0.52	53	15.7	11.5	—	33.4	—
	TIMOTHY *Phleum pratense*												
465	fresh, late vegetative	2-04-903	26	0.71	0.58	0.35	0.20	16	4.8	2.6	—	8.5	—
466			100	2.69	2.21	1.34	0.77	61	18.0	10.0	—	32.1	—
467	fresh, midbloom	2-04-905	29	0.80	0.66	0.40	0.23	18	2.7	1.4	9	9.8	1
468			100	2.73	2.24	1.38	0.80	62	9.1	4.9	31	33.5	4
469	hay, sun-cured, late vegetative	1-04-881	89	2.56	2.10	1.31	0.78	58	15.2	10.2	25	24.1	3
470			100	2.87	2.35	1.47	0.88	65	17.0	11.4	28	27.0	3
471	hay, sun-cured, early bloom	1-04-882	90	2.21	1.81	1.06	0.55	51	13.4	7.3	28	25.1	4
472			100	2.47	2.03	1.18	0.61	56	15.0	8.2	31	28.0	4
473	hay, sun-cured, midbloom	1-04-883	89	2.35	1.93	1.17	0.66	53	8.1	4.9	29	27.6	4
474			100	2.65	2.17	1.31	0.74	60	9.1	5.6	33	31.0	5
475	hay, sun-cured, late bloom	1-04-885	88	2.14	1.76	1.00	0.51	49	6.9	3.1	30	28.7	6
476			100	2.43	1.99	1.14	0.58	55	7.8	3.5	34	32.5	7
477	silage	3-04-922	34	0.90	0.74	0.44	0.25	20	3.5	1.9	—	12.1	—
478			100	2.65	2.17	1.31	0.74	60	10.1	5.6	—	35.6	—
	TREFOIL, BIRDSFOOT *Lotus corniculatus*												
479	fresh	2-20-786	24	0.67	0.55	0.34	0.07	15	5.1	4.0	—	6.0	—
480			100	2.78	2.28	1.41	0.83	63	21.0	16.3	—	24.7	—
481	hay, sun-cured	1-05-044	92	2.36	1.93	1.14	0.63	53	15.0	10.3	22	28.3	8
482			100	2.56	2.10	1.24	0.68	58	16.3	11.2	24	30.7	9
	TURNIP *Brassica rapa rapa*												
483	aerial part, fresh	2-05-063	14	0.42	0.35	0.23	0.15	10	2.9	1.1	—	1.4	—
484			100	3.13	2.57	1.67	1.06	71	21.2	8.1	—	10.3	—
485	aerial part, silage	3-05-066	14	0.45	0.37	0.23	0.15	10	2.1	1.5	—	2.4	—
486			100	3.13	2.57	1.67	1.06	71	14.8	10.7	—	17.0	—
487	roots, fresh	4-05-067	9	0.35	0.29	0.19	0.13	8	1.1	0.8	—	1.1	1
488			100	3.79	3.11	2.12	1.45	86	11.8	8.9	—	11.5	10
	VETCH, *Vicia* spp												
489	fresh	2-05-111	22	0.60	0.49	0.29	0.16	13	4.7	3.5	—	6.2	—
490			100	2.65	2.17	1.31	0.74	60	20.9	15.7	—	27.7	—
491	fresh, late vegetative	2-05-108	22	0.58	0.48	0.28	0.16	13	4.6	3.5	—	6.2	—
492			100	2.60	2.13	1.28	0.71	59	20.8	15.8	—	27.7	—
493	hay, sun-cured	1-05-106	89	2.16	1.77	1.01	0.52	49	18.5	14.0	—	27.3	7
494			100	2.43	1.99	1.14	0.58	55	20.8	15.7	—	30.6	8
495	hay, sun-cured, early vegetative	1-05-098	93	2.58	2.11	1.31	0.77	59	23.4	18.8	—	24.2	6
496			100	2.78	2.28	1.41	0.83	63	25.2	20.3	—	26.1	6
497	hay, sun-cured, early bloom	1-05-099	83	2.16	1.77	1.06	0.59	49	19.3	14.7	—	23.7	—
498			100	2.60	2.13	1.28	0.71	59	23.3	17.7	—	28.6	—
499	hay, sun-cured, midbloom	1-05-100	91	2.29	1.88	1.10	0.58	52	18.9	15.2	—	26.7	8
500			100	2.51	2.06	1.21	0.64	57	20.8	16.6	—	29.3	9
	WHEAT *Triticum aestivum*												
501	bran	4-05-190	89	2.78	2.28	1.49	0.94	63	15.2	11.8	9	10.0	3
502			100	3.13	2.57	1.67	1.06	71	17.1	13.3	11	11.3	3
503	flour by-product, less than 9.5%	4-05-205	89	3.21	2.63	1.78	1.20	72	16.4	13.2	—	7.3	—
504	fiber (wheat middlings)		100	3.62	2.97	2.00	1.35	82	18.4	14.8	—	8.2	—
505	fresh, early vegetative	2-05-176	22	0.73	0.60	0.39	0.26	17	6.3	5.0	5	3.9	1
506			100	3.31	2.71	1.79	1.16	75	28.6	22.6	24	17.4	4
507	grain	4-05-211	89	3.41	2.80	1.91	1.32	78	14.2	11.4	7	2.6	—
508			100	3.84	3.15	2.15	1.48	87	16.0	12.8	8	2.9	—
509	grain, hard red spring	4-05-258	88	3.48	2.85	1.97	1.36	78	15.1	11.3	7	2.5	—
510			100	3.97	3.25	2.24	1.55	90	17.2	13.0	8	2.9	—
511	grain, hard red winter	4-05-268	88	3.42	2.81	1.92	1.32	78	12.7	9.1	—	2.5	—
512			100	3.88	3.18	2.18	1.50	88	14.4	10.4	—	2.8	—
513	grain, soft red winter	4-05-294	88	3.42	2.81	1.92	1.32	78	11.5	8.6	—	2.2	—
514			100	3.88	3.18	2.18	1.50	88	13.0	9.8	—	2.4	—
515	grain, soft white winter, Pacific coast	4-08-555	89	3.50	2.87	1.97	1.35	79	10.0	6.7	—	2.5	—
516			100	3.92	3.22	2.21	1.52	89	11.2	7.5	—	2.8	—
517	grain screenings	4-05-216	89	2.95	2.42	1.59	1.03	67	14.1	10.1	5	6.9	7
518			100	3.31	2.71	1.79	1.16	75	15.8	11.3	6	7.7	8
519	hay, sun-cured	1-05-172	88	2.01	1.65	0.92	0.43	45	7.4	4.0	—	24.6	6
520			100	2.29	1.88	1.04	0.49	52	8.5	4.6	—	28.1	7
521	straw	1-05-175	89	1.60	1.32	0.57	0.10	36	3.2	-3.1	35	36.9	12
522			100	1.81	1.48	0.64	0.11	41	3.6	-3.5	39	41.6	14

Entry Number	Calcium (%)	Chlorine (%)	Cobalt (mg/kg)	Copper (mg/kg)	Fluorine (mg/kg)	Iodine (mg/kg)	Iron (mg/kg)	Magnesium (%)	Manganese (mg/kg)	Molybdenum (mg/kg)	Phosphorus (%)	Potassium (%)	Selenium (mg/kg)	Sodium (%)	Sulfur (%)	Zinc (mg/kg)	Provitamin A (Carotene) (mg/kg)	Vitamin E (mg/kg)	Vitamin D2 (IU/g)
463	1.11	0.32	—	9	—	—	133	0.43	94	—	0.22	1.40	—	0.08	0.41	—	86	—	1636
464	1.27	0.37	—	10	—	—	152	0.49	108	—	0.25	1.60	—	0.09	0.47	—	99	—	1874
465	0.10	—	—	—	—	—	53	0.04	—	—	0.08	0.63	—	0.05	0.03	—	62	—	—
466	0.39	—	—	—	—	—	200	0.15	—	—	0.32	2.40	—	0.19	0.13	—	235	—	—
467	0.11	0.19	—	3	—	—	52	0.04	56	—	0.09	0.60	—	0.06	0.04	—	57	—	—
468	0.38	0.64	—	11	—	—	179	0.14	192	—	0.30	2.06	—	0.19	0.13	—	195	—	—
469	0.59	—	—	23	—	—	179	0.13	79	—	0.30	1.50	—	0.16	—	60	112	—	—
470	0.66	—	—	26	—	—	200	0.14	89	—	0.34	1.68	—	0.18	—	67	125	—	—
471	0.48	—	—	57	—	—	179	0.13	92	—	0.22	—	—	0.16	—	56	47	12	—
472	0.53	—	—	64	—	—	200	0.14	103	—	0.25	—	—	0.18	—	62	53	13	—
473	0.43	—	—	5	—	—	151	0.14	—	—	0.20	1.41	—	0.16	—	38	47	—	1764
474	0.48	—	—	5	—	—	170	0.16	—	—	0.22	1.59	—	0.18	—	43	53	—	1985
475	0.34	—	—	—	—	—	141	0.12	—	—	0.16	1.42	—	0.06	—	—	40	—	—
476	0.38	—	—	—	—	—	160	0.13	—	—	0.18	1.61	—	0.07	—	—	45	—	—
477	0.19	—	—	2	—	—	37	0.05	31	—	0.10	0.58	—	0.04	0.04	—	31	—	—
478	0.55	—	—	6	—	—	110	0.15	90	—	0.29	1.69	—	0.11	0.13	—	90	—	—
479	0.46	—	0.05	—	—	—	97	0.07	—	—	0.05	0.48	—	0.02	0.06	—	—	—	—
480	1.91	—	0.21	—	—	—	400	0.28	—	—	0.22	1.99	—	0.07	0.25	—	—	—	—
481	1.57	—	0.10	9	—	—	210	0.47	26	—	0.25	1.77	—	0.06	0.23	—	173	—	1421
482	1.70	—	0.11	9	—	—	228	0.51	29	—	0.27	1.92	—	0.07	0.25	—	188	—	1544
483	0.40	0.26	—	2	—	—	54	0.07	55	—	0.05	0.41	—	0.15	0.04	5	—	—	—
484	2.93	1.93	—	18	—	—	403	0.54	409	—	0.39	3.03	—	1.13	0.27	37	—	—	—
485	0.41	—	—	3	—	—	54	0.07	58	—	0.08	0.54	—	—	—	—	71	3	—
486	2.87	—	—	18	—	—	380	0.47	409	—	0.58	3.79	—	—	—	—	501	22	—
487	0.05	0.06	—	2	—	—	11	0.02	4	—	0.02	0.28	—	0.10	0.04	3	—	—	—
488	0.59	0.65	—	21	—	—	118	0.22	43	—	0.26	2.99	—	1.05	0.43	29	—	—	—
489	—	0.42	0.07	—	—	—	—	—	—	—	—	—	—	0.11	0.03	—	—	—	—
490	—	1.85	0.30	—	—	—	—	—	—	—	—	—	—	0.49	0.15	—	—	—	—
491	—	—	—	—	—	—	—	—	—	—	—	—	—	—	—	—	—	—	—
492	—	—	—	—	—	—	—	—	—	—	—	—	—	—	—	—	—	—	—
493	1.05	—	0.32	9	—	0.44	374	0.22	65	—	0.29	2.07	—	0.46	0.13	—	411	—	—
494	1.18	—	0.36	10	—	0.49	420	0.25	73	—	0.32	2.32	—	0.52	0.15	—	461	—	—
495	—	—	—	—	—	—	—	—	—	—	—	—	—	—	—	—	358	—	—
496	—	—	—	—	—	—	—	—	—	—	—	—	—	—	—	—	386	—	—
497	—	—	—	—	—	—	—	—	—	—	—	—	—	—	—	—	—	—	—
498	—	—	—	—	—	—	—	—	—	—	—	—	—	—	—	—	—	—	—
499	—	—	—	—	—	—	—	—	—	—	—	—	—	—	—	—	—	—	—
500	—	—	—	—	—	—	—	—	—	—	—	—	—	—	—	—	—	—	—
501	0.11	0.05	0.10	13	—	0.07	114	0.53	111	—	1.22	1.38	0.38	0.04	0.22	114	3	18	—
502	0.13	0.05	0.11	14	—	0.07	128	0.60	125	—	1.38	1.56	0.43	0.04	0.25	128	3	21	—
503	0.11	0.04	0.09	19	—	0.11	83	0.36	112	—	0.88	1.00	0.74	0.17	0.17	103	3	23	—
504	0.13	0.04	0.10	22	—	0.12	93	0.40	126	—	0.99	1.13	0.83	0.19	0.20	116	3	25	—
505	0.09	—	—	—	—	—	22	0.05	—	—	0.09	0.78	—	0.04	0.05	—	115	—	—
506	0.42	—	—	—	—	—	100	0.21	—	—	0.40	3.50	—	0.18	0.22	—	520	—	—
507	0.04	0.07	0.12	6	—	0.09	54	0.15	37	—	0.37	0.38	0.26	0.04	0.16	44	0	15	—
508	0.04	0.08	0.14	7	—	0.10	61	0.16	42	—	0.42	0.42	0.30	0.05	0.18	50	0	17	—
509	0.03	0.08	0.12	6	—	—	56	0.15	37	—	0.38	0.36	0.25	0.02	0.15	45	0	13	—
510	0.04	0.09	0.13	7	—	—	64	0.17	42	—	0.43	0.41	0.29	0.03	0.17	52	0	14	—
511	0.04	0.05	0.14	5	—	—	31	0.11	29	—	0.38	0.43	0.40	0.02	0.13	38	—	11	—
512	0.05	0.06	0.16	5	—	—	35	0.13	33	—	0.43	0.49	0.45	0.02	0.15	43	—	12	—
513	0.04	0.07	0.10	6	—	—	27	0.10	32	—	0.38	0.41	0.04	0.01	0.11	42	—	16	—
514	0.05	0.08	0.12	7	—	—	30	0.11	36	—	0.43	0.46	0.05	0.01	0.12	48	—	18	—
515	0.09	—	—	—	—	—	54	0.13	—	—	0.30	0.45	—	0.09	0.16	—	—	—	—
516	0.10	—	—	—	—	—	60	0.15	—	—	0.34	0.51	—	0.10	0.18	—	—	—	—
517	0.13	—	—	—	—	—	54	0.16	29	—	0.35	0.52	0.61	0.09	0.20	—	—	—	—
518	0.15	—	—	—	—	—	60	0.18	33	—	0.39	0.58	0.68	0.10	0.22	—	—	—	—
519	0.13	—	—	—	—	—	175	0.11	—	—	0.17	0.87	—	0.18	0.19	—	75	—	1352
520	0.15	—	—	—	—	—	200	0.12	—	—	0.20	1.00	—	0.21	0.22	—	85	—	1544
521	0.16	0.28	0.04	3	—	—	140	0.11	36	—	0.04	1.26	—	0.13	0.17	6	2	—	587
522	0.18	0.32	0.05	4	—	—	157	0.12	41	—	0.05	1.42	—	0.14	0.19	6	2	—	662

TABLE 13 Composition of Some Sheep Feeds; Data Expressed on an As-Fed and Dry Basis (100% Dry Matter)—*Continued*

Entry Number	Feed Name Description[a]	International Feed Number	Dry Matter (%)	DE Sheep (Mcal/kg)	ME Sheep (Mcal/kg)	NE$_m$ (Mcal/kg)	NE$_g$ (Mcal/kg)	TDN Sheep (%)	Crude Protein (%)	Dig. Protein (%)	Cellulose (%)	Crude Fiber (%)	Lignin (%)
	WHEATGRASS, CRESTED *Agropyron desertorum*												
523	fresh, early vegetative	2-05-420	28	0.92	0.76	0.50	0.32	21	6.0	5.1	—	6.2	—
524			100	3.31	2.71	1.79	1.16	75	21.5	18.3	—	22.2	—
525	fresh, late vegetative	2-05-421	34	0.91	0.75	0.46	0.26	21	4.8	3.4	—	7.8	—
526			100	2.69	2.21	1.34	0.77	61	14.0	10.0	—	22.9	—
527	fresh, early bloom	2-05-422	37	0.93	0.76	0.45	0.24	21	4.4	3.0	—	9.9	—
528			100	2.51	2.06	1.21	0.64	57	12.0	8.2	—	26.9	—
529	fresh, full bloom	2-05-424	45	1.11	0.91	0.53	0.27	25	4.4	1.8	—	13.6	—
530			100	2.47	2.03	1.18	0.61	56	9.8	4.0	—	30.3	—
531	fresh, milk stage	2-05-425	48	1.16	0.95	0.53	0.28	26	3.8	2.1	—	16.8	—
532			100	2.43	1.99	1.14	0.58	55	8.0	4.4	—	35.0	—
533	fresh, mature	2-05-427	60	1.43	1.17	0.67	0.33	32	3.3	1.3	—	23.2	—
534			100	2.38	1.95	1.11	0.55	54	5.5	2.1	—	38.7	—
535	fresh, post ripe	2-05-428	80	1.91	1.56	0.89	0.44	43	2.5	−0.1	—	32.2	—
536			100	2.38	1.95	1.11	0.55	54	3.1	−0.1	—	40.3	—
537	fresh, stem-cured	2-08-558	81	1.89	1.55	0.87	0.42	43	2.7	1.2	—	31.7	—
538			100	2.34	1.92	1.07	0.52	53	3.3	1.5	—	39.1	—
539	hay, sun-cured	1-05-418	93	2.17	1.78	1.00	0.48	49	11.5	7.4	—	30.5	5
540			100	2.34	1.92	1.07	0.52	53	12.4	8.0	—	32.9	6
541	hay, sun-cured, early vegetative	1-05-411	94	3.14	2.57	1.71	1.12	71	18.0	15.3	—	19.6	—
542			100	3.35	2.75	1.82	1.19	76	19.2	16.3	—	20.9	—
543	hay, sun-cured, late vegetative	1-20-201	92	2.39	1.96	1.18	0.65	55	19.6	14.4	—	25.2	4
544			100	2.60	2.13	1.28	0.71	59	21.3	15.6	—	27.4	5
545	hay, sun-cured, early bloom	1-05-412	92	2.31	1.89	1.11	0.59	52	12.9	8.4	—	30.8	—
546			100	2.51	2.06	1.21	0.64	57	14.0	9.1	—	33.5	—
547	hay, sun-cured, midbloom	1-05-413	96	2.38	1.95	1.13	0.59	54	12.8	8.2	—	33.0	6
548			100	2.47	2.03	1.18	0.61	56	13.2	8.5	—	34.3	6
549	hay, sun-cured, full bloom	1-05-414	95	2.30	1.89	1.08	0.55	52	8.3	4.2	—	34.2	—
550			100	2.43	1.99	1.14	0.58	55	8.7	4.4	—	36.0	—
551	hay, sun-cured, milk stage	1-05-415	93	2.16	1.77	1.00	0.48	49	6.9	3.1	—	34.2	—
552			100	2.34	1.92	1.07	0.52	53	7.5	3.3	—	37.0	—
553	hay, sun-cured, mature	1-05-416	94	1.99	1.63	0.85	0.33	45	5.3	3.3	—	36.4	—
554			100	2.12	1.74	0.90	0.35	48	5.6	3.5	—	38.7	—
555	**WINTERFAT, COMMON** *Eurotia lanata* fresh, stem cured	2-26-142	80	1.24	1.01	0.33	—	28	8.7	5.4	—	—	8
556			100	1.54	1.27	0.41	—	35	10.8	6.7	—	—	10

[a]See Table 15 for stage-of-maturity terms.

Entry Number	Calcium (%)	Chlorine (%)	Cobalt (mg/kg)	Copper (mg/kg)	Fluorine (mg/kg)	Iodine (mg/kg)	Iron (mg/kg)	Magnesium (%)	Manganese (mg/kg)	Molybdenum (mg/kg)	Phosphorus (%)	Potassium (%)	Selenium (mg/kg)	Sodium (%)	Sulfur (%)	Zinc (mg/kg)	Provitamin A (Carotene) (mg/kg)	Vitamin E (mg/kg)	Vitamin D₂ (IU/g)
523	0.13	—	—	—	—	—	—	0.08	—	—	0.10	—	—	—	—	—	126	—	—
524	0.46	—	—	—	—	—	—	0.28	—	—	0.34	—	—	—	—	—	451	—	—
525	0.08	—	—	—	—	—	—	—	—	—	0.07	—	—	—	—	—	123	—	—
526	0.23	—	—	—	—	—	—	—	—	—	0.20	—	—	—	—	—	361	—	—
527	0.09	—	—	—	—	—	—	—	—	—	0.07	—	—	—	—	—	—	—	—
528	0.24	—	—	—	—	—	—	—	—	—	0.18	—	—	—	—	—	—	—	—
529	0.18	—	—	3	—	—	—	0.04	19	—	0.13	0.47	—	0.00	0.21	6	69	—	—
530	0.39	—	—	7	—	—	—	0.09	43	—	0.28	1.04	—	0.01	0.47	13	154	—	—
531	0.15	—	—	—	—	—	—	—	—	—	0.12	—	—	—	—	—	41	—	—
532	0.31	—	—	—	—	—	—	—	—	—	0.25	—	—	—	—	—	86	—	—
533	0.16	—	—	—	—	—	—	—	—	—	0.09	—	—	—	—	—	45	—	—
534	0.27	—	—	—	—	—	—	—	—	—	0.15	—	—	—	—	—	75	—	—
535	0.22	—	0.20	7	—	—	—	—	42	—	0.06	—	—	—	—	—	0	—	—
536	0.27	—	0.25	8	—	—	—	—	53	—	0.07	—	—	—	—	—	0	—	—
537	0.16	—	—	—	—	—	—	—	—	—	0.07	—	—	—	—	—	—	—	—
538	0.20	—	—	—	—	—	—	—	—	—	0.09	—	—	—	—	—	—	—	—
539	0.31	—	0.22	15	—	—	165	0.15	34	—	0.20	1.85	0.37	—	—	30	21	—	—
540	0.33	—	0.24	16	—	—	178	0.16	36	—	0.21	2.00	0.40	—	—	32	22	—	—
541	0.40	—	—	—	—	—	—	—	—	—	0.25	—	—	—	—	—	213	—	—
542	0.43	—	—	—	—	—	—	—	—	—	0.26	—	—	—	—	—	228	—	—
543	—	—	—	—	—	—	—	—	—	—	—	—	—	—	—	—	—	—	—
544	—	—	—	—	—	—	—	—	—	—	—	—	—	—	—	—	—	—	—
545	0.31	—	—	15	—	—	164	0.15	33	—	0.20	1.84	0.37	—	—	29	—	—	—
546	0.34	—	—	16	—	—	178	0.16	36	—	0.22	2.00	0.40	—	—	32	—	—	—
547	—	—	—	—	—	—	—	—	—	—	—	—	—	—	—	—	—	—	—
548	—	—	—	—	—	—	—	—	—	—	—	—	—	—	—	—	—	—	—
549	0.25	—	—	—	—	—	—	—	—	—	0.15	—	—	—	—	—	—	—	—
550	0.26	—	—	—	—	—	—	—	—	—	0.16	—	—	—	—	—	—	—	—
551	0.24	—	—	—	—	—	—	—	—	—	0.10	—	—	—	—	—	—	—	—
552	0.26	—	—	—	—	—	—	—	—	—	0.11	—	—	—	—	—	—	—	—
553	0.18	—	—	—	—	—	—	0.03	—	—	0.11	0.45	—	—	—	—	29	—	—
554	0.19	—	—	—	—	—	—	0.03	—	—	0.12	0.48	—	—	—	—	31	—	—
555	1.58	—	—	—	—	—	—	—	—	—	0.09	—	—	—	—	—	14	—	—
556	1.98	—	—	—	—	—	—	—	—	—	0.12	—	—	—	—	—	18	—	—

TABLE 14 Composition of Mineral Supplements; Data Expressed on an As-Fed and Dry Basis (100% Dry Matter)[a]

Entry Number	Feed Name Description	International Feed Number	Dry Matter (%)	Protein Equivalent N × 6.25 (%)	Calcium (Ca) (%)	Chlorine (Cl) (%)	Magnesium (Mg) (%)	Phosphorus (P) (%)	Potassium (K) (%)	Sodium (Na) (%)	Sulfur (S) (%)	Cobalt (Co) (mg/kg)	Copper (Cu) (mg/kg)	Fluorine (F) (mg/kg)	Iodine (I) (mg/kg)	Iron (Fe) (mg/kg)	Manganese (Mn) (mg/kg)	Selenium (Se) (mg/kg)	Zinc (Zn) (mg/kg)
	AMMONIUM																		
01	phosphate, monobasic, $(NH_4)H_2PO_4$ (monoammonium phosphate)	6-09-338	97	68.8	0.27	—	0.45	24.00	0.01	0.06	1.42	10	10	2,400	—	16,900	388	—	97
02			100	70.9	0.28	—	0.46	24.74	0.01	0.06	1.46	10	10	2,500	—	17,400	400	—	100
03	phosphate, dibasic, $(NH_4)_2H_2PO_4$ (diammonium phosphate)	6-00-370	97	112.4	0.50	—	0.45	20.00	0.01	0.05	2.10	—	10	2,037	—	12,028	388	—	97
04		6-09-339	100	115.9	0.52	—	0.46	20.60	0.01	0.05	2.16	—	10	2,100	—	12,400	400	—	100
05	sulfate		100	134.1	—	—	—	—	—	—	24.10	—	1	—	—	10	1	—	—
06			100	134.1	—	—	—	—	—	—	24.10	—	1	—	—	10	1	—	—
	BONE																		
07	charcoal (bone black) (bone char)	6-00-402	90	—	27.10	—	0.53	12.73	0.14	—	—	—	—	—	—	—	—	—	—
08			100	—	30.11	—	0.59	14.14	0.16	—	—	—	—	—	—	—	—	—	—
09	meal, steamed	6-00-400	97	8.1	30.58	0.01	0.62	13.79	0.18	0.39	0.20	—	14	—	30	757	33	—	332
10			100	8.4	31.53	0.01	0.64	14.22	0.19	0.40	0.21	—	14	—	31	780	34	—	342
	CALCIUM																		
11	carbonate, $CaCO_3$	6-01-069	100	—	39.39	—	0.05	0.04	0.06	0.06	0.09	—	—	—	—	300	300	—	—
12			100	—	39.39	—	0.05	0.04	0.06	0.06	0.09	—	—	—	—	300	300	—	—
13	phosphate, monobasic, from defluorinated phosphoric acid (monocalcium phosphate)	6-01-082	97	—	15.91	—	0.59	20.95	0.08	0.06	1.19	10	10	2,000	—	15,300	350	—	87
14			100	—	16.40	—	0.61	21.60	0.08	0.06	1.22	10	10	2,100	—	15,800	360	—	90
15	phosphate, dibasic, from defluorinated phosphoric acid (dicalcium phosphate)	6-01-080	97	—	21.30	—	0.57	18.70	0.07	0.05	1.11	10	10	1,746	—	14,000	291	—	97
16			100	—	22.00	—	0.59	19.30	0.07	0.05	1.14	10	10	1,800	—	14,400	300	—	100
17	sulfate, anhydrous (gypsum), $CaSO_4$	6-01-087	85	—	22.02	—	2.21	0.01	—	—	20.01	—	—	—	—	1,710	—	—	—
18			100	—	25.90	—	2.61	0.01	—	—	23.54	—	—	—	—	2,010	—	—	—
	COBALT																		
19	carbonate, $CoCO_3$	6-01-566	99[b]	—	—	—	—	—	—	—	0.20	4,554	—	—	—	490	—	—	—
20			100	—	—	—	—	—	—	—	0.20	4,600	—	—	—	500	—	—	—
	COLLOIDAL																		
21	clay (soft rock phosphate)	6-03-947	99[b]	—	17.00	—	0.38	9.00	—	0.10	—	—	—	14,900	—	19,000	—	—	—
22			100	—	17.17	—	0.38	9.09	—	0.10	—	—	—	15,000	—	19,200	—	—	—
	COPPER (CUPRIC)																		
23	sulfate, pentahydrate $CuSO_4 \cdot 5H_2O$, cp[c]	6-01-720	100	—	—	—	—	—	—	—	12.84	—	254,500	—	—	—	—	—	—
24			100	—	—	—	—	—	—	—	12.84	—	254,500	—	—	—	—	—	—
	CURACAO																		
25	phosphate	6-05-586	99[b]	—	34.00	—	0.80	14.00	—	0.20	—	—	—	5,400	—	3,465	—	—	—
26			100	—	34.34	—	0.81	14.14	—	0.20	—	—	—	5,500	—	3,500	—	—	—
	IRON (FERROUS)																		
27	sulfate, heptahydrate	6-20-734	98[b]	—	—	—	—	—	—	—	12.10	—	—	—	—	214,000	—	—	—
28			100	—	—	—	—	—	—	—	12.35	—	—	—	—	218,400	—	—	—

No.	Ingredient	IFN No.	DM %	Ca	Cl	Mg	P	K	Na	S	Co	Cu	F	I	Fe	Mn	Se	Zn
	LIMESTONE																	
29	limestone	6-02-632	98	33.32	0.03	2.02	0.02	0.12	0.06	0.04	—	—	—	—	3,430	—	—	—
30			100	34.00	0.03	2.06	0.02	0.12	0.06	0.04	—	—	—	—	3,500	—	—	—
31	magnesium (dolomitic)	6-02-633	99[b]	22.08	0.12	9.89	0.04	0.36	—	—	—	—	—	—	760	—	—	—
32			100	22.30	0.12	9.99	0.04	0.36	—	—	—	—	—	—	770	—	—	—
	MAGNESIUM																	
33	carbonate, $MgCO_3Mg(OH)_2$	6-02-754	98[b]	0.02	0.00	30.20	—	—	—	—	—	—	—	—	210	—	—	—
34			100	0.02	0.00	30.81	—	—	—	—	—	—	—	—	220	—	—	—
35	oxide, MgO	6-02-756	98	3.00	—	54.90	—	—	—	—	—	—	—	—	—	98	—	—
36			100	3.07	—	56.20	—	—	—	—	—	—	—	—	—	100	—	—
	MANGANESE (MANGANOUS)																	
37	oxide, MnO, cp[c]	6-03-056	99[b]	—	—	—	—	—	—	—	—	—	—	—	—	766,700	—	—
38			100	—	—	—	—	—	—	—	—	—	—	—	—	774,500	—	—
	OYSTERSHELL																	
39	ground (flour)	6-03-481	99	37.62	0.01	0.30	0.07	0.10	0.21	—	—	—	—	—	2,840	99	—	—
40			100	38.00	0.01	0.30	0.07	0.10	0.21	—	—	—	—	—	2,870	100	—	—
	PHOSPHATE																	
41	defluorinated	6-01-780	100	32.00	—	0.42	18.00	0.08	4.90	—	10	20	1,800	—	6,700	200	—	60
42			100	32.00	—	0.42	18.00	0.08	4.90	—	10	20	1,800	—	6,700	200	—	60
	POTASSIUM																	
43	bicarbonate, $KHCO_3$, cp[c]	6-29-493	99[b]	—	—	—	—	38.65	—	—	—	—	—	—	—	—	—	—
44			100	—	—	—	—	39.05	—	—	—	—	—	—	—	—	—	—
45	iodide, KI	6-03-759	100[b]	—	—	—	—	21.00	—	—	—	—	—	681,700	—	—	—	—
46			100	—	—	—	—	21.00	—	—	—	—	—	681,700	—	—	—	—
	SODIUM																	
47	bicarbonate, $NaHCO_3$	6-04-272	100	—	—	—	—	—	27.00	—	—	—	—	—	—	—	—	—
48			100	—	—	—	—	—	27.00	—	—	—	—	—	—	—	—	—
49	chloride, NaCl	6-04-152	100	—	60.66	—	—	—	39.34	—	—	—	—	—	—	—	—	—
50			100	—	60.66	—	—	—	39.34	—	—	—	—	—	—	—	—	—
51	phosphate, monobasic, monohydrate, $NaH_2PO_4 \cdot H_2O$ (monosodium phosphate)	6-04-288	97	—	—	·	21.80	—	16.18	—	—	—	—	—	—	—	—	—
52			100	—	—	—	22.50	—	16.68	—	—	—	—	—	—	—	—	—
53	selenite, Na_2SeO_3	6-26-013	98[b]	—	—	—	—	—	26.07	—	—	—	—	—	—	—	447,000	—
54			100	—	—	—	—	—	26.60	—	—	—	—	—	—	—	456,000	—
55	sulfate decahydrate, $Na_2SO_4 \cdot 10H_2O$, cp[c]	6-04-292	97[b]	—	—	—	—	—	13.84	9.65	—	—	—	—	—	—	—	—
56			100	—	—	—	—	—	14.27	9.95	—	—	—	—	—	—	—	—
57	tripolyphosphate, $Na_5P_3O_{10}$	6-08-076	96	—	—	—	24.00	—	29.80	—	—	—	—	—	38	—	—	—
58			100	—	—	—	25.00	—	31.00	—	—	—	—	—	40	—	—	—
	ZINC																	
59	oxide, ZnO	6-05-553	100	—	—	0.05	—	—	—	—	—	—	—	—	—	1.0	—	780,000
60			100	—	—	0.05	—	—	—	—	—	—	—	—	—	1.0	—	780,000
61	sulfate, monohydrate, $ZnSO_4 \cdot H_2O$	6-05-555	99[b]	0.02	0.015	—	—	—	—	17.50	—	—	—	—	10	10	—	360,000
62			100	0.02	0.015	—	—	—	—	17.68	—	—	—	—	10	10	—	363,600

[a] The composition of mineral ingredients that are hydrated (e.g., $CaSO_4 \cdot 2H_2O$) is shown, including the waters of hydration. Mineral composition of feed grade mineral supplements vary by source, mining site, and manufacturer. Use manufacturer's analysis when available.

[b] Dry matter values have been estimated for these minerals.

[c] cp = Chemically pure.

TABLE 15 Stage-of-Maturity Terms Used in Table 13

Preferred Term	Definition	Comparable Terms
For Plants That Bloom		
Germinated	Stage in which the embryo in a seed resumes growth after a dormant period	Sprouted
Early vegetative	Stage at which the plant is vegetative and before the stems elongate	Fresh new growth, before heading out, before inflorescence emergence, immature prebud stage, very immature, young
Late vegetative	Stage at which stems are beginning to elongate to just before blooming; first bud to first flowers	Before bloom, bud stage, budding plants, heading to in bloom, heads just showing, jointing and boot (grasses), prebloom, preflowering, stems elongated
Early bloom	Stage between initiation of bloom and stage in which 1/10 of the plants are in bloom; some grass heads are in anthesis	Early anthesis, first flower, headed out, in head, up to 1/10 bloom
Midbloom	Stage in which 1/10 to 2/3 of the plants are in bloom; most grass heads are in anthesis	Bloom, flowering, flowering plants, half bloom, in bloom, mid anthesis
Full bloom	Stage in which 2/3 or more of the plants are in bloom	3/4 to full bloom, late anthesis
Late bloom	Stage in which blossoms begin to dry and fall and seeds begin to form	15 days after silking, before milk, in bloom to early pod, late to past anthesis
Milk stage	Stage in which seeds are well formed but soft and immature	After anthesis, early seed, fruiting, in tassel, late bloom to early seed, past bloom, pod stage, post anthesis, post bloom, seed developing, seed forming, soft, soft immature
Dough stage	Stage in which the seeds are of dough-like consistency	Dough stage, nearly mature, seeds dough, seeds well developed, soft dent
Mature	Stage in which plants are normally harvested for seed	Dent, dough to glazing, fruiting, fruiting plants, in seed, kernels ripe, ripe seed
Post ripe	Stage that follows maturity; seeds are ripe and plants have been cast and weathering has taken place (applies mostly to range plants)	Late, seed, over ripe, very mature
Stem cured	Stage in which plants are cured on the stem; seeds have been cast and weathering has taken place (applies mostly to range plants)	Dormant, mature and weathered, seeds cast
Regrowth early vegetative	Stage in which regrowth occurs without flowering activity; vegetative crop aftermath; regrowth in stubble (applies primarily to fall regrowth in temperate climates); early dry season regrowth	Vegetative recovery growth
Regrowth late vegetative	Stage in which stems begin to elongate to just before blooming; first bud to first flowers; regrowth in stubble with stem elongation (applies primarily to fall regrowth in temperate climates)	Recovery growth, stems elongating, jointing and boot (grasses)
For Plants That Do Not Bloom[a]		
1 to 14 days' growth	A specified length of time after plants have started to grow	2 weeks' growth
15 to 28 days' growth	A specified length of time after plants have started to grow	4 weeks' growth
29 to 42 days' growth	A specified length of time after plants have started to grow	6 weeks' growth
43 to 56 days' growth	A specified length of time after plants have started to grow	8 weeks' growth
57 to 70 days' growth	A specified length of time after plants have started to grow	10 weeks' growth

[a]These classes are for species that remain vegetative for long periods and apply primarily to the tropics. When the name of a feed is developed, the age classes form part of the name (e.g., Pangolagrass, 15 to 28 days' growth). Do not use terms which apply to plants that bloom and those which do not bloom in same name. For plants growing longer than 70 days, the interval is increased by increments of 14 days.

TABLE 16   Weight-Unit Conversion Factors

Units Given	Units Wanted	For Conversion Multiply by
lb	g	453.6
lb	kg	0.4536
oz	g	28.35
kg	lb	2.2046
kg	mg	1,000,000.
kg	g	1,000.
g	mg	1,000.
g	μg	1,000,000.
mg	μg	1,000.
mg/g	mg/lb	453.6
mg/kg	mg/lb	0.4536
μg/kg	μg/lb	0.4536
Mcal	kcal	1,000.
kcal/kg	kcal/lb	0.4536
kcal/lb	kcal/kg	2.2046
ppm	μg/g	1.
ppm	mg/kg	1.
ppm	mg/lb	0.4536
mg/kg	%	0.0001
ppm	%	0.0001
mg/g	%	0.1
g/kg	%	0.1

TABLE 17   Weight Equivalents

1 lb = 453.6 g = 0.4536 kg = 16 oz
1 oz = 28.35 g
1 kg = 1,000 g = 2.2046 lb
1 g = 1,000 mg
1 mg = 1,000 μg = 0.001 g
1 μg = 0.001 mg = 0.000001 g
1 μg per g or 1 mg per kg is the same as ppm

References

NUTRIENT REQUIREMENTS AND SIGNS
OF DEFICIENCY

Energy

Agricultural Research Council. 1980. The Nutrient Requirements of Ruminant Livestock. Slough: Commonwealth Agricultural Bureaux.

Ames, D. R. 1969. Normal Responses of Sheep to Acute Thermal Stress. Ph.D. dissertation. Michigan State University, East Lansing.

Andrews, R. P., M. Kay, and E. R. Ørskov. 1969. The effect of different dietary energy concentrations on the voluntary intake and growth of intensively fed lambs. Anim. Prod. 11:73.

Andrews, R. P., and E. R. Ørskov. 1970. The nutrition of the early weaned lamb. II. The effect of dietary protein concentration, feeding level and sex on body composition at two live weights. J. Agric. Sci. 75:19.

Arehart, L. A., Jr., J. M. Lewis, F. C. Hinds, and M. E. Mansfield. 1969. Space allowances for lambs on slotted floors. J. Anim. Sci. 29:638.

Arehart, L. A., Jr., J. M. Lewis, F. C. Hinds, and M. E. Mansfield. 1972. Space allowance for lactating ewes confined to slotted floors when penned with single or twin lambs. J. Anim. Sci. 34:180.

Arnold, G. W., and M. L. Dudzinski. 1967. Studies on the diet of the grazing animal. 2. The effect of physiological status in ewes and pasture availability on herbage intake. Aust. J. Agric. Res. 18:349.

Bergman, E. N., and D. E. Hogue. 1967. Glucose turnover and oxidation rates in lactating sheep. Am. J. Physiol. 213:1378.

Black, J. L. 1974. Manipulation of body composition through nutrition. Proc. Aust. Soc. Anim. Prod. 10:211.

Blaxter, K. L. 1966. The Energy Metabolism of Ruminants. Springfield, Ill.: Charles C Thomas.

Blaxter, K. L., and A. W. Boyne. 1978. The estimation of the nutritive value of feeds as energy sources for ruminants and the derivation of feeding systems. J. Agric. Sci. 90:47.

Blaxter, K. L., and A. W. Boyne. 1982. Fasting and maintenance metabolism of sheep. J. Agric. Sci. 99:611.

Blaxter, K. L., and F. W. Wainman. 1964. The utilization of energy of different rations by sheep and cattle for maintenance and for fattening. J. Agric. Sci. 63:113.

Blaxter, K. L., J. L. Clapperton, and F. W. Wainman. 1966. The extent of differences between six British breeds of sheep in their metabolism, feed intake and utilization, and resistance to climatic stress. Br. J. Nutr. 20:283.

Brink, D. R., and D. R. Ames. 1975. Effect of ambient temperature on lamb performance. J. Anim. Sci. 41:264. (Abstr.)

Brockway, J. M., J. D. Pullar, and J. D. McDonald. 1969. Direct and indirect calorimetric techniques for the evaluation of the expenditure of standing and lying sheep. Pp. 423-427 in Energy Metabolism of Farm Animals, K. L. Blaxter, J. Kielanowski, and G. Thorbek, eds. Newcastle-upon-Tyne, England: Oriel Press Ltd.

Bull, L. S., J. T. Reid, and D. E. Johnson. 1970. Energetics of sheep concerned with the utilization of acetic acid. J. Nutr. 100:262.

Burton, J. H., and J. T. Reid. 1969. Interrelationship among energy input, body size, age and body composition in sheep. J. Nutr. 97:517.

Chiou, P. W. S., and R. M. Jordan. 1973. Ewe milk replacer diets for young lambs. 4. Protein and energy requirements of young lambs. J. Anim. Sci. 37:581.

Christopherson, R. J., and P. M. Kennedy. 1983. Effect of the thermal environment on digestion in ruminants. Can. J. Anim. Sci. 63:477.

Clapperton, J. L. 1964a. The effect of walking upon the utilization of food by sheep. Br. J. Nutr. 18:39.

Clapperton, J. L. 1964b. The energy metabolism of sheep walking on the level and on gradient. Br. J. Nutr. 18:47.

Clarke, R. A., and W. K. Roberts. 1967. Ruminal and fecal fatty acids and apparent ration digestibility in lambs as affected by dietary fatty acids. Can. J. Anim. Sci. 47:31.

Cook, C. W., L. A. Stoddart, and L. E. Harris. 1952. Determining the digestibility and metabolizable energy of winter range plants by sheep. J. Anim. Sci. 11:578.

Coop, I. E. 1962. The energy requirements of sheep for maintenance and gain. 2. Pen fed sheep. J. Agric. Sci. 58:179.

Coop, I. E., and M. K. Hill. 1962. The energy requirements of sheep for maintenance and gain. 2. Grazing sheep. J. Agric. Sci. 58:187.

Corbett, J. L., R. A. Leng, and B. A. Young. 1969. Measurement of energy expenditure by grazing sheep and the amount of energy supplied by volatile fatty acids produced in the rumen. Pp. 177-186 in Energy Metabolism of Farm Animals, K. L. Blaxter, J. Kielanowski, and G. Thorbek, eds. Newcastle-upon-Tyne, England: Oriel Press Ltd.

Curtis, S. E. 1981. Environmental management in animal agriculture. Animal Environment Services, Mohamet, Ill.

Doane, B. B., U. S. Garrigus, E. E. Hatfield, and H. W. Norton. 1962. Hand-fed corn silage ration compared with self-fed rations containing roughage, largely corncob or oat hay, for wintering bred and lactating ewes. University of Illinois, Urbana, Anim. Sci. Mimeo. AS-582, pp. 30-35.

Drew, K. R., and J. T. Reid. 1975a. Compensatory growth in immature sheep. I. Effects of weight loss and realimentation on whole body composition. J. Agric. Sci. 85:193.

Drew, K. R., and J. T. Reid. 1975b. Compensatory growth in immature sheep. II. Some changes in the physical and chemical composition of sheep. J. Agric. Sci. 85:201.

Egan, A. R. 1965. Nutritional status and intake regulation in sheep. 3. The relationship between improvement of nitrogen status and increase in voluntary intake of low-protein roughages by sheep. Aust. J. Agric. Res. 16:463.

Farrell, D. J., R. A. Leng, and J. L. Corbett. 1972. Undernutrition in grazing sheep. I. Changes in the composition of the body, blood and rumen contents. Aust. J. Agric. Res. 23:483.

Ferrell, C. L., J. D. Crouse, R. A. Field, and J. L. Chant. 1979. Effects of sex, diet, and stage of growth upon energy utilization by lambs. J. Anim. Sci. 49:790.

Gardner, R. W., and D. E. Hogue. 1964. Effects of energy intake and number of lambs suckled on milk yield, milk composition and energetic efficiency of lactating ewes. J. Anim. Sci. 23:935.

Garrett, W. N. 1980. Energy utilization of growing cattle as determined in 72 comparative slaughter experiments. P. 3 in Energy Metabolism, L. E. Mount, ed. EAAP Publ. No. 26.

Garrett, W. N., J. H. Meyer, and G. P. Lofgreen. 1959. The comparative energy requirements of sheep and cattle for maintenance and gain. J. Anim. Sci. 18:528.

Garrigus, U. S. 1967. Influence of management and nutrition on "consumer-preferred lamb." J. Anim. Sci. 26:89.

Garrigus, U. S. 1970. Self-feeding breeding ewes. University of Illinois, Urbana, Anim. Sci. Mimeo. AS-659.

Graham, N. McC. 1967. The metabolic rate of fasting sheep in relation to total and lean body weight and the estimation of maintenance requirements. Aust. J. Agric. Res. 18:127.

Graham, N. McC. 1968. Effects of undernutrition in late pregnancy on the nitrogen and energy metabolism of ewes. Aust. J. Agric. Res. 19:555-565.

Graham, N. McC., and T. W. Searle. 1972. Balances of energy and matter in growing sheep at several ages, body weights, and planes of nutrition. Aust. J. Agric. Res. 23:97.

Graham, N. McC., and T. W. Searle. 1982. Energy and nitrogen utilization for body growth in young sheep from two breeds with differing capacities for wool growth. Aust. J. Agric. Res. 33:607.

Hutchinson, J. C. D. 1968. Deaths of sheep after shearing. Aust. J. Exp. Agric. Anim. Husb. 8:393.

Johnson, D. E. 1972. Heat increment of acetate and corn and effects of casein infusions with growing lambs. J. Nutr. 102:1093.

Jordan, R. M. 1966. Effect of energy as supplied by hay or high concentrate rations and frequency of feeding on the performance of ewes. J. Anim. Sci. 25:624.

Jordan, R. M., and H. E. Hanke. 1977. Effect of level of grain fed ewes during late lactation on lamb production. J. Anim. Sci. 45:945.

Jordan, R. M., H. E. Hanke, G. C. Marten, and J. W. Rust. 1968. Year-round sheep nutrition and feeding programs. Minn. Agric. Exp. Stn. Bull. 489.

Joyce, J. P., and K. L. Blaxter. 1965. The effect of wind on heat losses of sheep. Pp. 355-367 in Energy Metabolism, K. L. Blaxter, ed. New York: Academic Press.

Joyce, J. P., K. L. Blaxter, and C. Park. 1966. The effect of natural outdoor environments on the energy requirements of sheep. Res. Vet. Sci. 7:342.

Kelloway, R. C. 1973. The effects of plane of nutrition, genotype and sex on growth, body composition and wool production in grazing sheep. J. Agric. Sci. 80:17.

Koong, L. J., C. L. Ferrell, and J. A. Nienaber. 1982. Effects of plane of nutrition on organ size and fasting heat production in swine and sheep. P. 245 in Energy Metabolism of Farm Animals, A. Ekern and F. Sundskol, eds. Proc. 9th Symp. on Energy Metabolism, EAAP Publ. No. 29.

Langlands, J. P., J. L. Corbett, I. McDonald, and J. D. Pullar. 1963a. Estimates of energy required for maintenance by adult sheep. 1. Housed sheep. Anim. Prod. 5:1.

Langlands, J. P., J. L. Corbett, I. McDonald, and G. W. Reid. 1963b. Estimates of the energy required for maintenance by adult sheep. 2. Grazing sheep. Anim. Prod. 5:11.

Lofgreen, G. P., and W. N. Garrett. 1968. A system for expressing net energy requirements and feed values for growing and finishing beef cattle. J. Anim. Sci. 27:793.

Mansfield, M. E., J. M. Lewis, and G. E. McKibben. 1967. Rearing lambs free of gastrointestinal nematodes. J. Am. Vet. Med. Assoc. 151:1182.

Modyanov, A. V. 1969. Energy metabolism in sheep under different physiological conditions. Pp. 171-176 in Energy Metabolism of Farm Animals, K. L. Blaxter, J. Kielanowski, and G. Thorbek, eds. Newcastle-upon-Tyne, England: Oriel Press Ltd.

Monteath, M. A. 1971. The effect of sub-maintenance feeding of ewes during mid-pregnancy on lamb and wool production. Proc. N. Z. Soc. Anim. Prod. 31:105.

National Research Council. 1975. Nutrient Requirements of Sheep. Washington, D.C.: National Academy of Sciences.

National Research Council. 1981. Effect of Environment on Nutrient Requirements of Domestic Animals. Washington, D.C.: National Academy Press.

Owen, J. B. 1971. Complete diets for ruminants. Agriculture (August): 331-333.

Paladines, O. L., and M. Giergoff. 1969. Use of an indirect approach for the measurement of the energy value of pasture by grazing sheep. Pp.253-260 in Energy Metabolism of Farm Animals, K. L. Blaxter, J. Kielanowski, and G. Thorbek, eds. Newcastle-upon-Tyne, England: Oriel Press Ltd.

Panaretto, B. A. 1968. Some metabolic effects of cold stress on undernourished non-pregnant ewes. Aust. J. Agric. Res. 19:273.

Parker, C. F., and C. B. Boyles. 1970. Bi-weekly vs. daily winter-feeding of ewes during early and mid-gestation. Ohio Agric. Res. Dev. Ctr. Res. Summ. 42:27.

Parker, C. F., and A. L. Pope. 1983. The U.S. sheep industry: Changes and challenges. J. Anim. Sci. 57(Suppl. 2):75.

Pattie, W. A., and A. J. Williams. 1967. Selection for weaning weight in Merino sheep. 3. Maintenance requirements and the efficiency of conversion of feed to wool in mature ewes. Aust. J. Exp. Agric. Anim. Husb. 7:117.

Rattray, P. V., W. N. Garrett, N. E. East, and N. Hinman. 1973a. Net energy requirements of ewe lambs for maintenance, gain and pregnancy and net energy values of feedstuffs for lambs. J. Anim. Sci. 37:853.

Rattray, P. V., W. N. Garrett, N. Hinman, I. Garcia, and J. Castillo. 1973b. A system for expressing the net energy requirements and net energy content of feeds for young sheep. J. Anim. Sci. 36:115.

Rattray, P. V., W. N. Garrett, H. H. Meyer, G. E. Bradford, N. Hinman, and N. E. East. 1973c. Net energy requirements for growth of lambs age three to five months. J. Anim. Sci. 37:1386.

Rattray, P. V., W. N. Garrett, N. E. East, and N. Hinman. 1974. Efficiency of utilization of metabolizable energy during pregnancy and energy requirements for pregnancy in sheep. J. Anim. Sci. 38:383.

Reid, J. T., A. Bensadoun, L. S. Bull, J. H. Burton. P. A. Gleeson, I. K. Han, Y. D. Joo, D. E. Johnson, W. R. McManus, O. L. Paladines, J. W. Stroud, H. F. Tyrrell, B. D. H. Van Niekerk, and G. W. Wellington. 1968. Some peculiarities in the body composition of animals. Pp. 19-44 in Body Composition of Animals and Man. Publ. No. 1598. Washington, D.C.: National Academy of Sciences.

Slee, J., and M. L. Ryder. 1967. The effect of cold exposure on wool growth in Scottish Blackface and Merino × Cheviot sheep. J. Agric. Sci. 69:449.

Theriez, M., Y. Villette, and C. Castrillo. 1982a. Influence of metabolizable energy content of the diet and of feeding level on lamb performance. I. Growth and body composition. Livestock Prod. Sci. 9:471.

Theriez, M., C. Castrillo, and Y. Villette. 1982b. Influence of metabolizable energy content of the diet and of feeding level on lamb performance. II. Utilization of metabolizable energy for growth and fattening. Livestock Prod. Sci. 9:487.

Ulyatt, M. J., K. L. Blaxter, and I. McDonald. 1967. The relation between the apparent digestibility of roughages in the rumen and lower gut of sheep, the volume of fluid in the rumen and voluntary feed intake. Anim. Prod. 9:463.

Webster, M. E. D., and K. G. Johnson. 1968. Some aspects of body temperature regulation in sheep. J. Agric. Sci. 71:61.

Webster, M. E. D., and J. J. Lynch. 1966. Some physiological and behavioural consequences of shearing. Aust. Soc. Anim. Prod. Bull. 6:234.

Young, B. A., and J. L. Corbett. 1972. Maintenance energy requirement of grazing sheep in relation to herbage availability. I. Calorimetric estimates. Aust. J. Agric. Res. 23:57.

Protein

Agricultural Research Council. 1980. The Nutrient Requirements of Ruminant Livestock. Commonwealth Agricultural Bureaux. Surrey: The Gresham Press.

Allison, M. S. 1969. Biosynthesis of amino acids by ruminant microorganisms. J. Anim. Sci. 29:797.

Amos, H. E., D. Burdick, and T. L. Huber. 1974. Effects of formaldehyde treatment of sunflower and soybean meal on nitrogen balance in lambs. J. Anim. Sci. 38:702.

Armstrong, D. G., and E. F. Annison. 1973. Amino acid requirements and amino acid supply in the sheep. Proc. Nutr. Soc. 32:107.

Bartley, E. E., T. B. Avery, T. G. Nagaraja, B. R. Watt, A. Davidovich, S. Galitzer, and B. Lassman. 1981. Ammonia toxicity in cattle. V. Ammonia concentration of lymph and portal, carotid and jugular blood after the ingestion of urea. J. Anim. Sci. 53:494.

Bartley, E. E., A. Davidovich, G. W. Barr, G. W. Griffel, A. D. Dayton, D. W. Deyoe, and R. M. Bechtle. 1976. Ammonia toxicity in cattle. I. Rumen and blood changes associated with toxicity and treatment methods. J. Anim. Sci. 43:835.

Bhattacharya, A. N., and A. R. Khan. 1973. Wheat straw and urea in pelleted rations for growing-fattening sheep. J. Anim. Sci. 37:136.

Bhattacharya, A. N., and E. Pervez. 1973. Effect of urea supplementation on intake and utilization of diets containing low quality roughages in sheep. J. Anim. Sci. 36:976.

Black, A. L., M. Kleiber, A. H. Smith, and P. N. Stewart. 1957. Acetate as a precursor of amino acids of casein in the intact dairy cow. Biochim. Biophys. Acta 23:54.

Black, J. L., G. R. Pearce, and D. E. Tribe. 1973. Protein requirements of growing lambs. Br. J. Nutr. 30:45.

Black, J. L., G. E. Robards, and R. Thomas. 1973. Effects of protein and energy intakes on the wool growth of Merino wethers. Aust. J. Agric. Res. 24:339.

Bouchard, R., and G. J. Brisson. 1969. Changes in protein fractions of ewes' milk throughout lactation. Can. J. Anim. Sci. 48:143.

Briggs, M. H., ed. 1967. Urea as a Protein Supplement. New York: Pergamon Press.

Brisson, G. J., and J. P. Lemay. 1968. Comparison between rations of different protein: Energy ratio for lambs weaned at three or fifteen days of age. Can. J. Anim. Sci. 48:307.

Brooks, I. M., F. N. Owens, R. E. Brown, and U. S. Garrigus. 1973. Amino acid oxidation and plasma amino acid levels in sheep with abomasal infusions of graded amounts of lysine. J. Anim. Sci. 36:965.

Broster, W. H. 1973. Protein-energy interrelationships in growth and lactation of cattle and sheep. Proc. Nutr. Soc. 32:115.

Bryant, M. P., and I. M. Robinson. 1963. Apparent incorporation of ammonia and amino acid carbon during growth of selected species of ruminal bacteria. J. Dairy Sci. 46:150.

Carver, L. A., and W. H. Pfander. 1973. Urea utilization by sheep in the presence of potassium nitrate. J. Anim. Sci. 36:581.

Chalupa, W. 1972. Metabolic aspects of nonprotein nitrogen utilization in ruminant animals. Fed. Proc. 31:1152.

Chalupa, W. 1973. Utilization of nonprotein nitrogen in the production of animal protein. Proc. Nutr. Soc. 32:99.

Chalupa, W. 1975. Rumen bypass and protection of proteins and amino acids. J. Dairy Sci. 58:1198.

Chalupa, W. 1984. Symposium: Protein nutrition of the lactating dairy cow: Discussion. J. Dairy Sci. 67:1134.

Clemens, E. T., and R. R. Johnson. 1973. Biuretolytic activity of rumen microorganisms as influenced by the frequency of feeding biuret supplement. J. Anim. Sci. 37:1027.

Cowan, R. T., J. J. Robinson, I. McHattie, and K. Pennie. 1981. Effects of protein concentration in the diet on milk yield, change in body composition and the efficiency of utilization of body tissue for milk production in ewes. Anim. Prod. 33:111.

Crampton, E. W. 1964. Nutrient-to-calorie ratios in applied nutrition. J. Nutr. 82:353.

Daniels, L. B., M. E. Muhrer, J. R. Campbell, and F. A. Martz. 1971. Feeding heated urea-cellulose preparations to ruminants. J. Anim. Sci. 32:348.

Davies, P. J. 1968. The effect of cereal and protein source on the energy intake and nitrogen balance of fattening lambs given all-concentrate diets. Anim. Prod. 10:311.

Digenis, G. A., H. E. Amos, K. Yang, G. E. Mitchell, Jr., C. O. Little, J. V. Swintoski, R. C. Parish, G. T. Schelling, E. M. Dretz, and R. E. Tucker. 1974. Methionine substitutes in ruminant nutrition. I. Stability of nitrogenous compounds related to methionine during vitro incubation with rumen microorganisms. J. Pharmacol. Sci. 63:744.

Downes, A. M. 1961. On the amino acids essential for the tissues of the sheep. Aust. J. Biol. Sci. 14:254.

Driedger, A., and E. E. Hatfield. 1972. Influence of tannins on the nutritive value of soybean meal for ruminants. J. Anim. Sci. 34:456.

Egan, A. R. 1965. The influence of sustained duodenal infusions of casein or urea upon voluntary intake of low-protein roughages by sheep. Aust. J. Agric. Res. 16:451.

Eskeland, B., W. H. Pfander, and R. L. Preston. 1973. Utilization of volatile fatty acids and glucose for protein deposition in lambs. Br. J. Nutr. 29:347.

Eskeland, B., W. H. Pfander, and R. L. Preston. 1974. Intravenous energy infusion: Effects on nitrogen retention, plasma free amino acids and plasma urea nitrogen. Br. J. Nutr. 31:201.

Faichney, G. J., and R. H. Weston. 1971. Digestion by ruminant lambs of a diet containing formaldehyde-treated casein. Aust. J. Agric. Res. 22:461.

Farlin, S. D., U. S. Garrigus, and E. E. Hatfield. 1968. Changes in metabolism of biuret during adjustment to a biuret-supplemented diet. J. Anim. Sci. 27:785.

Fenderson, C. L., and W. G. Bergen. 1976. Effect of excess dietary protein on feed intake and nitrogen metabolism in steers. J. Anim. Sci. 42:1323.

Ferguson, K. A., J. A. Hemsley, and P. J. Reis. 1967. Nutrition and wool growth. Aust. J. Sci. 30:215.

Fick, K. R., C. B. Ammerman, C. H. McGowan, P. E. Loggins, and J. A. Cornell. 1973. Influence of supplemental energy and biuret nitrogen on the utilization of low quality roughage by sheep. J. Anim. Sci. 36:137.

Garrigus, U. S. 1968. Conversion of nonprotein nitrogen to animal protein for human consumption. Ill. Agric. Exp. Stn. Spec. Publ. 12:19.

Garrigus, U. S. 1968. Less expensive protein (nitrogen) for sheep diets. Pp. 115-140 *in* Sheep Nutrition and Feeding. Proceedings of a symposium. Iowa State University, Ames.

Gonzalez, J. S., J. J. Robinson, I. McHattie, and C. Fraser. 1982. The effect in ewes of source and level of dietary protein on milk yield and the relationship between the intestinal supply of non-ammonium nitrogen and the production of milk protein. Anim. Prod. 34:31.

Hanke, H. E. and R. M. Jordan. 1983. Lamb response to various protein supplements when fed in conjunction with either alfalfa hay or corn silage. Proc. 55th Sheep Rep. University of Minnesota, St. Paul.

Hatfield, E. E. 1970. Selected topics related to the amino acid nutrition of the growing ruminant. Fed. Proc. 29:44.

Hatfield, E. E., U. S. Garrigus, R. M. Forbes, A. L. Neumann, and W. Gaither. 1959. Biuret—a source of NPN for ruminants. J. Anim. Sci. 18:1208.

Hinman, D. D., and R. R. Johnson. 1973. Zero time rate technique for evaluating nitrogen supplements for high roughage rations. J. Anim. Sci. 36:571.

Hogan, J. P. 1975. Quantitative aspects of nitrogen utilization in ruminants. J. Dairy Sci. 58:1164.

Hogan, J. P., and R. H. Weston. 1967. The digestion of two diets of differing protein content but with similar capacities to sustain wool growth. Aust. J. Agric. Res. 19:973.

Hogue, D. E. 1967. Protein requirements of lactating ewes. Pp. 118-122 *in* Cornell Nutr. Conf. Cornell University, Ithaca, N.Y.

Hogue, D. E. 1968. The nutritional requirements of lactating ewes. Pp. 32-39 *in* Sheep Nutrition and Feeding. Proceedings of a symposium. Iowa State University, Ames.

Hogue, D. E., C. J. Sniffen, and B. H. McGee. 1979. The effect of protein solubility on gain and efficiency of rapidly growing lambs. Pp. 98-101 *in* Cornell Nutr. Conf. Cornell University, Ithaca, N.Y.

Huber, J. T., and L. Kung, Jr. 1981. Protein and nonprotein nitrogen utilization in dairy cattle. J. Dairy Sci. 64:1170.

Hungate, R. E. 1966. The Rumen and Its Microbes. New York: Academic Press.

Jacobson, D. R., H. H. Van Horn, and C. J. Sniffen. 1970. Amino acids in ruminant nutrition. Lactating ruminants. Fed. Proc. 29:35.

Johnson, R. R. 1976. Influence of carbohydrate solubility on nonprotein nitrogen utilization in the ruminant. J. Anim. Sci. 43:184.

Johnson, R. R., and E. T. Clemens. 1973. Adaptation of rumen microorganisms to biuret as an NPN supplement to low quality roughage rations for cattle and sheep. J. Nutr. 103:494.

Jones, G. M., A. Cecyre, and J. M. Gaudreau. 1973. Effects of dietary protein and cellulose content of semipurified diets on voluntary feed intake and digestibility by sheep. Can. J. Anim. Sci. 53:445.

Jordan, R. M. 1953. Urea for pregnant ewes. S.D. Agric. Exp. Stn. Bull. 429.

Jordan, R. M., and H. E. Hanke. 1980. Effect of protein supplement source on lamb gains. 72nd Meet. Am. Soc. Anim. Sci. (Abstr. p. 373.)

Klosterman, E. W., D. W. Bolin, M. L. Buchanan, and W. E. Dinusson. 1953. Protein requirements of ewes during breeding and pregnancy. J. Anim. Sci. 12:451.

Knight, W. M., and F. N. Owens. 1973. Interval urea infusion for lambs. J. Anim. Sci. 36:145.

Kromann, R. P., A. E. Joyner, and J. E. Sharp. 1971. Influence of certain nutritional and physiological factors on urea toxicity in sheep. J. Anim. Sci. 32:732.

Leibholtz, J. 1972. II. The flow of amino acids into the duodenum from dietary and microbial sources. Aust. J. Agric. Res. 23:1073.

Leibholtz, J., and P. E. Hartmann. 1972. Nitrogen metabolism in sheep. I. The effect of protein and energy intake on the flow of digesta into the duodenum and on the digestion and absorption of nutrients. Aust. J. Agric. Res. 23:1059.

Leng, R. A., and J. V. Nolan. 1984. Nitrogen metabolism in the rumen. J. Dairy Sci. 67:1072.

LeRoy, R., S. Z. Zelter, and A. C. Francois. 1965. Protection of proteins in feeds against deaminization in the rumen. Nutr. Abstr. Rev. 35:444.

Little, C. O., and G. E. Mitchell, Jr. 1967. Abomasal vs. oral administration of proteins to wethers. J. Anim. Sci. 26:411.

Loosli, J. K., H. H. Williams, W. E. Thomas, F. H. Ferris, and L. A. Maynard. 1949. Synthesis of amino acids in the rumen. Science 110:144.

Ludwick, R. L., J. P. Fontenot, and R. E. Tucher. 1971. Studies of the adaptation phenomenon by lambs fed urea as the sole nitrogen source: Digestibility and nutrient balance. J. Anim. Sci. 331:1298.

McCarthy, R. D., R. A. Patton, and L. C. Griel, Jr. 1970. Amino acid nutrition of lactating ruminants. Fed. Proc. 29:41.

McIntyre, K. H. 1971. The effects of continuous intravenous and intraruminal infusion of urea on nitrogen metabolism in sheep. Aust. J. Agric. Res. 22:429.

McLaren, G. A., G. C. Anderson, L. I. Tsai, and K. M. Barth. 1965. Level of readily fermentable carbohydrates and adaptation of lambs to all-urea supplemental rations. J. Nutr. 87:331.

Moir, R. J., M. Somers, and A. C. Bray. 1967-1968. Utilization of dietary sulphur and nitrogen by ruminants. Sulphur Inst. J. 3:15.

National Research Council. 1975. Nutrient Requirements of Sheep. Washington, D.C.: National Academy of Sciences.

National Research Council. 1976. Nutrient Requirements of Beef Cattle. Washington, D.C.: National Academy of Sciences.

National Research Council. 1978. Nutrient Requirements of Dairy Cattle. Washington, D.C.: National Academy of Sciences.

National Research Council. 1984. Nutrient Requirements of Beef Cattle. Washington, D.C.: National Academy Press.

National Research Council. 1985. Ruminant Nitrogen Usage. Washington, D.C.: National Academy Press.

Neudoerffer, T. S., D. B. Duncan, and F. D. Horney. 1971. The extent of release of encapsulated methionine in the intestine of cattle. Br. J. Nutr. 25:343.

Nikolic, J. A., A. Pavlicevic, D. Zeremski, and D. Negovanovic. 1980. Adaptation to diets containing significant amounts of non-protein nitrogen. Pp. 603-620 *in* Digestive Physiology and Metabolism in Ruminants, Y. Ruckebusch and P. Thivend, eds. Westport, Conn.: AVI Publishing.

Nimrick, K. O., E. E. Hatfield, and F. N. Owens. 1970. Qualitative assessment of supplemental amino acid needs for growing lambs fed urea as the sole nitrogen source. J. Nutr. 100:1293.

Nolan, J. V., B. W. Norton, and R. A. Leng. 1973. Nitrogen cycling in sheep. Proc. Nutr. Soc. 32:93.

Oltjen, R. R. 1969. Effects of feeding ruminants non-protein nitrogen as the only nitrogen source. J. Anim. Sci. 29:673.

Ørskov, E. R. 1982. Protein Nutrition in Ruminants. New York: Academic Press.

Ørskov, E. R. 1983. Nutrition of lambs from birth to slaughter. Pp. 155-165 *in* Sheep Production. Proc. Nottingham Easter School. W. Haresign, ed. London: Butterworth.

Owens, F. N. ed. 1982. Protein Requirements for Cattle: Symposium. Oklahoma State University, Stillwater.

Owens, F. N., and W. G. Bergen. 1983. Nitrogen metabolism of ruminant animals: Historical perspective, current understanding and future implications. J. Anim. Sci. 57(Suppl. 2): 498.

Owens, F. N., W. M. Knight, and K. O. Nimrick. 1973. Intraruminal urea infusion and abomasal amino acid passage. J. Anim. Sci. 37:1000.

Pisulewski, P. M., A. J. Okome, P. J. Buttery, W. R. Haresign, and D. Lewis. 1981. Ammonia concentrations and protein synthesis in the rumen. J. Sci. Food Agric. 32:759.

Poe, S. E., D. G. Ely, G. E. Mitchell, Jr., H. A. Glimp, and W. P. Deweese. 1971. Rumen development in lambs. II. Rumen metabolite changes. J. Anim. Sci. 32:989.

Poe, S. E., G. E. Mitchell, Jr., and D. G. Ely. 1972. Rumen development in lambs. III. Microbial B-vitamin synthesis. J. Anim. Sci. 34:826.

Preston, R. L. 1966. Protein requirements of growing-finishing cattle and lambs. J. Nutr. 90:157.

Preston, R. L., D. D. Schnakenberg, and W. H. Pfander. 1965. Protein utilization in ruminants. 1. Blood urea nitrogen as affected by protein intake. J. Nutr. 86:281.

Purser, D. B. 1970a. Amino acid requirements of ruminants. Fed. Proc. 29:51.

Purser, D. B. 1970b. Nitrogen metabolism in the rumen: Microorganisms as a source of protein for the ruminant animal. J. Anim. Sci. 30:988.

Reis, P. J. 1967. The growth and composition of wool. 4. The differential response of growth and sulfur content of wool to the level of sulfur-containing amino acids given per abomasum. Aust. J. Biol. Sci. 20:809.

Reis, P. J., and P. G. Schinckel. 1963. Some effects of sulphur-containing amino acids on the growth and composition of wool. Aust. J. Biol. Sci. 16:218.

Reis, P. J., and D. A. Tunks. 1969. Evaluation of formaldehyde treated casein for wool growth and nitrogen retention. Aust. J. Agric. Res. 20:775.

Robards, G. E. 1971. The wool growth of Merino sheep receiving an exponential pattern of methionine infusion to the abomasum. Aust. J. Agric. Res. 22:261.

Robinson, J. J., and T. J. Forbes. 1966. A study of the protein requirements of the mature breeding ewe. Br. J. Nutr. 20:263.

Robinson, J. J., and T. J. Forbes. 1968. The effect of protein intake during gestation on ewe and lamb performance. Anim. Prod. 10:297.

Satter, L. D., and R. E. Roffler. 1975. Nitrogen requirement and utilization in dairy cattle. J. Dairy Sci. 58:1219.

Satter, L. D., and L. L. Slyter. 1974. Effect of ammonia concentration on rumen microbial protein production in vitro. Br. J. Nutr. 32:199.

Satter, L. D., L. W. Whitlow, and G. L. Beardsley. 1977. Resistance of protein to rumen degradation and its significance to the dairy cow. Distill. Feed Res. Counc. Conf. Proc. 32:63. Des Moines, Ia.

Schelling, G. T., and E. E. Hatfield. 1968. Effect of abomasally infused nitrogen sources on nitrogen retention of growing lambs. J. Nutr. 96:319.

Schelling, G. T., J. E. Chandler, and G. C. Scott. 1973. Postruminal supplemental methionine infusion to sheep fed high quality diets. J. Anim. Sci. 37:1034.

Schiehzadek, S. A., and L. H. Harbers. 1974. Soybean meal, urea and extruded starch-urea products compared as protein supplements in high-roughage lamb rations. J. Anim. Sci. 38:206.

Schmidt, S. P., N. J. Benevenga, and N. A. Jorgensen. 1974. Effect of formaldehyde treatment of soybean meal on the performance of growing steers and lambs. J. Anim. Sci. 38:646.

Sibbald, I. R., T. C. Loughheed, and J. H. Linton. 1968. A methionine supplement for ruminants. Proc. 2nd World Conf. Anim. Prod., College Park, Md. (Abstr. No. 113)

Storm, E., and E. R. Ørskov. 1982. Biological value and digestibility of rumen microbial protein in lamb small intestine. Proc. Nutr. Soc. 41:78A.

Streeter, C. L., C. O. Little, G. E. Mitchell, Jr., and R. A. Scott. 1973. Influence of rate of ruminal administration of urea on nitrogen utilization in lambs. J. Anim. Sci. 37:796.

Velloso, L., T. W. Perry, R. C. Peterson, and W. M. Beeson. 1971. Effect of dehydrated alfalfa meal and of fish solubles on growth and nitrogen and energy balance of lambs and beef cattle fed a high urea liquid supplement. J. Anim. Sci. 32:764.

Walker, D. M., and B. W. Norton. 1971. Nitrogen balance studies with the milk-fed lamb. 9. Energy and protein requirements for maintenance, live weight gain and wool growth. Br. J. Nutr. 26:15.

Weston, R. H. 1971. Factors limiting the intake of feed by sheep. V. Feed intake and the productive performance of the ruminant lamb in relation to the quantity of crude protein digested in the intestine. Aust. J. Agric. Res. 22:307.

Weston, R. H. 1973. Factors limiting the intake of feed by sheep. VII. The digestion of a medium quality roughage and the effect of postruminal infusion of casein on its consumption by young sheep. Aust. J. Agric. Res. 24:387.

Williams, V. J. 1969. The relative rates of absorption of amino acids from the small intestines of the sheep. Comp. Biochem. Physiol. 29:865.

Young, P. W., G. T. Schelling, R. E. Tucker, and G. E. Mitchell, Jr. 1981. Plasma amino acid response to abomasal infusions of amino acids in sheep. J. Anim. Sci. 52:1421.

Zinn, R. A., and F. N. Owens. 1983. Influence of feed intake level on site of digestion in steers fed a high concentrate diet. J. Anim. Sci. 56:471.

Minerals

Agricultural Research Council. 1980. The Nutrient Requirements of Ruminant Livestock. Slough: Commonwealth Agricultural Bureaux.

Allaway, W. H., D. P. Moore, J. E. Oldfield, and O. H. Muth. 1966. Movement of physiological levels of selenium from soils through plants to animals. J. Nutr. 88:411.

Ammerman, C. B. 1981. Cobalt. Anim. Nutr. Health 36:26.

Ammerman, C. B., and P. R. Henry. 1983. Dietary magnesium requirements in ruminants and nonruminants. Pp. 93-106 in Proc. John Lee Pratt Int. Symp. on the Role of Magnesium in Animal Nutrition, J. P. Fontenot, G. E. Bunce, K. E. Webb, Jr., and V. G. Allen, eds. Blacksburg, Va.: Virginia Polytechnic Institute and State University.

Ammerman, C. B., C. F. Chicco, P. E. Loggins, and L. R. Arrington. 1972. Availability of different inorganic salts of magnesium to sheep. J. Anim. Sci. 34:122.

Ammerman, C. B., C. F. Chicco, J. E. Moore, P. A. Van Walleghem, and L. R. Arrington. 1971. Effect of dietary magnesium on voluntary feed intake and rumen fermentations. J. Dairy Sci. 54:1288.

Amos, R. L., G. J. Crissman, R. F. Keefer, and D. J. Horvath. 1975. Serum magnesium levels of ewes grazing orchardgrass topdressed with dolomite or calcite. J. Anim. Sci. 41:198.

Anke, M., and B. Groppel. 1970. Manganese deficiency and radioisotope studies on manganese metabolism. Pp. 133-135 in Trace Element in Animals, C. F. Mills, ed. London: E and S Livingstone.

Apgar, J., and H. F. Travis. 1979. Effect of a low zinc diet on the ewe during pregnancy and lactation. J. Anim. Sci. 48:1234.

Arora, S. P., E. E. Hatfield, U. S. Garrigus, T. G. Lohman, and B. B. Doane. 1969. Zinc-65 uptake by rumen tissue. J. Nutr. 97:25.

Barry, T. N., S. J. Duncan, W. A. Sadler, K. R. Millar, and A. D. Sheppard. 1983. Iodine metabolism and thyroid hormone relationships in growing sheep fed on kale (Brassica oleracea) and ryegrass (Lolium perenne)-clover (Trifolium repens) fresh-forage diets. Br. J. Nutr. 49:241.

Becker, D. E., and S. E. Smith. 1951. The level of cobalt tolerance in yearling sheep. J. Anim. Sci. 10:266.

Beede, D. K., P. L. Schnieder, P. G. Mallonee, R. J. Collier, and C. J. Wilcox. 1983. Potassium nutrition and the relationship with heat stress in lactating dairy cattle. Proc. 6th Ann. Int. Miner. Conf., St. Petersburg, Fla.

Beeson, W. M., R. F. Johnson, D. W. Bolin, and C. W. Hickman. 1944. The phosphorus requirement for fattening lambs. J. Anim. Sci. 3:63.

Bird, P. R. 1974. Sulphur metabolism and excretion studies in ruminants. XIII. Intake and utilization of wheat straw by sheep and cattle. Aust. J. Agric. Res. 25:631.

Braithwaite, G. D. 1982. Endogenous faecal loss of calcium by ruminants. J. Agric. Sci. 99:355.

Braithwaite, G. D. 1983a. Calcium and phosphorus requirements of the ewe during pregnancy and lactation. 1. Calcium. Br. J. Nutr. 50:711.

Braithwaite, G. D. 1983b. Calcium and phosphorus requirements of the ewe during pregnancy and lactation. 2. Phosphorus. Br. J. Nutr. 50:723.

Braithwaite, G. D. 1984a. Changes in phosphorus metabolism of sheep in response to the increased demands for P associated with an intravenous infusion of calcium. J. Agric. Sci. 102:135.

Braithwaite, G. D. 1984b. Some observations on phosphorus homoeostasis and requirements of sheep. J. Agric. Sci. 102:295.

Bray, A. C., and J. A. Hemsley. 1969. Sulphur metabolism of sheep. IV. The effect of a varied dietary sulphur content on some body fluid sulphate levels and on the utilization of urea-supplemented roughage by sheep. Aust. J. Agric. Res. 20:759.

Brink, M. F. 1961. Potassium Requirement of the Immature Ovine. Ph.D. dissertation. University of Missouri, Columbia.

Brisson, G. J., and R. Bouchard. 1970. Artificial rearing of lambs: Feeding cold milk ad libitum versus warm milk three times per day to appetite, and effects of an antibiotic-vitamin-iron supplement on growth, performance and digestibility of diet constituents. J. Anim. Sci. 31:810.

Buck, W. B., and R. M. Sharma. 1969. Copper toxicity in sheep. Iowa State Univ. Vet. 31:4.

Bull, L. S. 1979. Sulfur nutrition of ruminants. Pp. 111-130 in Proc. 2nd Ann. Int. Min. Conf. St. Petersburg Beach, Fla.

Burridge, J. C., J. W. S. Reith, and M. L. Berrow. 1983. Soil factors and treatments affecting trace elements in crops and herbage. Pp. 77-85 in Trace Elements in Animal Production and Veterinary Practice, N. F. Suttle, R. B. Gunn, W. M. Allen, K. A. Linklater, and G. Wiener, eds. Br. Soc. Anim. Prod. Occas. Publ. No. 7.

Calhoun, M. C., and M. Shelton. 1983. Source and level of potassium in high concentrate lamb diets. J. Anim. Sci. 57(Suppl. 1):423.

Campbell, J. K., and C. F. Mills. 1979. The toxicity of zinc to pregnant sheep. Environ. Res. 20:1.

Campbell, L. D., and W. K. Roberts. 1965. The requirements and role of potassium in ovine nutrition. Can. J. Anim. Sci. 45:147.

Care, A. D., J.-P. Barlet, and H. M. Abdel-Hafeez. 1980. Calcium and phosphate homeostasis in ruminants and its relationship to the aetiology and prevention of parturient paresis. Pp. 429-446 in Digestive Physiology and Metabolism in Ruminants, Y. Ruckebusch and P. Thivent, eds. Westport, Conn.: AVI Publishing.

Chicco, C. F., C. B. Ammerman, and P. E. Loggins. 1973a. Effect of age and dietary magnesium on voluntary feed intake and plasma magnesium in ruminants. J. Dairy Sci. 56:822.

Chicco, C. F., C. B. Ammerman, J. P. Feaster, and B. G. Dunavant. 1973b. Nutritional interrelationships of dietary calcium, phosphorus and magnesium in sheep. J. Anim. Sci. 36:986.

Clanton, D. C. 1980. Applied potassium nutrition in beef cattle. Pp. 17-32 in Proc. 3rd Ann. Int. Min. Conf. Orlando, Fla.

Cohen, R. D. H. 1980. Phosphorus in rangeland ruminant nutrition: A review. Livestock Prod. Sci. 7:25.

Davies, N. T., H. S. Soliman, W. Corrigall, and A. Flett. 1977. The susceptibility of suckling lambs to zinc toxicity. Br. J. Nutr. 38:153.

Denton, D. A. 1969. Salt appetite. Nutr. Abstr. Rev. 39:1043.

Devlin, T. J., and W. K. Roberts. 1963. Dietary maintenance requirement of sodium for wether lambs. J. Anim. Sci. 22:648.

Donald, H. P., and W. S. Russell. 1970. The relationship between live weight of ewe at mating and weight of newborn lamb. Anim. Prod. 12:273.

Doney, J. M., J. N. Peart, W. F. Smith, and F. Louda. 1979. A consideration of techniques for estimation of milk yield by suckled sheep and a comparison of estimates obtained by two methods in relation to the effect of breed, level of production and stage of lactation. J. Agric. Sci. 92:123.

Egan, A. R. 1972. Reproductive responses to supplemental zinc and manganese in Dorset Horn ewes. Aust. J. Exp. Agric. Anim. Husb. 12:131.

Egan, D. A. 1969. Control of an outbreak of hypomagnesaemic tetany in nursing ewes. Ir. Vet. J. 23:8.

Ellis, W. C., and W. H. Pfander. 1960. Further studies on molybdenum as a possible component of the "alfalfa ash factor" for sheep. J. Anim. Sci. 19:1260. (Abstr.)

Ellis, W. C., W. H. Pfander, M. E. Muhrer, and E. E. Pickett. 1958. Molybdenum as a dietary essential for lambs. J. Anim. Sci. 17:180.

Falconer, I. R. 1963. Iodide metabolism of the thyroid and mammary glands during lactation in sheep. J. Endocrinol. 25:533.

Falconer, I. R., and H. A. Robertson. 1961. Changes in thyroid activity during growth in the sheep. J. Endocrinol. 22:23.

Fenner, H. 1979. Magnesium nutrition of the ruminant. Pp. 57-91 in Proc. 2nd Ann. Int. Miner. Conf. St. Petersburg Beach, Fla.

Field, A. C. 1983a. Maintenance requirements of phosphorus and absorbability of dietary phosphorus in sheep. J. Agric. Sci. 100:231.

Field, A. C. 1983b. Dietary factors affecting magnesium utilization. Pp. 159-171 in Proc. John Lee Pratt Int. Symp. on the Role of Magnesium in Animal Nutrition. J. P. Fontenot, G. E. Bunce, K. E. Webb, Jr., and V. G. Allen, eds. Blacksburg, Va.: Virginia Polytechnic Institute and State University.

Field, A. C. 1984. Genetic variation in mineral utilization by ruminants and its large effect on requirements. Pp. 71-93 in Proc. 7th Ann. Int. Miner. Conf. Clearwater Beach, Fla.

Field, A. C., R. L. Coop, R. A. Dingwall, and C. S. Munro. 1982. The phosphorus requirements for growth and maintenance of sheep. J. Agric. Sci. 99:311.

Field, A. C., J. Kamphues, and J. A. Woolliams. 1983. The effect of dietary intake of calcium and phosphorus on the absorption and excretion of phosphorus in chimaera-derived sheep. J. Agric. Sci. 101:597.

Fontenot, J. P. 1980. Magnesium in ruminant nutrition. In NFIA Literature Review of Magnesium in Animal Nutrition. West Des Moines, Ia.: Natl. Feed Ingredients Assoc.

Godwin, K. O., R. E. Kuchel, and R. A. Buckley. 1970. The effect of selenium on infertility in ewes grazing improved pastures. Aust. J. Exp. Agric. Anim. Husb. 10:672.

Goodrich, R. D., and W. R. Thompson. 1981. Sulfur. Anim. Nutr. Health 36:24.

Goodrich, R. D., T. S. Kahlon, D. E. Pamp, and D. P. Cooper. 1978. Sulfur in Ruminant Nutrition. West Des Moines: Natl. Feed Ingredients Assoc.

Grace, N. D. 1975. Studies on the flow of zinc, cobalt, copper and manganese along the digestive tract of sheep given fresh perennial ryegrass, or white or red clover. Br. J. Nutr. 34:73.

Grace, N. D. 1981. Phosphorus kinetics in sheep. Br. J. Nutr. 45:367.

Grace, N. D. 1983. Amounts and distribution of mineral elements associated with fleece-free empty body weight gains in grazing sheep. N. Z. J. Agric. Res. 26:59.

Grace, N. D., and N. F. Suttle. 1979. Some effects of sulphur intake on molybdenum in sheep. Br. J. Nutr. 41:125.

Grant, A. B., and A. D. Sheppard. 1983. Selenium in New Zealand pastures. N. Z. Vet. J. 31:131.

Greene, L. W., J. P. Fontenot, and K. E. Webb, Jr. 1983a. Effect of dietary potassium on absorption of magnesium and other macroelements in sheep fed different levels of magnesium. J. Anim. Sci. 56:1208.

Greene, L. W., K. E. Webb, Jr., and J. P. Fontenot. 1983b. Effect of potassium level on site of absorption of magnesium and other macroelements in sheep. J. Anim. Sci. 56:1214.

Griffiths, J. R., R. J. Bennett, and R. M. R. Bush. 1970. The effect of cobalt supplementation, as an oral drench or pasture treatment, on the growth of lambs. Anim. Prod. 12:89.

Guardiola, C. M., G. C. Fahey, Jr., J. W. Spears, U. S. Garrigus, O. A. Izquierdo, and C. Pedroza. 1983. The effects of sulphur supplementation on cellulose digestion in vitro and on nutrient digestion, nitrogen metabolism and rumen characteristics of lambs on good quality fescue and tropical star grass hays. Anim. Feed Sci. Technol. 8:129.

Hagsten, I., T. W. Perry, and J. B. Outhouse. 1975. Salt requirements of lambs. J. Anim. Sci. 40:329.

Handreck, K. A., and K. O. Godwin. 1970. Distribution in the sheep of selenium derived from ^{75}Se-labelled ruminal pellets. Aust. J. Agric. Res. 21:71.

Harris, L. E., R. J. Raleigh, M. A. Madsen, J. L. Shupe, J. E. Butcher, and D. A. Greenwood. 1963. Effect of various levels of fluorine, stilbestrol, and oxytetracycline in the fattening ration of lambs. J. Anim. Sci. 22:51.

Hartley, W. J. 1963. Selenium and ewe fertility. Proc. N. Z. Soc. Anim. Prod. 23:20.

Hayter, S., and G. Wiener. 1973. Variation in the concentration of copper in the blood plasma of Finnish Landrace and Merino sheep and their crosses with reference to reproductive performance and age. Anim. Prod. 16:261.

Henneman, H. A., E. P. Reineke, and S. A. Griffin. 1955. The thyroid secretion rate of sheep as affected by season, age, breed, pregnancy and lactation. J. Anim. Sci. 14:419.

Hidiroglou, M. 1979a. Manganese in ruminant nutrition. Can. J. Anim. Sci. 59:217.

Hidiroglou, M. 1979b. Trace element deficiencies and fertility in ruminants: a review. J. Dairy Sci. 62:1195.

Hidiroglou, M., S. K. Ho, and J. F. Standish. 1978. Effects of dietary manganese levels on reproductive performance of ewes and on tissue mineral composition of ewes and day-old lambs. Can. J. Anim. Sci. 58:35.

Holz, R. C., T. W. Perry, and W. M. Beeson. 1961. Hemoglobin levels of lambs from birth to eight weeks of age and the effects of iron-dextran on suckling lambs. J. Anim. Sci. 20:445.

Hoskins, F. H., and S. L. Hansard. 1964. Placental transfer and fetal tissue iron utilization in sheep. J. Nutr. 83:10.

Howell, J. McC. 1970. The pathology of swayback. Pp. 103-105 in Trace Element Metabolism in Animals. C. F. Mills, ed. London: E and S Livingstone.

Howell, J. McC. 1983. Toxicity problems associated with trace elements in domestic animals. Pp. 107-117 in Trace Elements in Animal Production and Veterinary Practice, N. F. Suttle, R. G. Gunn, W. M. Allen, K. A. Linklater, and G. Wiener, eds. Br. Soc. Anim. Prod. Occas. Publ. No. 7.

Hutcheson, D. P., N. A. Cole, J. B. McLaren, and G. B. Thompson. 1979. Preshipment and postshipment diets for light weight stressed feeder calves. J. Anim. Sci. 49(Supp. 1):191.

Jackson, H. M., R. P. Kromann, and E. E. Ray. 1971. Energy retention in lambs as influenced by various levels of sodium and potassium in the rations. J. Anim. Sci. 33:872.

Jamison, H. M., R. C. Carter, J. A. Gaines, and C. M. Kincaid. 1961. The effect of breed of sire on body size of lambs at birth. J. Anim. Sci. 20:154.

Johnson, W. H., R. D. Goodrich, and J. C. Meiske. 1970. Appearance in the blood plasma and excretion of 35S from three chemical forms of sulfur by lambs. J. Anim. Sci. 31:1003.

Jones, O. H., Jr., and W. B. Anthony. 1970. Influence of dietary cobalt on fecal vitamin B_{12} and blood composition in lambs. J. Anim. Sci. 31:440.

Jordan, R. M., and H. E. Hanke. 1982. Effect of mineral additions to trace mineralized salt on daily intake of salt and minerals. Proc. 54th Sheep and Lamb Feeders Day. Minn. Agric. Exp. Stn. Rep. S-182.

Kubota, J. 1975. Areas of molybdenum toxicity to grazing animals in the western states. J. Range Manage. 28:252.

Kubota, J., W. H. Allaway, D. L. Carter, E. E. Cary, and V. A. Lazar. 1967. Selenium in crops in the United States in relation to selenium-responsive diseases of animals. J. Agric. Food Chem. 15:488.

Kuchel, R. E., and R. A. Buckley. 1969. The provision of selenium to sheep by means of heavy pellets. Aust. J. Agric. Res. 20:1099.

Kuttler, K. L., D. W. Marble, and C. Blincoe. 1961. Serum and tissue residues following selenium injections in sheep. Am. J. Vet. Res. 22:422.

Lamprecht, W. O., Jr., J. G. Darroch, and H. R. Crookshank. 1969. Statistical analysis of dietary mineral intake and the occurrence of urolithiasis in sheep. J. Anim. Sci. 28:386.

Langlands, J. P. 1973. Milk and herbage intakes by grazing lambs born to Merino ewes and sired by Merino, Border Leicester, Corriedale, Dorset Horn and Southdown rams. Anim. Prod. 16:285.

Larvor, P. 1983. Physiological and Biochemical Functions of Magnesium in Animals. Pp. 81-91 in Proc. John Lee Pratt Int. Symp. on the Role of Magnesium in Animal Nutrition. J. P. Fontenot, G. E. Bunce, K. E. Webb, Jr., and V. G. Allen, eds. Blacksburg, Va.: Virginia Polytechnic Institute and State University.

Lassiter, J. W., and J. D. Morton. 1968. Effects of low manganese diet on certain ovine characteristics. J. Anim. Sci. 27:776.

Lawlor, M. J., W. H. Smith, and W. M. Beeson. 1965. Iron requirement of the growing lambs. J. Anim. Sci. 24:742.

Lee, H. J., and H. R. Marston. 1969. The requirement for cobalt of sheep grazed on cobalt-deficient pastures. Aust. J. Agric. Res. 20:905.

MacPherson, A. 1983. Oral treatment of trace element deficiencies in ruminant livestock. Pp. 93-103 in Trace Elements in Animal Production and Veterinary Practice, N. F. Suttle, R. G. Gunn, W. M. Allen, K. A. Linklater and G. Wiener, eds. Br. Soc. Anim. Prod. Occas. Publ. No. 7.

Mansfield, M. E., J. M. Lewis, and G. E. McKibben. 1967. Rearing lambs free of gastrointestinal nematodes. J. Am. Vet. Med. Assoc. 151:1182.

Marston, H. R. 1970. The requirement of sheep for cobalt or for vitamin B_{12}. Br. J. Nutr. 24:615.

Martens, H., and Y. Rayssiquier. 1980. Magnesium metabolism and hypomagnesaemia. Pp. 447-466 in Digestive Physiology and Metabolism in Ruminants, Y. Ruckebusch and P. Thivend, eds. Westport, Conn.: AVI Publishing.

Masters, D. G., and R. G. Moir. 1983. Effect of zinc deficiency on the pregnant ewe and developing foetus. Br. J. Nutr. 49:365.

McAleese, D. M., and R. M. Forbes. 1959. Experimental production of magnesium deficiency in lambs on a diet containing roughage. Nature (London) 184:2025.

McCauley, E. H., J. G. Linn, and R. D. Goodrich. 1973. Experimentally induced iodide toxicosis in lambs. Am. J. Vet. Res. 34:65.

McClymont, C. L., K. N. Wynne, P. K. Briggs, and M. C. Franklin. 1957. Sodium chloride supplementation of high-grain diets for fattening Merino sheep. Aust. J. Agric. Res. 8:83.

McDonald, I. W. 1968. The nutrition of grazing ruminants. Nutr. Abstr. Rev. 38:381.

Meyer, J. H., and W. C. Weir. 1954. The tolerance of sheep to high intakes of sodium chloride. J. Anim. Sci. 13:443.

Meyer, J. H., W. C. Weir, N. R. Ittner, and J. D. Smith. 1955. The influence of high sodium chloride intakes by fattening sheep and cattle. J. Anim. Sci. 14:412.

Miller, W. J. 1979a. Copper in ruminant nutrition: A review. Pp. 1-38 in Copper and Zinc in Animal Nutrition. West Des Moines, Ia.: Natl. Feed Ingredients Assoc.

Miller, W. J. 1979b. Zinc in ruminant nutrition: A review. Pp. 39-72 in Copper and Zinc in Animal Nutrition. West Des Moines, Ia.: Natl. Feed Ingredients Assoc.

Mills, C. F., and A. C. Dalgarno. 1967. The influence of dietary calcium concentration on epidermal lesions of zinc deficiency in lambs. Proc. Nutr. Soc. 26:19. (Abstr.)

Mills, C. F., A. C. Dalgarno, R. B. Williams, and J. Quarterman. 1967. Zinc deficiency and the zinc requirements of calves and lambs. Br. J. Nutr. 21:751-768.

Moir, R. J. 1979. Basic concepts of sulphur nutrition. Pp. 93-108 in Proc. 2nd Ann. Int. Miner. Conf. St. Petersburg Beach, Fla.

Moksnes, K., and G. Norheim. 1983. Selenium and glutathione peroxidase levels in lambs receiving feed supplemented with sodium selenite or selenomethionine. Acta Vet. Scand. 24:45.

Morris, J. G., and R. G. Peterson. 1975. Sodium requirements of lactating ewes. J. Nutr. 105:595.

Muth, O. H. 1970. Selenium-responsive disease of sheep. J. Am. Vet. Med. Assoc. 157:1507.

National Research Council. 1975. Nutrient Requirements of Sheep. Washington, D.C.: National Academy of Sciences.

National Research Council. 1980. Mineral Tolerance of Domestic Animals. Washington, D.C.: National Academy of Sciences.

National Research Council. 1982. United States-Canadian Tables of Feed Composition, 3rd ed. Washington, D.C.: National Academy Press.

National Research Council. 1983. Selenium in Nutrition. Washington, D.C.: National Academy Press.

Neville, W. E., Jr., A. B. Chapman, and A. L. Pope. 1958. Comparison of lambs from western (Columbia-Rambouillet) ewes and sired by rams of four down breeds. J. Anim. Sci. 17:763.

Oh, S. H., A. L. Pope, and W. G. Hoekstra. 1976. Dietary selenium requirements of sheep fed a practical-type diet as assessed by tissue glutathione peroxidase and other criteria. J. Anim. Sci. 42:984.

O'Hara, P. J., A. J. Fraser, and M. P. Jones. 1982. Superphosphate poisoning of sheep: The role of fluoride. N. Z. Vet. J. 30:199.

Oldfield, J. E., J. R. Schubert, and O. H. Muth. 1963. Implications of selenium in large animal nutrition. J. Agric. Food Chem. 11:388.

Ott, E. A., W. H. Smith, M. Stob, H. E. Parker, R. B. Harrington, and W. M. Beeson. 1965. Zinc requirement of the growing lamb fed a purified diet. J. Nutr. 87:459.

Ott, E. A., W. H. Smith, R. B. Harrington, and W. M. Beeson. 1966. Zinc toxicity in ruminants. 1. Effect of high levels of dietary zinc on gains, feed consumption and feed efficiency of lambs. J. Anim. Sci. 25:414.

Paulson, G. D., G. A. Broderick, C. A. Baumann, and A. L. Pope. 1968. Effect of feeding sheep selenium-fortified trace mineralized salt: effect of tocopherol. J. Anim. Sci. 27:195.

Paynter, D. I. 1979. Glutathione peroxidase and selenium in sheep. I. Effect of intraruminal selenium pellets on tissue glutathione peroxidase activities. Aust. J. Agric. Res. 30:695.

Paynter, D. I., J. W. Anderson, and J. W. McDonald. 1979. Glutathione peroxidase and selenium in sheep. II. The relationship between glutathione peroxidase and selenium-responsive unthriftiness in Merino lambs. Aust. J. Agric. Res. 30:703.

Perry, T. W. 1982. Feed Formulations. Danville, Ill.: Interstate Printers and Publishers, Inc.

Pert, J. N., R. A. Edwards, and E. Donaldson. 1975. The yield and composition of the milk of Finnish Landrace x Blackface ewes. II. Ewes and lambs grazed on pasture. J. Agric. Sci. 85:315.

Phillippo, M. 1983. The role of dose-response trials in predicting trace element deficiency disorders. Pp. 51-59 in Trace Elements in Animal Production and Veterinary Practice, N. F. Suttle, R. G. Gunn, W. M. Allen, K. A. Linklater, and G. Wiener, eds. Br. Soc. Anim. Prod. Occas. Publ. No. 7.

Piper, L. R., B. M. Bindon, J. F. Wilkins, R. J. Cox, Y. M. Curtis, and M. A. Cheers. 1980. The effect of selenium treatment on the fertility of Merino sheep. Proc. Aust. Soc. Anim. Prod. 13:241.

Pond, W. G. 1983. Effect of dietary calcium and zinc levels on weight gain and blood and tissue mineral concentrations of growing Columbia- and Suffolk-sired lambs. J. Anim. Sci. 56:952.

Pope, A. L. 1971. A review of recent mineral research with sheep. J. Anim. Sci. 33:1332.

Pope, A. L. 1975. Mineral interrelationships in ovine nutrition. J. Am. Vet. Med. Assoc. 166:264.

Pope, A. L., R. J. Moir, M. Somers, E. J. Underwood, and C. L. White. 1979. The effect of sulphur on ^{75}Se absorption and retention in sheep. J. Nutr. 109:1448.

Potter, B. J., G. B. Jones, R. A. Buckley, G. B. Belling, G. H. McIntosh, and B. S. Hetzel. 1980. Production of severe iodine deficiency in sheep using a prepared low-iodine diet. Aust. J. Biol. Sci. 33:53.

Powell, K., R. L. Reid, and J. A. Balasko. 1978. Performance of lambs on perennial rye grass, smooth brome grass, orchard grass and tall fescue pastures. 2. Mineral utilization, in vitro digestibility and chemical composition of herbage. J. Anim. Sci. 46:1503.

Preston, R. C. 1977. Phosphorus in beef cattle and sheep nutrition. Pp. 1-44 in NFIA Literature Review on Phosphorus in Ruminant Nutrition. West Des Moines, Ia.: Natl. Feed Ingredients Assoc.

Rastogi, R., W. J. Boylan, W. E. Rempel, and H. F. Windels. 1982. Crossbreeding in sheep with evaluation of the combining ability, heterosis and recombination effects for lamb growth. J. Anim. Sci. 54:524.

Robertson, H. A., and I. R. Falconer. 1961. The estimation of thyroid activity: An evaluation of certain parameters. J. Endocrinol. 21:411.

Rosa, I. V., P. R. Henry, and C. B. Ammerman. 1982. Interrelationship of dietary phosphorus, aluminum and iron on performance and tissue mineral composition in lambs. J. Anim. Sci. 55:1231.

Rook, J. A. F., and J. E. Storry. 1962. Magnesium in the nutrition of farm animals. Nutr. Abstr. Rev. 32:1055.

Ross, D. B. 1964. Chronic copper poisoning in lambs. Vet. Rec. 76:875.

Ross, D. B. 1966. The diagnosis, prevention and treatment of chronic copper poisoning in housed lambs. Br. Vet. J. 122:279.

Ross, D. B. 1970. The effect of oral ammonium molybdate and sodium sulphate given to lambs with high liver copper concentrations. Res. Vet. Sci. 11:295.

Rotruck, J. T., A. L. Pope, C. A. Baumann, W. G. Hoekstra, and G. D. Paulson. 1969. Effect of long-term feeding of selenized salt to ewes and their lambs. J. Anim. Sci. 29:170. (Abstr.)

Schubert, J. R., O. H. Muth, J. E. Oldfield, and L. F. Remmert. 1961. Experimental results with selenium in white muscle disease of lambs and calves. Fed. Proc. 20:689.

Scott, D., and A. F. McLean. 1981. Control of mineral absorption in ruminants. Proc. Nutr. Soc. 40:257.

Shelton, J. M. 1968. Lambing out of season and accelerated lambing. Pp. 136-149 in Proc. Symp. on Physiology of Reproduction in Sheep. Oklahoma State University, Stillwater.

Silverman, P. H., M. E. Mansfield, and H. L. Scott. 1970. Haemonchus contortus infection in sheep: Effects of various levels of primary infections on nontreated lambs. Am. J. Vet. Res. 31:841.

Singh, O. N., H. A. Henneman, and E. P. Reineke. 1956. The relationship of thyroid activity to lactation, growth and sex in sheep. J. Anim. Sci. 15:625.

Smith, W. H., E. A. Ott, M. Stob, and W. M. Beeson. 1962. Zinc deficiency syndrome in the young lamb. J. Anim. Sci. 21:1014. (Abstr.)

Standish, J. F., and C. B. Ammerman. 1971. Effect of excess dietary iron as ferrous sulfate and ferric citrate on tissue mineral composition of sheep. J. Anim. Sci. 33:481.

Stevenson, M. H., and E. F. Unsworth. 1978. Studies on the absorption of calcium, phosphorus, magnesium, copper and zinc by sheep fed on roughage-cereal diets. Br. J. Nutr. 40:491.

Stritzke, D. J., and J. Whiteman. 1982. Lamb growth patterns following different seasons of birth. J. Anim. Sci. 55:1002.

Suttle, N. F. 1975. The role of organic sulphur in the copper-molybdenum-S interrelationship in ruminant nutrition. Br. J. Nutr. 34:411.

Suttle, N. F. 1983a. Effects of molybdenum concentration in fresh herbage, hay and semi-purified diets on copper metabolism of sheep. J. Agric. Sci. 100:651.

Suttle, N. F. 1983b. Meeting the mineral requirements of sheep. Pp. 167-183 in Sheep Production (Proc. Nottingham Easter School), W. Haresign, ed. London: Butterworth.

Suttle, N. F. 1983c. The nutritional basis for trace element deficiencies in ruminant livestock. Pp. 19-25 in Trace Elements in Animal Production and Veterinary Practice, N. F. Suttle, R. G. Gunn, W. M. Allen, K. A. Linklater, and G. Wiener, eds. Br. Soc. Anim. Prod. Occas. Publ. No. 7.

Suttle, N. F., and A. C. Field. 1983. The effects of dietary supplements of thiomolybdates on copper and molybdenum metabolism in sheep. J. Comp. Pathol. 93:379.

Suttle, N. F., and M. McLauchlan. 1976. Predicting the effects of dietary molybdenum and sulphur on the availability of copper to ruminants. Proc. Nutr. Soc. 35:22A.

Sykes, A. R., R. L. Coop, and K. W. Angus. 1979. Chronic infection with Trichostrongylus vitrinus in sheep. Some effects on food utilization, skeletal growth and certain serum constituents. Res. Vet. Sci. 26:372.

Telfer, S. B., G. Zervas, and G. Carlos. 1984. Curing or preventing deficiencies in copper, cobalt and selenium in cattle and sheep using tracerglass. Can. J. Anim. Sci. 64(Suppl.):234.

Telle, P. P., R. L. Preston, L. D. Kintner, and W. H. Pfander. 1964. Definition of the ovine potassium requirement. J. Anim. Sci. 23:59.

Thomas, B. H., and S. S. Wheeler. 1932. The efficacy of copper in the regeneration of hemoglobin in anemic lambs. Pp. 204-208 in Proc. Am. Soc. Anim. Prod.

Thomas, F. M., and B. J. Potter. 1976. The effect and site of action of potassium upon magnesium absorption in sheep. Aust. J. Agric. Res. 27:873.

Thompson, J. K., and R. L. Reid. 1981. Mineral status of beef cows and sheep on spring pasture fertilized with kieserite. J. Anim. Sci. 52:969.

Thomson, G. G., and B. M. Lawson. 1970. Copper and selenium interaction in sheep. N. Z. Vet. J. 18:79.

Todd, J. R. 1969. Chronic copper toxicity of ruminants. Proc. Nutr. Soc. 28:189.

Tomas, F. M., R. J. Moir, and M. Somers. 1967. Phosphorus turnover in sheep. Aust. J. Agric. Res. 18:635.

Ullrey, D. E., P. S. Brady, P. A. Whetter, P. K. Ku, and W. T. Magee. 1977. Selenium supplementation of diets for sheep and beef cattle. J. Anim. Sci. 45:559.

Ullrey, D. E., M. R. Light, P. S. Brady, P. A. Whetter, J. E. Tilton, H. A. Henneman, and W. T. Magee. 1978. Selenium supplement in salt for sheep. J. Anim. Sci. 46:1515.

Underwood, E. J. 1977. Trace Elements in Human and Animal Nutrition. New York: Academic Press.

Underwood, E. J. 1981. The Mineral Nutrition of Livestock. Slough: Commonwealth Agricultural Bureaux.

Underwood, E. J., and M. Somers. 1969. Studies of zinc nutrition in sheep. 1. The relation of zinc to growth, testicular development and spermatogenesis in young rams. Aust. J. Agric. Res. 20:889.

Watkinson, J. H. 1983. Prevention of selenium deficiency in grazing animals by annual topdressing of pasture with sodium selenate. N. Z. Vet. J. 31:78.

Whanger, P. D., P. H. Weswig, J. A. Schmitz, and J. E. Oldfield. 1978. Effects of various methods of selenium administration on white muscle disease, glutathione peroxidase and plasma enzyme activities in sheep. J. Anim. Sci. 47:1157.

Wiener, G. 1979. Review of genetic aspects of mineral metabolism with particular reference to copper in sheep. Livestock Prod. Sci. 6:223.

Wiener, G., and J. A. Woolliams. 1983. Genetic variation in trace element metabolism. Pp. 27-35 in Trace Elements in Animal Production and Veterinary Practice, N. F. Suttle, R. G. Gunn, W. M. Allen, K. A. Linklater, and G. Wiener, eds. Br. Soc. Anim. Prod. Occas. Publ. No. 7.

Woolliams, J. A., N. F. Suttle, G. Wiener, A. C. Field, and C. Wolliams. 1982. The effect of breed of sire on the accumulation of copper in lambs, with particular reference to copper toxicity. Anim. Prod. 35:299.

Vitamins

Adams, C. R. 1982. Feedlot cattle need supplemental vitamin E. Feedstuffs 54(18):24.

Agricultural Research Council. 1980. The Nutrient Requirements of Ruminant Livestock. Commonwealth Agricultural Bureaux. Surrey: The Gresham Press.

Alderson, N. E., G. E. Mitchell, Jr., C. O. Little, R. L. Warner, and R. E. Tucker. 1971. Preintestinal disappearance of vitamin E in ruminants. J. Nutr. 101:655.

Andrews, E. D., and I. J. Cunningham. 1945. The vitamin D requirement of the sheep. N.Z. J. Sci. Technol. 27:223.

Anonymous. 1963. Vitamin A. New York: Charles Pfizer.

Barlow, R. M. 1983. Polioencephalomalacia. Pp. 85-86 in Diseases of Sheep, W. B. Martin, ed. Boston: Blackwell Scientific Publishers.

Bunnell, R. H., J. P. Keating, and A. J. Quaresimo. 1968. Alpha-tocopherol content of feedstuffs. J. Agric. Food Chem. 16:659.

Church, D. C., and W. G. Pond. 1974. Basic Animal Nutrition and Feeding. Albany, N.Y.: Albany Printing.

Crowley, J. P. 1961. Rickets in November-born lambs. Vet. Rec. 73:295-297.

DeLuca, H. F. 1974. Vitamin D: The vitamin and the hormone. Fed. Proc. 33:2211.

DeLuca, H. F. 1976. Metabolism of vitamin D: Current status. Am. J. Clin. Nutr. 29:1258.

Eaton, H. D. 1969. Chronic bovine hypo- and hypervitaminosis A and cerebrospinal fluid pressure. Am. J. Clin. Nutr. 22:1070.

Eveleth, D. F., D. W. Bolin, and A. I. Goldsby. 1949. Experimental avitaminosis A in sheep. Am. J. Vet. Res. 10:250.

Ewan, R. C., C. A. Baumann, and A. L. Pope. 1968. Effects of selenium and vitamin E on nutritional muscular dystrophy in lambs. J. Anim. Sci. 27:751.

Faruque, O., and D. M. Walker. 1970. The relative biological potencies of retinyl palmitate and β-carotene for the milk-fed lamb. Br. J. Nutr. 24:23.

Fitch, L. W. N. 1943. Osteodystrophic dieases of sheep in New Zealand. I. Rickets in hoggets: With a note on the aetiology and definition of the disease. Aust. Vet. J. 19:2.

Guilbert, H. R., C. E. Howell, and G. H. Hart. 1940. Minimum vitamin A and carotene requirements of mammalian species. J. Nutr. 19:91.

Guilbert, H. R., R. F. Miller, and E. H. Hughes. 1937. The minimum vitamin A and carotene requirement of cattle, sheep and swine. J. Nutr. 13:543.

Hazzard, D. G., C. G. Woelfel, M. C. Calhoun, J. E. Rousseau, Jr., H. D. Eaton, S. W. Nielsen, R. M. Grey, and J. J. Lucas. 1964. Chronic hypervitaminosis A in Holstein male calves. J. Dairy Sci. 47:391.

Hidiroglou, M., C. J. Williams, and M. Ivan. 1979. Pharmacokinetics and amounts of 25-hydroxycholecalciferol in sheep affected by osteodystrophy. J. Dairy Sci. 62:567.

Hintz, H. F., and D. E. Hogue. 1964. Effect of selenium, sulfur and sulfur amino acids on nutritional muscular dystrophy in the lamb. J. Nutr. 82:495.

Hopkins, L. L., Jr., A. L. Pope, and C. A. Baumann. 1964. Contrasting nutritional responses to vitamin E and selenium in lambs. J. Anim. Sci. 23:674.

Kivimae, A., and C. Carpena. 1973. The level of vitamin E content in some conventional feeding stuffs and the effects of genetic variety, harvesting, processing and storage. Acta Agric. Scand. Suppl. 19:161-168.

Martin, F. H., D. E. Ullrey, H. W. Newland, and E. R. Miller. 1968. Vitamin A activity of carotenes in corn silage fed to lambs. J. Nutr. 96:269.

Matschiner, J. T. 1970. Characterization of vitamin K from the contents of bovine rumen. J. Nutr. 100:190.

May, B. J. 1982. The Minimum Vitamin A Requirement for Growing and Finishing Lambs. M.S. thesis. Angelo State University, San Angelo, Tex.

McElroy, L. W., and H. Goss. 1940a. A quantitative study of vitamins in the rumen contents of sheep and cows fed vitamin-low diets. I. Riboflavin and vitamin K. J. Nutr. 20:527.

McElroy, L. W., and H. Goss. 1940b. A quantitative study of vitamins in the rumen contents of sheep and cows fed vitamin-low diets. II. Vitamin B$_6$ (pyridoxine). J. Nutr. 20:541.

McElroy, L. W., and H. Goss. 1941a. A quantitative study of vitamins in the rumen contents of sheep and cows fed vitamin-low diets. III. Thiamine. J. Nutr. 21:163.

McElroy, L. W., and H. Goss. 1941b. A quantitative study of vitamins in the rumen contents of sheep and cows fed vitamin-low diets. IV. Pantothenic acid. J. Nutr. 21:405.

Miller, R. F., G. H. Hart, and H. H. Cole. 1942. Fertility in sheep as affected by nutrition during the breeding season and pregnancy. Calif. Agric. Exp. Stn. Bull. 672.

Moore, T. 1957. Vitamin A. New York: Elsevier.

Muth, O. H., J. R. Schubert, and J. E. Oldfield. 1961. White muscle disease (myopathy) in lambs and calves. VII. Etiology and prophylaxis. Am. J. Vet. Res. 22:466.

Myers, G. S., Jr., H. D. Eaton, and J. E. Rousseau, Jr. 1959. Relative value of carotene from alfalfa and vitamin A from a dry carrier fed to lambs and pigs. J. Anim. Sci. 18:288.

National Research Council. 1975. Nutrient Requirements of Sheep. Washington, D.C.: National Academy of Sciences.

National Research Council. 1984. Nutrient Requirements of Beef Cattle. Washington, D.C.: National Academy Press.

Nisbet, D. I., E. J. Butler, B. S. W. Smith, J. M. Robertson, and C. C. Bannatyne. 1966. Osteodystrophic diseases of sheep. II. Rickets in young sheep. J. Comp. Pathol. 76:159.

Rammell, C. G. 1983. Vitamin E status of cattle and sheep. 1: A background review. N. Z. Vet. J. 31:179.

Rousseau, J. E., M. W. Dicks, R. Teichman, C. F. Helmboldt, E. L. Bacon, R. M. Prouty, K. L. Dolge, H. D. Eaton, E. L. Jungherr, and G. Beall. 1957. Relationships between plasma, liver and dietary tocopherol in calves, lambs and pigs. J. Anim. Sci. 16:612.

Sharman, G. A. M. 1973. Deficiencies of vitamin E and selenium as factors limiting the intensification of sheep production. Acta Agric. Scand. Suppl. 19:181.

Suttle, N. F., and K. A. Linklater. 1983. Disorders related to trace element deficiencies. Pp. 173-175 in Diseases of Sheep, W. B. Martin, ed. Boston: Blackwell.

Ullrey, D. E. 1972. Biological availability of fat-soluble vitamins: Vitamin A and carotene. J. Anim. Sci. 35:648.

Weber, F. 1983. Biochemical mechanisms of vitamin A action. Proc. Nutr. Soc. 42:31.

Windholz, M., S. Budavari, R. F. Blumetti, and E. S. Otterbein. 1983. The Merck Index: An Encyclopedia of Chemicals, Drugs and Biologicals. Rahway, N.J.: Merck and Co., Inc., p. 1436.

Winegar, A. H., P. B. Pearson, and H. Schmidt. 1940. The synthesis of nicotinic acid in the body of sheep. Science 91:508.

Water

Asplund, J. M., and W. H. Pfander. 1972. Effects of water restriction on nutrient digestibility in sheep receiving fixed water:feed ratios. J. Anim. Sci. 35:1271.

Bailey, C. B., R. Hironaka, and S. B. Slen. 1962. Effects of the temperature of the environment and the drinking water on the temperature and water consumption of sheep. Can. J. Anim. Sci. 42:1.

Brod, D. L., K. K. Bolsen, and B. E. Brent. 1982. Effect of water temperature on rumen temperature, digestion and rumen fermentation in sheep. J. Anim. Sci. 54:179.

Brown, J. D., and J. J. Lynch. 1972. Some aspects of the water balance of sheep at pasture when deprived of drinking water. Aust. J. Agric. Res. 23:669.

Butcher, J. E. 1970. Is snow adequate and economical as a water source for sheep? Natl. Wool Grower 60:28.

Calder, R. W., J. W. G. Nicholson, and H. M. Cunningham. 1964. Water restriction for sheep on pasture and rate of consumption with other feeds. Can. J. Anim. Sci. 44:266.

Choi, S. S. 1961. Effects of Atmospheric Temperatures on the Feed and Water Consumption of the Sheep and the Digestibility of Nutrients. M.S. thesis. Utah State University, Logan.

Forbes, J. M. 1968. The water intake of ewes. Br. J. Nutr. 22:33.

Gordon, J. G. 1965. The effect of water deprivation upon the rumination behavior of housed sheep. J. Agric. Sci. 64:31.

James, L. F., J. E. Butcher, and K. R. Van Kampen. 1970. Relationship between *Halogeton glomeratus* consumption and water intake by sheep. J. Range Manage. 23:123.

Lynch, J. J., G. D. Brown, P. F. May, and J. B. Donnelly. 1972. The effect of withholding drinking water on wool growth and lamb production of grazing Merino sheep in a temperate climate. Aust. J. Agric. Res. 23:659.

Macfarlane, W. V., B. Howard, and B. D. Siebert. 1967. Water metabolism of Merino and Border Leicester sheep grazing salt-brush. Aust. J. Agric. Res. 18:947.

Pierce, A. W. 1968. Studies on salt tolerance of sheep. Aust. J. Agric. Res. 19:589.

Purohit, G. R., P. K. Ghosh, and G. C. Taneja. 1972. Water metabolism in desert sheep. Effects of various degrees of water restriction on the distribution of body water in Marwari sheep. Aust. J. Agric. Res. 23:685.

Squires, V. R., and A. D. Wilson. 1971. Distance between food and water supply and its effect on drinking frequency, and food and water intake of Merino and Border Leicester sheep. Aust. J. Agric. Res. 22:283.

Taneja, G. C. 1966. Effects of restricted watering in sheep. Indian Vet. J. 43:493.

Tomas, F. M., G. B. Jones, B. J. Potter, and G. L. Langsford. 1973. Influence of saline drinking water on mineral balances in sheep. Aust. J. Agric. Res. 24:377.

Wallace, J. D., D. N. Hyder, and K. L. Knox. 1972. Water metabolism in sheep fed forage rations differing in digestibility. Am. J. Vet. Res. 33:921.

Wilson, A. D. 1968. The effect of high salt intake or restricted water intake on diet selection by sheep. Br. J. Nutr. 22:583.

Wilson, A. D. 1970. Water economy and food intake of sheep when watered intermittently. Aust. J. Agric. Res. 21:273.

Wilson, A. D., and M. L. Dudzinski. 1973. Influence of the concentration and volume of saline water on the food intake of sheep and on their excretion of sodium and water in urine and faeces. Aust. J. Agric. Res. 24:245.

NUTRITION DISORDERS

Enterotoxemia

Buxton, D. 1983. Clostridial Diseases. Pp. 35-41 in Diseases of Sheep, W. B. Martin, ed. Boston: Blackwell.

Jensen, R. 1974. Diseases of Sheep. Philadelphia: Lea and Febiger.

Oxer, D. T., D. W. Minty, and C. E. Liefman. 1971. Vaccination trials in sheep with Clostridial vaccines with special reference to passively acquired CL. Welchii type D antitoxin in lambs. Aust. Vet. J. 47:134.

Polioencephalomalacia

Chick, B. F., S. N. Carrol, C. Kennedy, and B. V. McCleary. 1981. Some biochemical features of an outbreak of polioencephalomalacia in sheep. Aust. Vet. J. 57:251.

Davies, E. T., A. H. Pill, D. F. Collins, J. A. J. Venn, and G. D. Bridges. 1965. Cerebrocortical necrosis in calves. Vet. Rec. 77:290.

Edwin, E. E. 1970. Plasma enzyme concentrations in CCN. Vet. Rec. 87:396.

Edwin, E. E. 1975. Cerebrocortical necrosis and thiaminase I. Proc. 9th Int. Congr. Nutr., Mexico, Vol. 2, pg. 272.

Edwin, E. E., and R. Jackman. 1982. Ruminant thiamine requirement in perspective. Vet. Res. Comm. 5:237.

Edwin, E. E., R. Jackman, and P. Jones. 1982. Some properties of thiaminases associated with cerebrocortical necrosis. J. Agric. Sci. 99:271.

Edwin, E. E., L. M. Markson, J. Shreeve, R. Jackman, and P. J. Carroll. 1979. Diagnostic aspects of cerebrocortical necrosis. Vet. Rec. 104:4.

Jensen, R., L. A. Griner, and O. R. Adams. 1956. Polioencephalomalacia of cattle and sheep. J. Am. Vet. Med. Assoc. 129:311.

Loew, F. M. 1972. Pathophysiologic sequelae of intensive livestock production. 1. Polioencephalomalacia (cerebrocortical necrosis) of ruminants. Rev. Cubana Cienc. Agric. (English ed.) 6:301.

McKenzie, D. P., and P. Steele. 1980. Polioencephalomalacia—An increasing problem with sheep in the Great Southern. J. Agric. W. Aust. 21:57.

Mueller, R. E., and J. M. Asplund. 1981. Evidence in the ovine that polioencephalomalacia is not a result of an uncomplicated thiamine deficiency. Nutr. Rep. Int. 24:95.

Pill, A. H. 1967. Evidence of thiamine deficiency in calves affected with cerebrocortical necrosis. Vet. Rec. 81:178.

Roberts, G. W., and J. W. Boyde. 1974. Cerebrocortical necrosis in ruminants. Occurrence of thiaminase in the gut of normal and affected animals and its effect on thiamine status. J. Comp. Pathol. 84:365.

Spicer, E. M., and B. J. Horton. 1981. Biochemistry of natural and amprolium-induced polioencephalomalacia in sheep. Aust. Vet. J. 57:230.

Terlecki, S., and L. M. Markson. 1959. Cerebrocortical necrosis. Vet. Rec. 71:508.

Terlecki, S., and L. M. Markson. 1961. Cerebrocortical necrosis in cattle and sheep. Vet. Rec. 73:23.

Pregnancy Disease

Reid, R. L. 1968. The physiopathology of undernourishment in pregnant sheep with particular reference to pregnancy toxemia. Pp. 163-238 in Advances in Veterinary Science, 12, C. A. Brandly and C. E. Cornelius, eds. New York: Academic Press.

Robinson, J. J. 1983. Nutrition of the pregnant ewe. Pp. 11-131 in Sheep Production, W. Haresign, ed. London: Butterworth.

Russell, A. J. F. 1979. The nutrition of the pregnant ewe. Pp. 221-241 in The Management and Diseases of Sheep. Slough: Commonwealth Agricultural Bureaux.

Urinary Calculi

Bailey, C. B. 1978. Composition of kidney and bladder calculi from cattle on a diet known to cause formation of siliceous urinary calculi. Can. J. Anim. Sci. 58:513.

Crookshank, H. R. 1968. Prevention and control of urinary calculi in sheep. Pp. 162-171 in Proc. Symp. on Sheep Diseases and Health. University of California, Davis.

Crookshank, H. R. 1970. Effect of ammonium salts on the production of ovine urinary calculi. J. Anim. Sci. 30:1002.

Emerick, R. J., and L. B. Embry. 1963. Calcium and phosphorus levels related to the development of phosphate urinary calculi in sheep. J. Anim. Sci. 22:510.

Emerick, R. J., L. B. Embry, and O. E. Olson. 1959. Effect of sodium silicate on the development of urinary calculi and the excretion of various urinary constituents in sheep. J. Anim. Sci. 18:1025.

Field, A. C. 1969. Urinary calculi in ruminants. Proc. Nutr. Soc. 28:198.

Jensen, R. 1974. Diseases of Sheep. Philadelphia: Lea and Febiger.

Lamprecht, W. O., Jr., J. G. Darroch, and H. R. Crookshank. 1969. Statistical analysis of dietary mineral intake and the occurrence of urolithiasis in sheep. J. Anim. Sci. 28:386.

OTHER ASPECTS OF SHEEP NUTRITION

Pastures

Greenhalgh, J. F. D., and G. W. Reid. 1967. Separating the effects of digestibility and palatability of food intake in ruminant animals. Nature (London) 214:744.

Jordan, R. M., and G. C. Marten. 1968a. Effect of weaning, age of weaning and grain feeding on the performance and production of grazing lambs. J. Anim. Sci. 27:174.

Jordan, R. M., and G. C. Marten. 1968b. A note on the management of grazing non-lactating ewes. Anim. Prod. 10:121.

Marten, G. C., R. M. Jordan, and A. W. Hovin. 1981. Improved lamb performance associated with breeding for alkaloid reduction in reed canarygrass. Crop Sci. 21:295.

Price, D. A., K. R. Frederiksen, and R. D. Humphrey. 1968. Response of ewe lambs to hay quality and feeding method. Idaho Agric. Exp. Stn. Bull. 495.

Van Soest, P. J. 1965. Symposium on factors influencing the voluntary intake of herbage by ruminants: Voluntary intake in relation to chemical composition and digestibility. J. Anim. Sci. 24:834.

Wedin, W. F., and R. M. Jordan. 1961. Evaluation of annual crops as pasture for early-weaned lambs. J. Anim. Sci. 20:886.

Weston, R. H. 1968. Factors limiting the intake in feed by sheep. 3. The mean retention time of feed particles in sections of the alimentary tract. Aust. J. Agric. Res. 18:261.

Range Sheep

Bryant, F. C., M. M. Kothmann, and L. B. Merrill. 1979. Diets of sheep, angora goats, Spanish goats and white tailed deer under excellent range conditions. J. Range Manage. 32:412.

Clapperton, J. L. 1964. The energy metabolism of sheep working on the level and on gradients. Br. J. Nutr. 18:47.

Cook, C. W., L. A. Stoddart, and L. E. Harris. 1954. The nutritive value of winter range plants in the Great Basin as determined with digestion trials with sheep. Utah Agric. Exp. Stn. Bull. 372.

Cook, C. W., L. A. Stoddart, and L. E. Harris. 1956. Comparative nutritive value and palatability of some introduced and native forage plants for spring and summer grazing. Utah Agric. Exp. Stn. Bull. 385.

Harris, L. E., C. W. Cook, and J. E. Butcher. 1959. Symposium on forage evaluation. 5. Intake and digestibility techniques and supplemental feeding in range forage evaluation. J. Agron. 51:226.

Harris, L. E., C. W. Cook, and L. A. Stoddart. 1956. Feeding phosphorus, protein, and energy supplements to ewes on winter ranges of Utah. Utah Agric. Exp. Stn. Bull. 398.

Harris, L. E., G. P. Lofgreen, C. J. Kercher, R. J. Raleigh, and V. R. Bohman. 1967. Techniques of research in range livestock nurition. Utah Agric. Exp. Stn. Bull. 471.

Huston, J. E. 1983. Production of fine-wool ewes on yearlong rangeland in west Texas. I. Effects of season, stage of production and supplemental feed on intake. J. Anim. Sci. 56:1269.

Huston, J. E., B. S. Rector, L. B. Merrill and B. S. Engdahl. 1981. Nutritional value of range plants in the Edwards Plateau region of Texas. Tex. Agric. Exp. Stn. Bull. 1357.

James, L. F., R. F. Keeler, A. E. Johnson, M. L. Williams, E. N. Crenin, and J. D. Olson. 1980. Plants poisonous to livestock in the western states. USDA Bull. 419.

National Research Council. 1981. Effect of Environment on Nutrient Requirements of Domestic Animals. Washington, D.C.: National Academy Press.

Parker, C. F. 1976. Feeding and breeding ewes in confinement housing. Ohio Sheep Day Rep.

Weir, W. C., and D. T. Torell. 1967. Supplemental feeding of sheep grazing on dry range. Calif. Agric. Exp. Stn. Bull. 832.

Young, B. A., and J. L. Corbett. 1972. Maintenance energy requirement of grazing sheep in relation to herbage availability. Aust. J. Agric. Res. 23:57.

Flushing

Bellows, R. A., A. L. Pope, A. B. Chapman, and L. E. Casida. 1963. Effect of level and sequence of feeding and breed on ovulation rate, embryo survival and fetal growth in the mature ewe. J. Anim. Sci. 22:101.

Boshier, D. P. 1969. A histological and histochemical examination of implantation and early placentome formation in sheep. J. Reprod. Fertil. 19:51.

Coop, I. E. 1966. Effect of flushing on reproductive performance of ewes. J. Agric. Sci. 67:305.

Doney, J. M. 1979. Nutrition and the reproductive function in female sheep. Pp. 152-160 in The Management and Diseases of Sheep. Slough: Commonwealth Agricultural Bureaux.

Doney, J. M., and R. G. Gunn. 1981. Nutritional and other factors in breeding performance of ewes. Pp. 169-177 in Environmental Factors in Mammalian Reproduction, D. P. Gilmore and B. Cook, eds. London (New York): Macmillan.

Edey, T. N. 1969. Prenatal mortality in sheep: A review. Anim. Breed. Abstr. 78:173.

Edey, T. N. 1976. Embryo mortality. Pp. 400-410 in Sheep Breeding. G. J. Tomes, D. E. Robertson, and R. J. Lightfoot, eds. Armidale, New Zealand: New England University.

El-Sheikh, A. S., C. V. Hulet, A. L. Pope, and L. E. Casida. 1955. The effect of level of feeding on the reproductive capacity of the ewe. J. Anim. Sci. 14:919.

Foote, W. C., and D. H. Mathews. 1983. The relationship of body weight and size to reproduction and production performance. Pp. 131 in Proc. 1983 NC-111 Tech. Comm., Increased Efficiency of Sheep Production.

Foote, W. C., A. L. Pope, A. B. Chapman, and L. E. Casida. 1959. Reproduction in the yearling ewe as affected by breed and sequence of feeding levels. 2. Effects on fetal development. J. Anim. Sci. 18:463.

Gunn, R. G. 1983. The influence of nutrition on the reproductive performance of ewes. Pp. 99-110 in Sheep Production, W. Haresign, ed. London: Butterworth.

Howland, B. E., R. L. Kirkpatrick, A. L. Pope, and L. E. Casida. 1966. Pituitary and ovarian function in ewes fed on two nutritional levels. J. Anim. Sci. 25:716.

Lawson, R. A. S. 1977. Research application of embryo transfer in sheep and goats. Pp. 72-78 in Embryo Transfer in Farm Animals. Monograph 16. Agriculture Canada, Ottawa.

Memon, G. N., R. J. Antoniewicz, N. J. Benevenga, A. L. Pope, and L. E. Casida. 1969. Some effects of differences in dietary energy and protein levels on the ovary and the anterior pituitary gland of the ewe. J. Anim. Sci. 28:57.

Parr, R. A., I. A. Cumming, and I. J. Clark. 1982. Effects of maternal nutrition and plasma progesterone concentrations on survival and growth of the sheep embryo in early gestation. J. Agric. Sci. 98:39.

Robinson, J. J. 1977. The influence of maternal nutrition on ovine foetal growth. Pro. Nutr. Soc. 36:9.

Robinson, J. J. 1983. Nutrition of the pregnant ewe. Pp. 111-131 in Sheep Production, W. Haresign, ed. London: Butterworth.

Russell, A. J. F. 1979. The nutrition of the pregnant ewe. Pp. 221-241 in The Management and Diseases of Sheep. Slough: Commonwealth Agricultural Bureaux.

Thomas, D. L., J. L. Goodyear, A. R. Cobb, J. M. Stookey, and P. J. Dzuik. 1984. Ovulation rate of ewes provided supplemental grain, phenobarbital or mineral oil prior to estrus. Abstr. 103, Midwest Sec. Meet. Am. Soc. Anim. Sci.

Treacher, T. T. 1979. The nutrition of the lactating ewe. Pp. 242-256 in The Management and Diseases of Sheep. Slough: Commonwealth Agricultural Bureaux.

Treacher, T. T. 1983. Nutrient requirements of the lactating ewe. Pp. 133-153 in Sheep Production, W. Haresign, ed. London: Butterworth.

Creep Feeding

Fredriksen, K. R., R. M. Jordan, and C. E. Terrill. 1980. Rearing lambs on milk replacers. Farmers Bull. 2270. Science and Education Administration, U.S. Department of Agriculture, Washington, D.C.

Jordan, R. M., and C. E. Gates. 1961. Effect of grain feeding the ewe and lamb on subsequent lamb growth. J. Anim. Sci. 20:809.

Ørskov, E. R. 1975. Physiological conditioning in ruminants and its practical implications. World Anim. Rev. 16:31.

Ørskov, E. R. 1982. Very intensive systems. Chapter 21 in Sheep and Goat Production, I. E. Coop, ed. Amsterdam: Elsevier.

Ørskov, E. R. 1983. Nutrition of lambs from birth to slaughter. Pp. 155-165 in Sheep Production, W. Haresign, ed. London: Butterworth.

Robinson, J. J., C. Fraser, and I. McHattie. 1974. The effect of dietary crude protein concentration and time of weaning on milk production and body weight changes in the ewe. Anim. Prod. 19:331.

Early Weaning

Jordan, R. M., and H. E. Hanke. 1970. Protein requirements of young lambs. J. Anim. Sci. 31:593.

Jordan, R. M., and H. E. Hanke. 1977. Effect of level of grain fed ewes during late lactation on lamb production. J. Anim. Sci. 45:945.

Artificial Rearing

Franken, P., and L. Elving. 1982. Een vergelijking van een aantal parameters in het bloed van normal opgefokte lammeren en van lammeren die zwoegervrij, met rundercolostrum zijn opgefokte. (Comparison of a number of parameters in the blood of lambs reared free from Maedi on bovine colostrum.) Tijdschr. Diergenseesk. 107:315.

Frederiksen, K. R., R. M. Jordan, and C. E. Terrill. 1980. Rearing lambs on milk replacers. Farmers Bull. 2270. Science and Education Administration, U.S. Department of Agriculture, Washington, D.C.

Glimp, H. 1972. The effect of diet composition on the performance of lambs reared from birth on milk replacers. J. Anim. Sci. 34:1085.

Gorrill, A. D. L., G. J. Brisson, D. B. Emmons, and G. J. St.-Laurent. Revised 1982 by J. W. G. Nicholson. Artificial rearing of young lambs. Publ. 1507/E, Communication Branch, Agriculture Canada, Ottawa.

Heaney, D. P., J. N. B. Shrestha, and H. F. Peters. 1982a. Performance of lambs fed milk replacers having two levels of fat. Can. J. Anim. Sci. 62:837.

Heaney, D. P., J. N. B. Shrestha, and H. F. Peters. 1982b. Potential alternatives to lamb milk replacer for the artificial rearing of lambs. Can. J. Anim. Sci. 62:1135.

Heaney, D. P., J. N. B. Shrestha, and H. F. Peters. 1983. Effects of postweaning protein regimens and urea on the performance of intensively reared lambs. Can. J. Anim. Sci. 63:631.

Heaney, D. P., J. N. B. Shrestha, and H. F. Peters. 1984. Postweaning performance of artificially reared lambs weaned at 21 vs 28 days of age under two postweaning housing regimes. Can. J. Anim. Sci. 64:667.

Large, R. V., and P. D. Penning. 1967. The artificial rearing of lambs on cold reconstituted whole milk and on milk substitute. J. Agric. Sci. 69:405.

Larsen, R. E., A. C. S. Ward, K. R. Frederiksen, W. B. Ardrey, and F. W. Frank. 1974. Capability of lambs to absorb immunoproteins from freeze-dried bovine colostrum. Am. J. Vet. Res. 35:1061.

Logan, E. F., W. H. Foster, and D. Irwin. 1978. A note on bovine colostrum as an alternative source of immunoglobulin for lambs. Anim. Prod. 26:93.

Meat and Livestock Commission. 1976. Artificial rearing of lambs. Tech. Rep. Sheep Improvement Ser. Meat and Livestock Comm., Box 44, Queensway House, Queensway, Bletchley, Milton Keynes MK2 2EF, England.

Peters, H. F., and D. P. Heaney. 1974. Factors influencing the growth of lambs reared artificially or with their dams. Can. J. Anim. Sci. 54:9.

Feed Additives

Anonymous. 1984a. Feed Additive Compendium. Minneapolis: Miller Publishing.

Anonymous. 1984b. FDA approves Bovatec for confined sheep. Feedstuffs 56(27):4.

Foreyt, W. J., N. L. Gates, and R. B. Wescott. 1979. Effects of lasalocid and monensin against experimentally induced coccidiosis in confinement-reared lambs from weaning to market weight. Am. J. Vet. Res. 40:97.

Hays, V. W. 1969. Biological basis for the use of antibiotics in livestock production. Pp. 11-30 in the Use of Drugs in Animal Feeds. Publ. 1679. Washington, D.C.: National Academy of Sciences.

Horton, G. M. J., and P. H. G. Stockdale. 1981. Lasalocid and monensin in finishing diets for early weaned lambs with naturally occurring coccidiosis. Am. J. Vet. Res. 42:433.

Ott, E. A. 1968. Use of feed additives for lambs. Pp. 206-218 in Proc. Symp. on Sheep Nutrition and Feeding. Iowa State University, Ames.

Poisonous Plants

Binns, W. 1974. Range and pasture plants poisonous to sheep. J. Am. Vet. Med. Assoc. 164:284.

Dwyer, D. D. 1978. Impact of poisonous plants on western U. S. grazing systems and livestock operations. Pp. 13-21 in Effects of Poisonous Plants on Livestock, R. F. Keeler, K. R. Van Kampen, and L. F. James, eds. New York: Academic Press.

James, L. F., R. F. Keeler, A. E. Johnson, M. C. Williams, E. H. Cronin, and J. D. Olson. 1980. Plants Poisonous to Livestock in the Western States. USDA Bull. 419.

Kingsbury, J. M. 1964. Poisonous Plants of the United States and Canada. Englewood Cliffs, N.J.: Prentice-Hall.

Merrill, L. B., and J. L. Schuster. 1978. Grazing management practices affect livestock losses from poisonous plants. J. Range Manage. 31:351.

Schuster, J. L. 1978. Poisonous plant management problems and control measures on U.S. rangelands. Pp. 23-34 in Effects of Poisonous Plants on Livestock, R. F. Keeler, K. R. Van Kampen, and L. F. James, eds. New York: Academic Press.

Sperry, O. E., J. W. Dollahite, G. O. Hoffman, and B. J. Camp. 1964. Texas Plants Poisonous to Livestock. Tex. Agric. Exp. Stn. Bull. 1028.

Ration Alternatives

Beardsley, D. W. 1964. Symposium on forage utilization: Nutritive value of forages as affected by physical form. 2. Beef cattle and sheep studies. J. Anim. Sci. 23:239.

Esplin, A. L. 1968. Effect of feed processing in lamb rations. Pp. 193-205 in Sheep Nutrition and Feeding. Ames: Iowa State University.

Garrett, W. N., J. H. Meyer, G. P. Lofgreen, and J. B. Dobie. 1961. Effect of pellet size and composition on feedlot performance, carcass characteristics and rumen parakeratosis of fattening steers. J. Anim. Sci. 20:833.

Jordan, R. M. 1966. Effect of energy as supplied by hay or high concentrate rations and frequency of feeding on the performance of ewes. J. Anim. Sci. 25:624.

Jordan, R. M., and H. E. Hanke. 1963. Frequency of feeding, rough-age-concentrate ratio for pregnant ewes and summer drylot feeding of non-lactating ewes. J. Anim. Sci. 22:679.

Jordan, R. M., and H. E. Hanke. 1984. Effect of protein intake provided by corn gluten meal on lactating ewes. Proc. 55th Sheep and Lamb Feeders Report. S-200. University of Minnesota, St. Paul.

Loerch, S. C., K. E. McClure, and C. F. Parker. 1983. Effect of protein source in ewe diets on ewe and lamb performance. Proc. 1983. NC-111 Tech. Comm. Increased Efficiency of Sheep Production. Ottawa, Ontario, Canada.

Reynolds, P. J., and I. L. Lindahl. 1969. Effects of pelleting of forage on the *ad libitum* salt and water consumption and urine excretion of sheep. J. Anim. Sci. 28:563.

Woods, W., and R. W. Rhodes. 1962. Effect of varying roughage to concentrate ratios on the utilization by lambs of rations differing in physical form. J. Anim. Sci. 21:479.

Wright, P. L., A. L. Pope, and P. H. Phillips. 1962. Pelleted roughages for gestating and lactating ewes. Wis. Agric. Exp. Stn. Res. Bull. 239.

Wright, P. L., A. L. Pope, and P. H. Phillips. 1963. Effect of physical form of ration upon digestion and volatile fatty acid production in vivo and in vitro. J. Anim. Sci. 22:586.

Yapi, C. V., D. L. Thomas, A. R. Cobb, J. M. Stookey, G. C. Fahly, Jr., J. L. Goodyear, T. E. Long, and G. E. Ricketts. 1983. Effect of level and source of protein during lactation on ewe and lamb performance. Proc. 1983 NC-111 Tech. Comm. Increased Efficiency of Sheep Production. Ottawa, Canada.

COMPOSITION OF FEEDS

Crampton, E. W., L. E. Lloyd, and V. G. MacKay. 1957. The calorie value of TDN. J. Anim. Sci. 16:541.

Harris, L. E. 1963. Symposium on feeds and meats terminology. 3. A system for naming and describing feedstuffs, energy terminology, and the use of such information in calculating diets. J. Anim. Sci. 22:535.

Harris, L. E., J. M. Asplund, and E. W. Crampton. 1968. An international feed nomenclature and methods for summarizing and using feed data to calculate diets. Utah Agric. Exp. Stn. Bull. 479.

Harris, L. E., L. C. Kearl, and P. V. Fonnesbeck. 1972. Use of regression equations in predicting availability of energy and protein. J. Anim. Sci. 35:658.

Harris, L. E., L. C. Kearl, and P. V. Fonnesbeck. 1981. Rationale for naming a feed. Utah Agric. Exp. Stn. Bull. 501.

Harris, L. E., H. Haendler, R. Riviere, and L. Rechaussat. 1980. International feed databank system; an introduction into the system with instructions for describing feeds and recording data. International Network of Feed Information Centers. Publication 2. Prepared on behalf of INFIC by the International Feedstuffs Institute, Utah State University, Logan.

Knight, A. D., and L. E. Harris. 1966. Digestible protein estimation for NRC feed composition tables. Amer. Soc. Anim. Sci., West. Sec. Meet. 17:283.

National Research Council. 1982. United States-Canadian Tables of Feed Composition. Washington, D.C.: National Academy Press.

Swift, R. W. 1957. The caloric value of TDN. J. Anim. Sci. 16:753.

Index